Math
Lesson Guide

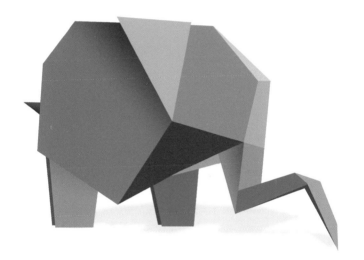

5

K12 Summit
CURRICULUM

Book Staff and Contributors

Lisa White   *Lead Content Specialist*
Megan Simmons   *Content Specialist*
Lauralyn Vaughn   *Manager, Instructional Design*
Susan Raley   *Text Editor*
Tricia Battipede   *Senior Creative Manager*
Jayoung Cho   *Senior Visual Designer*
Caitlin Gildrien   *Visual Designer*
Tricia Battipede, Mike Bohman, Shannon Palmer   *Cover Designers*
Deborah Benton, Dana Crisafulli, Michele Patrick, Maureen Steddin, Alisa Steel, David Stienecker   *Writers*
Amy Eward   *Senior Manager, Writers and Editors*
Abhilasha Parakh   *Senior Project Manager*

Doug McCollum   *Senior Vice President, Product Development*
Kristin Morrison   *Vice President, Design, Creative, and UX*
Rohit Lakhani   *Vice President, Program Management and Operations*
Kelly Engel   *Senior Director, Curriculum*
Christopher Frescholtz   *Senior Director, Program Management*
Erica Castle   *Director, Creative Services*
Lisa Dimaio Iekel   *Senior Production Manager*

Illustrations Credits

All illustrations © K12 unless otherwise noted
Characters: Tommy DiGiovanni, Matt Fedor, Ben Gamache, Shannon Palmer
Cover: Pastel wallpaper patterns © mxtama/iStock; Polygon © LPETTET/iStock.
Interior Pattern: Pastel wallpaper patterns © mxtama/iStock.

About K12 Inc.
K12 Inc. (NYSE: LRN) drives innovation and advances the quality of education by delivering state-of-the-art digital learning platforms and technology to students and school districts around the world. K12 is a company of educators offering its online and blended curriculum to charter schools, public school districts, private schools, and directly to families. More information can be found at K12.com.

ISBN: 978-1-60153-580-1

Printed by Walsworth, Marceline, MO, USA, March 2019

Table of Contents

K12 Summit Math 5 Overview .... **x**

How to Use This Guide ....**xxiii**

Numerical Expressions

Using Grouping Symbols (A) **2**

Using Grouping Symbols (B)....................................... **5**

Using Grouping Symbols (C)....................................... **8**

Using Grouping Symbols (D) **11**

Exploring Numerical Expressions (A)............................. **13**

Exploring Numerical Expressions (B)............................. **16**

Exploring Numerical Expressions (C)............................. **19**

Big Ideas: Mini-Project.. **21**

Multidigit Whole Number Multiplication and Division

Powers of 10 (A).. **24**

Powers of 10 (B).. **27**

Powers of 10 (C).. **29**

Multidigit Whole Number Multiplication (A)...................... **31**

Multidigit Whole Number Multiplication (B)...................... **34**

Multidigit Whole Number Multiplication (C)...................... **37**

Multidigit Division Strategies (A) **39**

Multidigit Division Strategies (B).............................. **42**

Multidigit Division Strategies (C) **45**

Multidigit Division Algorithm (A) **47**

Multidigit Division Algorithm (B) **50**

Multidigit Division Algorithm (C) **53**

Multidigit Division Algorithm (D)............................... **56**

Big Ideas: Extended Problems **58**

Addition and Subtraction of Fractions

Addition of Fractions (A) 60

Addition of Fractions (B).. 63

Addition of Fractions (C) 66

Addition of Fractions (D) 69

Addition of Fractions (E).. 72

Addition of Fractions (F) 75

Addition of Fractions (G) 78

Subtraction of Fractions (A) 80

Subtraction of Fractions (B) 83

Subtraction of Fractions (C) 85

Subtraction of Fractions (D).. 88

Subtraction of Fractions (E) 90

Subtraction of Fractions (F) 93

Big Ideas: Mini-Project.. 95

Addition and Subtraction of Mixed Numbers

Addition of Mixed Numbers (A) 98

Addition of Mixed Numbers (B) 101

Addition of Mixed Numbers (C) 103

Addition of Mixed Numbers (D) 105

Subtraction of Mixed Numbers (A)................................... 107

Subtraction of Mixed Numbers (B) 110

Subtraction of Mixed Numbers (C).................................. 112

Subtraction of Mixed Numbers (D).................................. 114

Addition and Subtraction of Mixed Numbers (A)...................... 116

Addition and Subtraction of Mixed Numbers (B)...................... 118

Addition and Subtraction of Mixed Numbers (C)...................... 121

Big Ideas: Extended Problems 123

Multiplication with Fractions and Mixed Numbers

Multiplying with Fractions (A) **126**

Multiplying with Fractions (B) **129**

Multiplying with Fractions (C) **132**

Multiplying with Fractions (D) **135**

Multiplying with Fractions (E) **138**

Multiplying with Fractions (F) **141**

Multiplying with Mixed Numbers (A) **143**

Multiplying with Mixed Numbers (B) **146**

Multiplying with Mixed Numbers (C) **148**

Multiplying with Mixed Numbers (D) **150**

Big Ideas: Mini-Project **152**

Division with Unit Fractions

Unit Fractions Divided by Whole Numbers (A) **154**

Unit Fractions Divided by Whole Numbers (B) **157**

Unit Fractions Divided by Whole Numbers (C) **159**

Unit Fractions Divided by Whole Numbers (D) **162**

Unit Fractions Divided by Whole Numbers (E) **164**

Unit Fractions Divided by Whole Numbers (F) **166**

Whole Numbers Divided by Unit Fractions (A) **168**

Whole Numbers Divided by Unit Fractions (B) **171**

Whole Numbers Divided by Unit Fractions (C) **173**

Whole Numbers Divided by Unit Fractions (D) **176**

Whole Numbers Divided by Unit Fractions (E) **178**

Whole Numbers Divided by Unit Fractions (F) **180**

Big Ideas: Challenge Problems **182**

Geometric Measurement: Volume

Measuring Volume (A) **184**

Measuring Volume (B) **187**

Measuring Volume (C) **190**

Calculating Volume (A) **192**

Calculating Volume (B) **195**

Calculating Volume (C) **197**

Calculating Volume (D) **199**

Volume and Problem Solving (A) **201**

Volume and Problem Solving (B) **203**

Volume and Problem Solving (C) **205**

Big Ideas: Extended Problems **207**

Decimals

Exploring Decimals (A) **210**

Exploring Decimals (B) **213**

Exploring Decimals (C) **216**

Exploring Decimals (D) **218**

Comparing Decimals (A) **220**

Comparing Decimals (B) **223**

Comparing Decimals (C) **225**

Rounding Decimals (A) **227**

Rounding Decimals (B) **230**

Rounding Decimals (C) **233**

Place Value Relationships to Thousandths (A) **235**

Place Value Relationships to Thousandths (B) **238**

Place Value Relationships to Thousandths (C) **241**

Big Ideas: Challenge Problems **243**

Addition and Subtraction of Decimals

Decimal Addition (A) **246**

Decimal Addition (B) **249**

Decimal Addition (C) **252**

Decimal Subtraction (A) **254**

Decimal Subtraction (B) **257**

Decimal Subtraction (C) **260**

Add and Subtract Decimals in the Real World (A) **262**

Add and Subtract Decimals in the Real World (B) **264**

Add and Subtract Decimals in the Real World (C) **266**

Add and Subtract Decimals in the Real World (D) **268**

Big Ideas: Extended Problems **270**

Multiplication with Decimals

Multiplying Whole Numbers by Decimals (A) **272**

Multiplying Whole Numbers by Decimals (B) **275**

Multiplying Whole Numbers by Decimals (C) **277**

Multiplying Whole Numbers by Decimals (D) **279**

Multiplying Decimals by Powers of 10 (A) **281**

Multiplying Decimals by Powers of 10 (B) **283**

Multiplying Decimals by Powers of 10 (C) **285**

Multiplying Two Decimals (A) **287**

Multiplying Two Decimals (B) **290**

Multiplying Two Decimals (C) **293**

Multiplying Two Decimals (D) **296**

Multiplying Two Decimals (E) **298**

Big Ideas: Challenge Problems **300**

Division with Decimals

Dividing Whole Numbers and Decimals (A) **302**
Dividing Whole Numbers and Decimals (B) **306**
Dividing Whole Numbers and Decimals (C) **310**
Dividing Whole Numbers and Decimals (D) **314**
Dividing Decimals by Powers of 10 (A) **316**
Dividing Decimals by Powers of 10 (B) **318**
Dividing Decimals by Powers of 10 (C) **320**
Decimal Division (A) **322**
Decimal Division (B) **326**
Decimal Division (C) **329**
Decimal Division (D) **333**
Decimal Division (E) **336**
Big Ideas: Extended Problems **338**

Points on a Coordinate Plane

Coordinate System (A) **340**
Coordinate System (B) **343**
Coordinate System (C) **345**
Coordinate System (D) **348**
Problem Solving on the Coordinate Plane (A) **350**
Problem Solving on the Coordinate Plane (B) **353**
Problem Solving on the Coordinate Plane (C) **356**
Problem Solving on the Coordinate Plane (D) **359**
Problem Solving on the Coordinate Plane (E) **362**
Big Ideas: Mini-Project **364**

Measurement and Unit Conversion

Using Units of Length (A) 366
Using Units of Length (B) 369
Using Units of Length (C) 372
Using Units of Liquid Volume (A).. 374
Using Units of Liquid Volume (B).. 377
Using Units of Liquid Volume (C).. 380
Using Units of Mass and Weight (A) 382
Using Units of Mass and Weight (B) 385
Using Units of Mass of Weight (C)... 388
Customary Units and Line Plots (A) 390
Customary Units and Line Plots (B) 392
Customary Units and Line Plots (C) 394
Big Ideas: Mini-Project.. 396

Classification of Two-Dimensional Figures

Triangles (A) 398
Triangles (B) 401
Triangles (C) 404
Polygons (A).. 406
Polygons (B).. 408
Polygons (C).. 411
Big Ideas: Extended Problems 413

End-of-Year Project

End-of-Year Project.. 416

K12 Summit Math 5 Overview

Welcome to Summit Math 5! We're grateful for this opportunity to play a role in your students' math education. We've provided the following overview of the content and structure of the course so that you can best support your students. At any time, if you have questions or would like further clarification, never hesitate to reach out to us. Let's get started!

Summit Math 5 encourages students to learn independently. As a Learning Coach, your role is to support and enhance the learning experience. Each lesson includes rich interactivity to ensure students build the depth of understanding they need to succeed on state assessments. Online interactions provide a wealth of data, so teachers know exactly where students are struggling. Additionally, the offline practice, during which students write directly in an Activity Book, offers variety. With rich content designed to engage and motivate students, and enough practice to reinforce each concept, Summit Math 5 includes the tools and technology that students need to succeed in math.

Course Components

Online Lessons

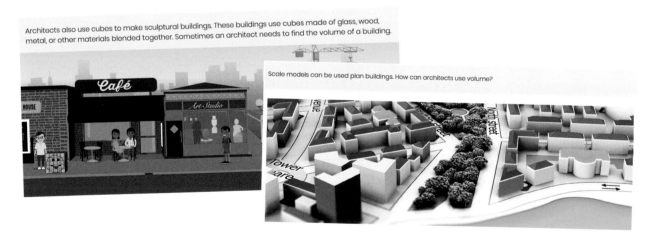

The online lessons provide the core instruction and multiple opportunities for practice in Summit Math 5. The online lessons include

- A predictable lesson structure
- Interactive **problems** and assessments that challenge students to use higher-order thinking skills
- A carefully thought-out progression from guided to independent practice
- Computer-scored practice with instant and meaningful feedback

- Learning experiences that support struggling students
- Explanations and exploratory interactions that support deep understanding, coupled with enough practice to build speed and accuracy
- Frequent practice with math facts, including games to engage and motivate students
- Student-friendly learning goals

In addition to the online lessons, rich print materials support learning.

Lesson Guide

Each course is accompanied by a Lesson Guide that makes it quick and easy for Learning Coaches to understand each lesson at a glance—without logging in. The Lesson Guide provides an overview of a lesson's content, activities, and materials; answer keys for Activity Book pages; alerts when special Learning Coach attention is needed; and other features to aid the Learning Coach in supporting students.

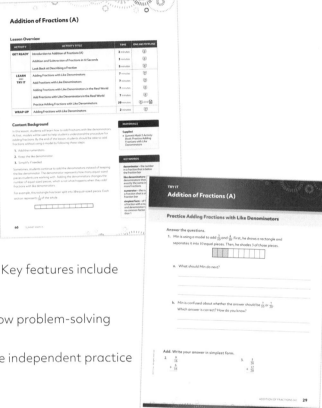

Activity Book

Summit Math 5 includes an Activity Book where students can put pencil to paper every instructional day. Key features include

- Full color pages with adequate space for answers
- Problems that require students to draw sketches, show problem-solving steps, evaluate answers, and write explanations
- Step-by-step problems that prepare students for the independent practice problems

Additional Supplied Materials

K12 supplies a base-10 blocks set, which is valuable for modeling place value and basic operations.

Also Needed

Students should obtain a binder or spiral notebook to use as their Math Notebook, in which they can work problems, make sketches, and take notes as they work through a lesson. Students should always have paper and a pencil handy.

Other common items that may be useful for some lessons include ruler and scissors.

Course Structure

Summit Math 5 is designed to lead students through a logical sequence of concepts based on current state and national academic standards. The material is structured to fit a typical, 180-day school year, but it can also be easily adapted to fit individual needs.

Summit Math 5 is divided into **units**. A typical unit is divided into a series of related **concepts**, which are in turn divided into **daily lessons**. The final lesson in each concept includes a review of the concept and a **Concept Quiz**. A separate **Big Ideas lesson** synthesizes the course content and appears at the end of the unit.

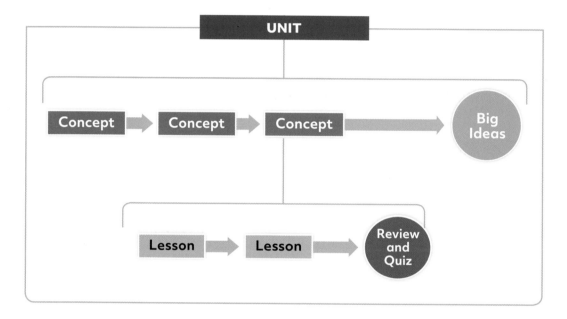

Lesson Model Overview

Concepts in Summit Math 5 follow a multiday learning cycle consisting of an initial lesson, one or more middle lessons, and a final lesson, each of which follows a consistent, predictable instructional formula.

INITIAL AND MIDDLE DAYS

During the initial and middle days, students learn and practice the core content. As students work through these lessons, they are asked to work more and more independently. They progress from concrete explorations and explicit instruction, through guided practice, to independent practice and application.

FINAL DAY

The final day of each concept includes practice problems that prepare students for the Concept Quiz. The Concept Quiz is computer graded and is based on the concept's key objectives. Students will also have an opportunity to practice in Stride on final days. Stride is a dynamic teaching tool that guides students to practice where they need it most.

	Initial Day	Middle Days	Final Day
GET READY			
Get Ready activities introduce and orient students to the lesson content.	Lesson Introduction 60-Second Math Look Back	Lesson Introduction Math Facts	Lesson Introduction
LEARN AND **TRY IT**			
Learn and **Try It** activities include multiple cycles of bite-sized instruction coupled with guided practice. The multiple cycles are followed by independent practice problems.	**LEARN** **TRY IT** Guided **TRY IT** Independent	**LEARN** **TRY IT** Guided **TRY IT** Independent	**TRY IT** Review
QUIZ			
			Concept Quiz
WRAP-UP			
Wrap-Up activities include one or two ungraded questions that serve to gauge student understanding as they exit the lesson or a graded quiz on the final day of each concept.	**WRAP-UP** Formative Assessment	**WRAP-UP** Formative Assessment	**STRIDE**

Activity Descriptions

This table briefly describes specific activity types in Summit Math 5.

GET READY	Description
Lesson Introduction	The Lesson Introduction introduces the content of the lesson within an engaging context. It also presents the objectives as student-friendly goals, defines any new keywords that students will encounter in the lesson, and lists the relevant state academic standards covered in the lesson.
60-Second Math	The 60-Second Math video is an engaging video designed to prompt curiosity and show how the concept students are about to study is used in the real world.
Look Back	The Look Back is a quick review of prerequisite skills that are essential to understanding the new concept. Students who struggle with the Look Back should seek additional help before proceeding.
Math Facts	A Math Facts practice provides independent practice of math facts. Students build speed and accuracy through interactive online questions and games.

LEARN AND TRY IT	Description
Learn	All initial and middle days include one or more bite-sized Learn and Try It cycles. These activities include a variety of approaches, including guided explorations and explicit instruction. Some particularly difficult concepts are explained in a video that features an expert teacher.
Try It (Guided)	Each Learn activity is followed by a short, guided Try It that allows students to immediately apply the concepts they have just learned. All problems include feedback based on student answers as well as complete solutions. The guided Try Its prepare students for the independent practice.

LEARN AND TRY IT	Description
Try It (Guided with Remediation)	Lessons with particularly important concepts include Try Its with branching pathways for struggling students. The questions in this activity are designed to uncover and correct misconceptions and common errors. As students work through the problem set, they receive targeted feedback depending on how they answer the questions. Struggling students are then guided through a reteaching activity to dispel the misconception or correct the common error.
Try It (Independent)	All initial and middle days include an independent Try It. The independent practice has two parts: an online part and an offline part. The independent online practice problems are like the types of problems students will encounter in the Concept Quiz. The offline problems are found in the student Activity Book.
Try It (Practice, Concept)	The final day of each concept includes a Try It that is designed to prepare students for the Concept Quiz. The review includes online interactive problems, which are sometimes in the form of a game.
WRAP-UP	Description
Formative Assessment	Initial and middle days end with a short check-in that includes one or two ungraded questions that gauge students' understanding at the end of the lesson. Although the questions are ungraded, the results are available to teachers.
Stride	Final days end with independent practice in Stride.

A Balance of Online and Offline Time

Summit Math 5 online activities make up about 75 percent of core lesson time. However, equally critical to learning is that students practice working out math calculations by hand. Summit Math 5 incorporates a daily offline activity in a predictable place within each lesson sequence. In the last Try It activity of each lesson day, after completing online practice in which instant feedback can help address any misunderstandings, students work out related problems in their Activity Book.

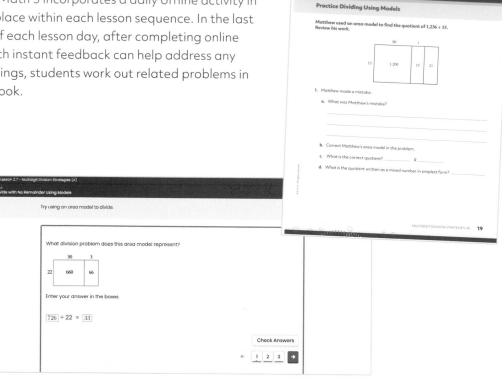

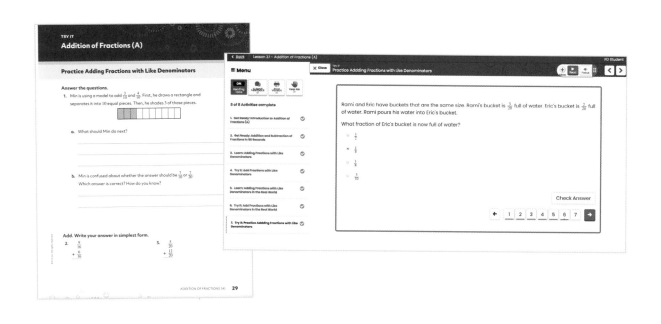

Special Features

In addition to the standard units and lessons, Summit Math 5 has these special features.

Big Ideas Lessons

Big Ideas lessons occur at the end of most units. In these lessons, students complete an assignment that gauges their ability to synthesize content and use higher-order thinking skills, such as analysis, evaluation, complex problem solving, and creativity. These assignments prepare students for the type of questions they will encounter on state assessments.

There are three types of Big Ideas lessons, which vary in the type of assignment students complete and submit:

- Extended Problems
- Mini-Project
- Challenge Problems

Note: The Extended Problems are intended to be used as graded assessments that should contribute a significant number of points toward students' grades.

Instant Recall: Facts Fluency

Students need to be able to recall addition, subtraction, multiplication, and division facts quickly and accurately. Summit Math 5 includes cycles of practice that look at specific sets of facts. There are three types of Math Facts practice.

1. Matching problems to provide scaffolding as students build familiarity
2. A set of fill-in-the-blank problems for the student to build mastery
3. A game for the students to continue to practice automatic recall of facts in a fun way

Virtual Manipulatives

Virtual manipulatives are digital versions of physical objects you might typically see in a math classroom. These highly interactive experiences allow students to play with and explore mathematical concepts. Virtual manipulatives provided in Summit Math 5 include

- Fraction Strips
- Pattern Blocks
- Base-10 Blocks
- Protractor

All explorations with virtual manipulatives are followed by direct explanations to ensure that students grasp the critical concepts. A version of these activities using printable or tactile manipulatives is available for students who need or prefer an offline version.

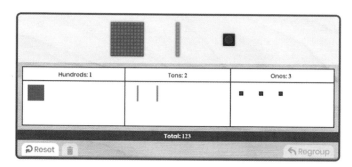

Base-10 Blocks

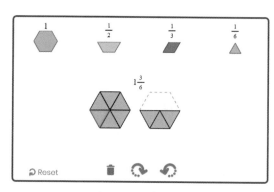

Pattern Blocks

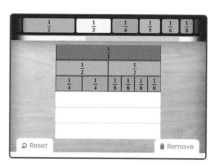

Fraction Strips

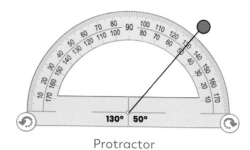

Protractor

End-of-Year Project

The end-of-year project is an extended, inquiry-based activity that is designed to build a deeper understanding of mathematics. Students use critical thinking skills and creativity as they explore an authentic, real-world problem. The project cuts across curricular areas, showing the impact and relevance of math while building twenty-first-century skills.

The project is structured around a question that is both engaging and relevant to students and their community. To find answers to the question, students will apply the mathematics they already know and then expand their knowledge to fill in the gaps. Students create and submit a final product that demonstrates what they have learned.

Assessment Overview

To ensure students can show what they have learned and to support high academic outcomes, students need exposure to the types questions they will see on state assessments.

Online Interactive Questions

Online interactive questions, similar in style and format to today's digital state assessments, provide powerful opportunities for students to demonstrate deep understanding. For this reason, a variety of online question types, including drag and drop and fill in the blank, are used throughout Summit Math 5.

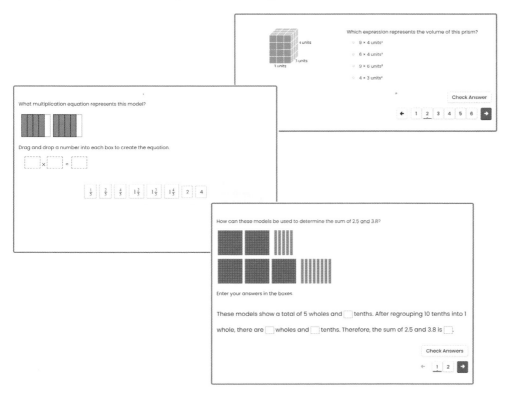

Graded Assessments

Summit Math 5 includes quizzes at the end of each concept, as well as teacher-graded assignments within Big Ideas lessons. Students are also asked to complete an in-depth project at the end of the year.

Assessment Type	How Many?
Concept Quiz	39
Big-Ideas: Extended Problems	6
Big-Ideas: Mini-Project	5
Big-Ideas: Challenge Problems	3
Mid-Year Assessment	1
End-of-Year Project	1
End-of-Year Assessment	1

Instructional Approach

Building Balanced Understanding and Efficiency

For a long period of time, most math instruction focused strictly on how—not why—to perform calculations. Summit Math 5 balances conceptual instruction and exploration to explain the why, with procedural practice designed to move students toward speed and accuracy. As you look across a lesson, a concept, and even a unit, you will see a careful progression in which students first use models to grasp why the math works, and then move toward more efficient methods of solving problems.

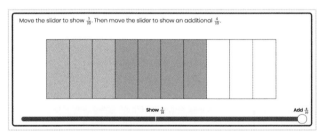

Conceptual Explorations

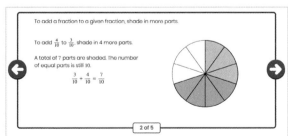

Conceptual Explanations

Procedural Explanations

Game-Like Embedded Practice

Repetition is an important part of building speed and accuracy. However, students must be motivated to practice in a variety of ways. Built-in games engage students to spend sufficient time practicing until key math tasks become natural and automatic.

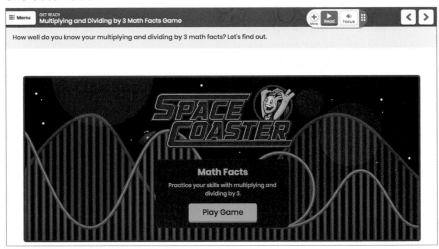

Making Math Relevant with Real-World, Concrete Examples

Summit Math 5 intentionally progresses from concrete real-world scenarios and models, to visual models, and finally to abstracted math to build a depth of knowledge.

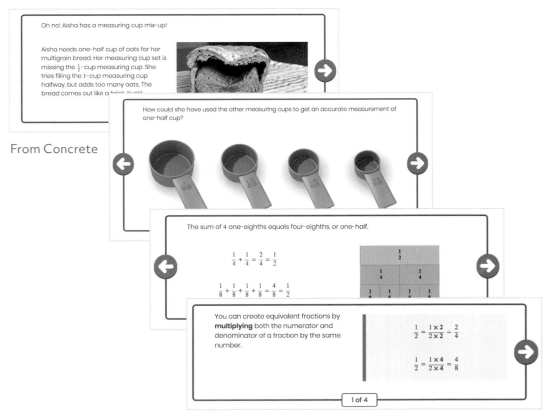

From Concrete

To Abstract

Content Focus

- Students expand understanding of operations with fractions by developing fluency with addition and subtraction of fractions with both like and unlike denominators, an understanding of multiplication of fractions, and an understanding of division of and by unit fractions.
- Students develop greater fluency with addition, subtraction, multiplication, and division of multidigit numbers.
- Students gain a greater understanding of the relationship between decimals and fractions as well as the relationship between decimals and whole umbers. They use this understanding to compare and round decimals, as well as perform the operations of addition, subtraction, multiplication, and division of decimals to the hundredths place.
- Students are introduced to the coordinate plane and develop an initial understanding of points in the first quadrant.
- Students explore the concept of volume in rectangular prisms and composite figures that can be divided into more than one rectangular prism.

Individualized Learning

Summit Math 5 is designed to help all students succeed.

Branching Pathways are practice problems for particularly difficult concepts to support struggling students. These problems are designed to uncover misconceptions and common errors. Students receive feedback targeted to their individual responses and are then led through a reteaching activity that corrects the misconception or common error, only if needed. Branching Pathways create a "tighter net" that catches struggling students at the point of instruction.

Stride is an engaging teaching tool that motivates students toward mastery and rewards learning with games. Following each Concept Quiz, students will practice related concepts based on their specific needs. Time to use Stride is integrated right into the course to ensure sufficient independent practice time.

Stride's adaptive technology guides students to practice where they need it most— and then serves a variety of content that's lively and engaging. Stride's vast database of questions, problems, video lessons, and printable resources deliver grade-level appropriate content aligned to the rigor of the Common Core and individual state standards. Stride's assessments identify where students are performing on specific grade-level standards throughout the year and help identify critical foundational gaps missed in prior grade levels. Test prep capabilities pinpoint student strengths and weaknesses for improved student outcomes on end-of-year assessments.

The Help Me button, which is located on the lesson menu, is an additional personalization feature that lets students opt into activities that are dynamically chosen based on the concept they are studying. Recommendations are powered by a sophisticated engine designed to serve up the activities most likely to be effective for individual students.

How to Use This Guide

The Lesson Guide contains information that will be helpful to you as you begin Summit Math 5 and daily as you work through the program. Here is what the Lesson Guide contains and how to use it.

Lesson Title

The title indicates the lesson topic and matches the title you will see in the online course.

Lesson Overview Table

This table has an overview of the lesson's activities, their approximate times, and whether they take place offline or online.

Content Background

This information will help you better understand the content students will be learning.

Materials

This box lists all materials needed for the lesson and indicates whether they are Supplied or Also Needed.

Keywords

The definitions of key terminology specific to the lesson are here.

Lesson Goals

The goals indicate what students will do in the lesson.

Answer Keys

The Lesson Guide includes answer keys for Activity Book pages.

Activities

Each lesson is broken down into two or more main sections: Get Ready, Learn and Try It, Concept Quiz (final days only), and Wrap-Up. Each section is broken down into individual activities. A brief explanation of each activity is included.

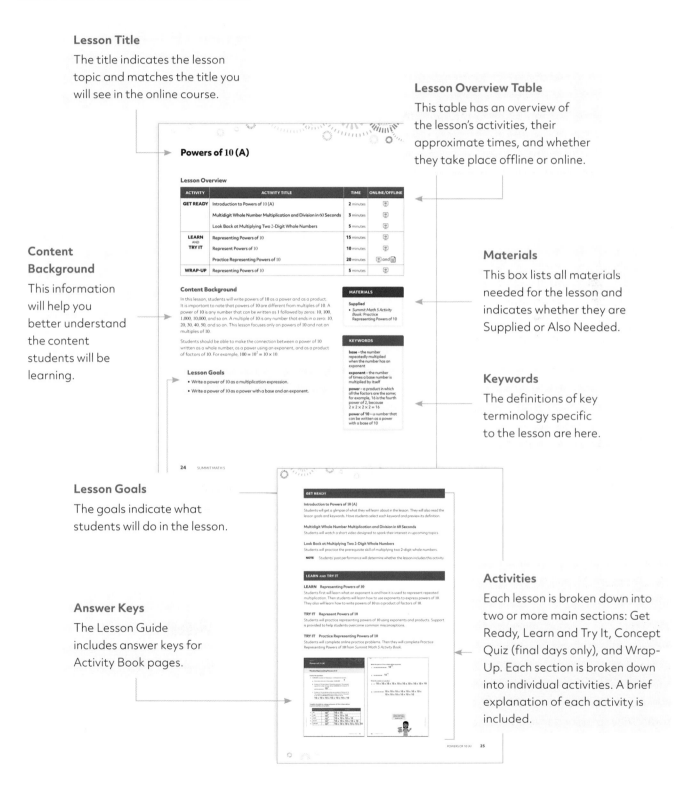

Lessons with Graded Assessments

Check in with students when a lesson has a graded assessment.

- The final lesson of every concept has a computer-scored quiz. Check to make sure students have completed and submitted the Concept Quiz.

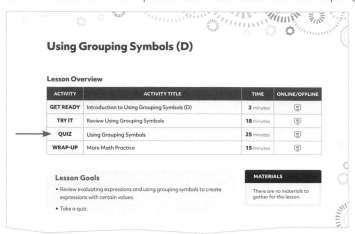

- Big Ideas lessons and the end-of-year project lesson have teacher-graded assignments. Students will complete and turn in the Extended Problems and Mini-Projects in the Big Ideas lessons, plus a project in the last lesson of the course. Teachers will grade these based on a standard rubric. Learning Coaches may need to help students submit their assignments to their teachers. Discuss the best method of turning in work with your students' teachers.

Remember

Academic support at home is critical to student success. While Summit Math 5 empowers students to work independently, this guide is designed help you support your students each day to help them maximize learning.

Numerical Expressions

Using Grouping Symbols (A)

Lesson Overview

ACTIVITY	ACTIVITY TITLE	TIME	ONLINE/OFFLINE
GET READY	Introduction to Using Grouping Symbols (A)	**2** minutes	🖥️
	Numerical Expressions in 60 Seconds	**3** minutes	🖥️
	Look Back at Adding, Subtracting, Multiplying, and Dividing	**5** minutes	🖥️
LEARN AND **TRY IT**	Evaluating an Expression	**7** minutes	🖥️
	Evaluate an Expression	**7** minutes	🖥️
	Using Properties with Order of Operations	**7** minutes	🖥️
	Use Properties with Order of Operations	**7** minutes	🖥️
	Practice Evaluating an Expression	**20** minutes	🖥️ and 📄
WRAP-UP	Evaluating an Expression	**2** minutes	🖥️

Content Background

In this lesson, students will use the order of operations to evaluate expressions with numbers. They will begin with expressions that use the four basic operations and use parentheses as the only grouping symbol.

The order of operations is a set of rules that states the order in which students need to perform computation problems that are written horizontally and include more than one operation. If students don't follow the correct order, they will not calculate the answer correctly. The order of operations is used to find the value of an expression, which is also known as evaluating an expression.

PMDAS

You may have learned the mnemonic device "PEMDAS" or "Please Excuse My Dear Aunt Sally" to help you remember the order of operations. Students at this level will not encounter problems with exponents, so the device should be shortened to "PMDAS." The order of operations follows this step-by-step priority:

1. **P**arentheses: If there are parentheses, complete the computations inside the parentheses. If two or more computations are within any parentheses, the following order is also used there.

MATERIALS

Supplied
- *Summit Math 5 Activity Book:* Practice Evaluating an Expression

KEYWORDS

evaluate – to find the value of an expression

expression – one or more numbers and symbols that show a certain value, such as $2 + 3$, or $3 \times ?$, or $10 - 4 + 1$

order of operations – a set of rules that tells the correct order to use to solve a problem that has more than one operation

2. Multiply or **D**ivide from left to right.

3. Add or **S**ubtract from left to right.

TIP Although multiplication and addition come first in PMDAS, you do not always multiply before dividing or add before subtracting. It depends on the order in which operations are listed from left to right.

Lesson Goals

- Use the order of operations to evaluate an expression without parentheses.
- Use the order of operations to evaluate an expression with parentheses.
- Use properties of arithmetic to evaluate an expression.

GET READY

Introduction to Using Grouping Symbols (A)

Students will get a glimpse of what they will learn about in the lesson. They will also read the lesson goals and keywords. Have students select each keyword and preview its definition.

Numerical Expressions in 60 Seconds

Students will watch a short video designed to spark their interest in upcoming topics.

Look Back at Adding, Subtracting, Multiplying, and Dividing

Students will practice the prerequisite skills of adding, subtracting, multiplying, and dividing.

LEARN AND TRY IT

LEARN   Evaluating an Expression

Students will learn what an expression is and how to evaluate an expression using the order of operations. Some expressions will include parentheses and some will not.

TRY IT   Evaluate an Expression

Students will practice evaluating expressions with and without parentheses. Support is provided to help students overcome common misconceptions.

LEARN   Using Properties with Order of Operations

Students will learn how the associative property, the commutative property, and the distributive property can be used as shortcuts in simplifying expressions.

TRY IT Use Properties with Order of Operations

Students will practice using the associative property, the commutative property, and the distributive property as shortcuts in simplifying expressions. Support is provided to help students overcome misconceptions.

TRY IT Practice Evaluating an Expression

Students will complete online practice problems. Then they will complete Practice Evaluating an Expression from *Summit Math 5 Activity Book*.

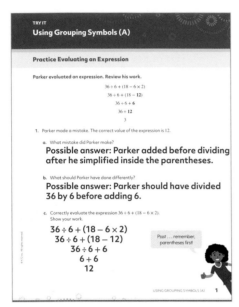

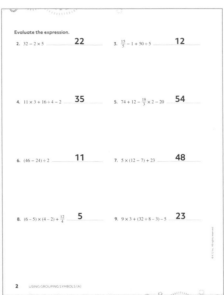

WRAP-UP

Evaluating an Expression

Students will solve a problem to show that they understand using the order of operations to evaluate an expression with parentheses.

Using Grouping Symbols (B)

Lesson Overview

ACTIVITY	ACTIVITY TITLE	TIME	ONLINE/OFFLINE
GET READY	Introduction to Using Grouping Symbols (B)	**2** minutes	🖥️
	Multiplying and Dividing by 5 and 10 Math Facts	**8** minutes	🖥️
LEARN AND **TRY IT**	Working with Nested Grouping Symbols	**15** minutes	🖥️
	Work with Nested Grouping Symbols	**10** minutes	🖥️
	Practice Working with Nested Grouping Symbols	**20** minutes	🖥️ and 📄
WRAP-UP	Working with Nested Grouping Symbols	**5** minutes	🖥️

Content Background

In this lesson, students will be introduced to nested grouping symbols as they use the order of operations to evaluate expressions with numbers. There are three different grouping symbols: parentheses ( ), brackets [ ], and braces { }. Nested grouping symbols occur when one set of grouping symbols appears inside another set of grouping symbols—for example, a set of brackets inside a set of parentheses. Students will not encounter problems with three levels of grouping symbols in this lesson (parentheses inside brackets inside braces).

PMDAS

The mnemonic device "PMDAS" or "Please My Dear Aunt Sally" still applies when there are multiple grouping symbols in an expression. The order of operations follows this step-by-step priority:

1. **P**arentheses: If there are parentheses, complete the computations inside the parentheses. *If there are multiple grouping symbols, students should work from the innermost grouping symbol and work their way outward.* If two or more computations are within any parentheses, the following order is also used there.

2. **M**ultiply or **D**ivide from left to right.

3. **A**dd or **S**ubtract from left to right.

Mastering the order of operations, particularly with nested grouping symbols, will greatly benefit students as they move into the formal study of algebra.

MATERIALS

Supplied
- *Summit Math 5 Activity Book:* Practice Working with Nested Grouping Symbols

KEYWORDS

grouping symbols – symbols used to set numbers or expressions apart, such as parentheses

Lesson Goals

- Find the value of an expression that has grouping symbols within grouping symbols.

Introduction to Using Grouping Symbols (B)

Students will get a glimpse of what they will learn about in the lesson. They will also read the lesson goals and keywords. Have students select each keyword and preview its definition.

Multiplying and Dividing by 5 and 10 Math Facts

Students will practice multiplying and dividing by 5 or 10.

LEARN AND TRY IT

LEARN Working with Nested Grouping Symbols

Students will be introduced to brackets and braces as additional types of grouping symbols. Then they will be introduced to nested grouping symbols and will be shown how to evaluate expressions with nested grouping symbols.

TRY IT Work with Nested Grouping Symbols

Students will practice translating a written phrase into an expression with multiple operations. Support is provided to help students overcome common misconceptions.

SUPPORT   For students having difficulty recognizing which operation to evaluate first, you can introduce PMDAS. The P stands for parentheses, but it includes any grouping symbols working from the inside out. Even though M comes before D in PMDAS, multiplication doesn't *always* come before division. Multiplication *or* division is evaluated in order from left to right. The same is true for addition and subtraction.

TRY IT   Practice Working with Nested Grouping Symbols

Students will complete online practice problems. Then they will complete Practice Working with Nested Grouping Symbols from *Summit Math 5 Activity Book*.

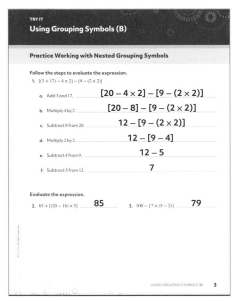

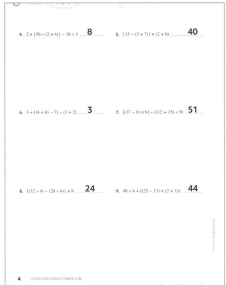

WRAP-UP

Working with Nested Grouping Symbols

Students will solve a problem to show that they understand how to evaluate an expression with nested grouping symbols.

Using Grouping Symbols (C)

Lesson Overview

ACTIVITY	ACTIVITY TITLE	TIME	ONLINE/OFFLINE
GET READY	Introduction to Using Grouping Symbols (C)	**2** minutes	🖥
	Multiplying and Dividing by 5 and 10 with Instant Recall	**8** minutes	🖥
LEARN AND **TRY IT**	Placing Grouping Symbols in an Expression	**7** minutes	🖥
	Place Grouping Symbols in an Expression	**7** minutes	🖥
	Placing Grouping Symbols in a Real-World Expression	**7** minutes	🖥
	Place Grouping Symbols in a Real-World Expression	**7** minutes	🖥
	Practice Placing Grouping Symbols	**20** minutes	🖥 and 📄
WRAP-UP	Placing Grouping Symbols	**2** minutes	🖥

Content Background

In this lesson, students will learn how to place parentheses (or other grouping symbols) in an expression to produce a specific value. They will find the correct placement of parentheses by guessing and then checking their guess. Students will also learn how to insert parentheses into an expression to represent a real-world problem. For reference, the order of operations follows this step-by-step priority:

1. Parentheses: If there are parentheses, complete the computations inside the parentheses. If there are multiple grouping symbols, students should work from the innermost grouping symbol and work their way outward. If two or more computations are within any parentheses, the following order is also used there.

2. Multiply or divide from left to right.

3. Add or subtract from left to right.

MATERIALS

Supplied
- *Summit Math 5 Activity Book:* Practice Placing Grouping Symbols

Lesson Goals

- Insert grouping symbols into an expression so that it has a particular value.
- Represent real-world situations with expressions that have grouping symbols.

GET READY

Introduction to Using Grouping Symbols (C)

Students will get a glimpse of what they will learn about in the lesson. They will also read the lesson goals.

Multiplying and Dividing by 5 and 10 with Instant Recall

Students will practice multiplying or dividing by 5 or 10.

LEARN AND TRY IT

LEARN   Placing Grouping Symbols in an Expression

Students will watch a video to learn how to change the value of an expression by inserting parentheses.

TRY IT   Place Grouping Symbols in an Expression

Students will complete two guided practice problems to practice creating an expression with a specific value by inserting parentheses.

SUPPORT   For students having difficulty knowing where to place parentheses, suggest first evaluating the expression without parentheses. Then ask them what would happen if the operations were completed in a different order. Finally encourage them to try placing parentheses around two numbers and an operation, and evaluating again. They can continue to guess and check until they find the correct placement.

LEARN   Placing Grouping Symbols in a Real-World Expression

Students will learn how to insert parentheses into an expression to represent a real-world problem.

TRY IT   Place Grouping Symbols in a Real-World Expression

Students will complete two guided problems to practice inserting parentheses into an expression to represent a real-world problem.

TRY IT   Practice Placing Grouping Symbols

Students will complete online practice problems. Then they will complete Practice Placing Grouping Symbols from *Summit Math 5 Activity Book*.

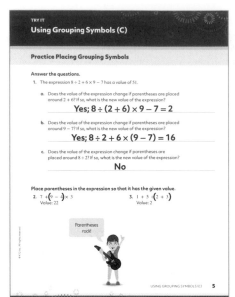

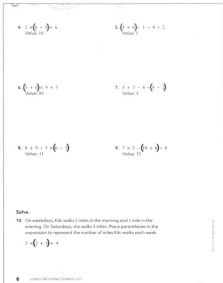

Placing Grouping Symbols

Students will solve a problem to show that they understand how to insert parentheses into an expression that represents a real-world problem to produce a specific value.

Using Grouping Symbols (D)

Lesson Overview

ACTIVITY	ACTIVITY TITLE	TIME	ONLINE/OFFLINE
GET READY	Introduction to Using Grouping Symbols (D)	**2** minutes	📶
TRY IT	Review Using Grouping Symbols	**18** minutes	📶
QUIZ	Using Grouping Symbols	**25** minutes	📶
WRAP-UP	More Math Practice	**15** minutes	📶

Lesson Goals

- Review evaluating expressions and using grouping symbols to create expressions with certain values.

- Take a quiz.

MATERIALS

There are no materials to gather for this lesson.

GET READY

Introduction to Using Grouping Symbols (D)

Students will read the lesson goals.

TRY IT

Review Using Grouping Symbols

Students will answer questions to review what they have learned about using grouping symbols to evaluate expressions.

QUIZ

Using Grouping Symbols

Students will complete the Using Grouping Symbols quiz.

More Math Practice

Students will practice skills according to their individual needs.

Exploring Numerical Expressions (A)

Lesson Overview

ACTIVITY	ACTIVITY TITLE	TIME	ONLINE/OFFLINE
GET READY	Introduction to Exploring Numerical Expressions (A)	**2** minutes	🖥️
	Look Back at Writing Equations to Solve Word Problems	**8** minutes	🖥️
LEARN AND **TRY IT**	Translating a Single-Step Expression from Words to Numbers	**7** minutes	🖥️
	Translate a Single-Step Expression from Words to Numbers	**7** minutes	🖥️
	Translating a Multistep Expression from Words to Numbers	**7** minutes	🖥️
	Translate a Multistep Expression from Words to Numbers	**7** minutes	🖥️
	Practice Translating an Expression from Words to Numbers	**20** minutes	🖥️ and 📄
WRAP-UP	Translating an Expression from Words to Numbers	**2** minutes	🖥️

Content Background

In this lesson, students will translate word expressions to numerical expressions using mathematical symbols, including grouping symbols. Vocabulary is important when determining which operation to use and which order to place numbers. Here are some common phrases to indicate each of the four basic operations:

- Addition: *added to, plus, the sum of, more than, increased by, the total of*

- Subtraction: *subtracted from, minus, the difference of, less than, decreased by, less, reduced by, fewer than*

- Multiplication: *multiplied by, times, the product of, of, combine equal groups, twice, double*

- Division: *divided by, the quotient of, separate into equal groups, share evenly with*

The order of operations will continue to be important for students to correctly represent a written phrase or sentence.

Lesson Goals

- Translate words into a mathematical expression.

Introduction to Exploring Numerical Expressions (A)

Students will get a glimpse of what they will learn about in the lesson. They will also read the lesson goals.

Look Back at Writing Equations to Solve Word Problems

Students will review the names of the results of computing each of the four basic operations: The result of adding is a *sum*. The result of subtracting is a *difference*. The result of multiplying is a *product*. The result of dividing is a *quotient*.

LEARN AND TRY IT

LEARN   Translating a Single-Step Expression from Words to Numbers

Students will learn how to translate a written phrase into a numerical expression with one operation. They must determine whether to add, subtract, multiply, or divide two numbers.

TRY IT   Translate a Single-Step Expression from Words to Numbers

Students will complete two guided problems to practice translating a written phrase into an expression with a single operation.

TIP   There can be more than one correct answer for addition and multiplication expressions. For example, the sum of 3 and 5 could be written $3 + 5$ or $5 + 3$. However, division and subtraction expressions only have one correct answer. For example, the quotient of 8 and 2 is $8 \div 2$ and not $2 \div 8$.

LEARN   Translating a Multistep Expression from Words to Numbers

Students will learn how to translate a written phrase into a numerical expression with multiple operations. Expressions may or may not need grouping symbols. An expression does not need grouping symbols if the operations should be computed in the same order as the order of operations. For example, 5 less than the product of 8 and 3 could be expressed as $8 \times 3 - 5$. Since multiplication is always performed before subtraction, inserting parentheses around 8×3 does not change the value of the expression. The expression is not technically wrong if parentheses *are* used, as the value of the expression is the same with or without them.

However, there are some cases where parentheses are necessary. For example, 5 times the sum of 8 and 3 must be expressed using parentheses. The numerical expression $5 \times (8 + 3)$ is not the same as $5 \times 8 + 3$. Without parentheses the multiplication would be computed first. Using parentheses around $8 + 3$ indicates that the addition should be computed first, which correctly represents the phrase.

TRY IT   Translate a Multistep Expression from Words to Numbers

Students will complete two guided problems to practice translating a written phrase into an expression with multiple operations. Some expressions may require grouping symbols.

TRY IT   Practice Translating an Expression from Words to Numbers

Students will complete online practice problems. Then they will complete Practice Translating an Expression from Words to Numbers from *Summit Math 5 Activity Book.*

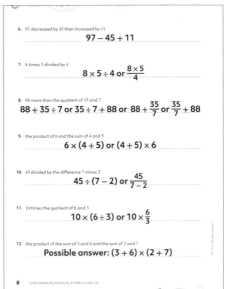

WRAP-UP

Translating an Expression from Words to Numbers

Students will solve a problem to show that they understand how to use a numerical expression to represent a written phrase.

Exploring Numerical Expressions (B)

Lesson Overview

ACTIVITY	ACTIVITY TITLE	TIME	ONLINE/OFFLINE
GET READY	Introduction to Exploring Numerical Expressions (B)	**2** minutes	🖥️
	Multiplying and Dividing by 5 and 10 Math Facts Game	**8** minutes	🖥️
LEARN AND **TRY IT**	Translating an Expression from Numbers to Words	**7** minutes	🖥️
	Translate an Expression from Numbers to Words	**7** minutes	🖥️
	Translating a Real-World Expression from Numbers to Words	**7** minutes	🖥️
	Translate a Real-World Expression from Numbers to Words	**7** minutes	🖥️
	Practice Translating an Expression from Numbers to Words	**20** minutes	🖥️ and 📄
WRAP-UP	Translating an Expression from Numbers to Words	**2** minutes	🖥️

Content Background

In this lesson, students will write phrases or sentences to represent numerical expressions, including expressions with grouping symbols. It is important that students use correct vocabulary to indicate a specific operation. Here are some common phrases to indicate each of the four basic operations:

- Addition: *added to, plus, the sum of, more than, increased by, the total of*

- Subtraction: *subtracted from, minus, the difference of, less than, decreased by, less, reduced by, fewer than*

- Multiplication: *multiplied by, times, the product of, of, combine equal groups, twice, double*

- Division: *divided by, the quotient of, separate into equal groups, share evenly with*

Understanding the order of operations will continue to be important for students to correctly translate a numerical expression into words.

> **MATERIALS**
>
> **Supplied**
> - *Summit Math 5 Activity Book:* Practice Translating an Expression from Numbers to Words

Lesson Goals
- Translate a mathematical expression into words.
- Determine real-world meaning for a mathematical expression.

Introduction to Exploring Numerical Expressions (B)

Students will get a glimpse of what they will learn about in the lesson. They will also read the lesson goals.

Multiplying and Dividing by 5 and 10 Math Facts Game

Students will practice multiplying and dividing by 5 and 10.

LEARN AND TRY IT

LEARN   Translating an Expression from Numbers to Words

Students will learn how to translate a numerical expression into a written phrase or sentence. There are often several correct translations for a numerical expression since there are many different phrases that represent each of the four basic operations. Students should approach each problem by first considering how the expression is evaluated using the order or operations.

SUPPORT   Sometimes certain words or phrases do not clearly describe an expression. For example, the expression $14 + 6 \div 2$ could be translated to "The sum of 14 and 6 divided by 2." However, this phrase does not clearly indicate whether the sum or the quotient should be computed first. In these cases, simply stating the operation is often the best solution. The best translation of $14 + 6 \div 2$ would be "14 plus 6 divided by 2."

TRY IT   Translate an Expression from Numbers to Words

Students will complete two guided problems to practice translating an expression from numbers to words. Extra support will be provided for students who struggle.

LEARN   Translating a Real-World Expression from Numbers to Words

Students will learn how to create real-world problems to represent numerical expressions. They should continue to approach each problem by first considering how the expression is evaluated using the order or operations.

TRY IT   Translate a Real-World Expression from Numbers to Words

Students will complete two guided problems to practice creating a real-world problem to describe a numerical expression.

TRY IT Practice Translating an Expression from Numbers to Words

Students will complete online practice problems. Then they will complete Practice Translating an Expression from Numbers to Words from *Summit Math 5 Activity Book*.

NOTE Students' answers may not exactly match the sample answers. Each operation can be described using many different phrases, and many different situations can be used to describe an expression.

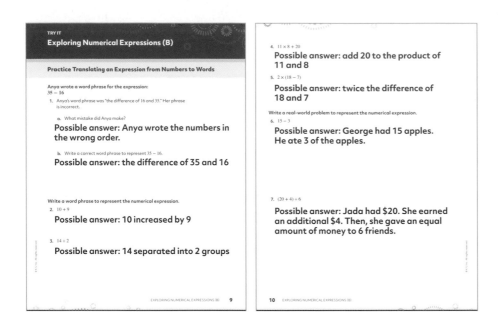

WRAP-UP

Translating an Expression from Numbers to Words

Students will solve a problem to show that they understand how to translate a numerical expression into words.

Exploring Numerical Expressions (C)

Lesson Overview

ACTIVITY	ACTIVITY TITLE	TIME	ONLINE/OFFLINE
GET READY	Introduction to Exploring Numerical Expressions (C)	**2** minutes	📶
TRY IT	Review Exploring Numerical Expressions	**18** minutes	📶
QUIZ	Explore Numerical Expressions	**25** minutes	📶
WRAP-UP	More Math Practice	**15** minutes	📶

Lesson Goals

- Review translating from words to numbers and from numbers to words.

- Take a quiz.

MATERIALS

There are no materials to gather for this lesson.

GET READY

Introduction to Exploring Numerical Expressions (C)

Students will read the lesson goals.

TRY IT

Review Exploring Numerical Expressions

Students will answer questions to review what they have learned about exploring numerical expressions.

QUIZ

Explore Numerical Expressions

Students will complete the Explore Numerical Expressions quiz.

More Math Practice

Students will practice skills according to their individual needs.

Big Ideas: Mini-Project

Lesson Overview

Big Ideas lessons provide students the opportunity to further apply the knowledge and skills acquired throughout previous units. Each Big Ideas lesson consists of three parts:

1. **Cumulative Review:** Students keep their skills fresh by reviewing prior content.

2. **Preview:** Students practice answering the types of questions they will commonly find on standardized tests.

3. **Synthesis:** Students complete an assignment that allows them to interweave and apply what they've learned. These synthesis assignments will vary throughout the course.

   In the Synthesis portion of this Big Ideas lesson, students will complete a small, creative project designed to tie together concepts and skills that students have encountered across units. These small projects are designed to emphasize a real-world application that connects mathematics to other subjects, including science, technology, engineering, art, and history. Students will need to use pencil and paper and/or technology to show their work.

   LEARNING COACH CHECK-IN   Make sure students complete, review, and submit the assignment to their teacher.

All materials needed for this lesson are linked online. The materials are not provided in this Lesson Guide or in the Activity Book.

Multidigit Whole Number Multiplication and Division

Powers of 10 (A)

Lesson Overview

ACTIVITY	ACTIVITY TITLE	TIME	ONLINE/OFFLINE
GET READY	Introduction to Powers of 10 (A)	**2** minutes	🖥️
	Multidigit Whole Number Multiplication and Division in 60 Seconds	**3** minutes	🖥️
	Look Back at Multiplying Two 2-Digit Whole Numbers	**5** minutes	🖥️
LEARN AND **TRY IT**	Representing Powers of 10	**15** minutes	🖥️
	Represent Powers of 10	**10** minutes	🖥️
	Practice Representing Powers of 10	**20** minutes	🖥️ and 📄
WRAP-UP	Representing Powers of 10	**5** minutes	🖥️

Content Background

In this lesson, students will write powers of 10 as a power and as a product. It is important to note that powers of 10 are different from multiples of 10. A power of 10 is any number that can be written as 1 followed by zeros: 10, 100, 1,000, 10,000, and so on. A multiple of 10 is any number that ends in a zero: 10, 20, 30, 40, 50, and so on. This lesson focuses only on powers of 10 and not on multiples of 10.

Students should be able to make the connection between a power of 10 written as a whole number, as a power using an exponent, and as a product of factors of 10. For example, $100 = 10^2 = 10 \times 10$.

Lesson Goals

- Write a power of 10 as a multiplication expression.
- Write a power of 10 as a power with a base and an exponent.

Introduction to Powers of 10 (A)

Students will get a glimpse of what they will learn about in the lesson. They will also read the lesson goals and keywords. Have students select each keyword and preview its definition.

Multidigit Whole Number Multiplication and Division in 60 Seconds

Students will watch a short video designed to spark their interest in upcoming topics.

Look Back at Multiplying Two 2-Digit Whole Numbers

Students will practice the prerequisite skill of multiplying two 2-digit whole numbers.

LEARN AND TRY IT

LEARN   Representing Powers of 10

Students first will learn what an exponent is and how it is used to represent repeated multiplication. Then students will learn how to use exponents to express powers of 10. They also will learn how to write powers of 10 as a product of factors of 10.

TRY IT   Represent Powers of 10

Students will practice representing powers of 10 using exponents and products. Support is provided to help students overcome common misconceptions.

TRY IT   Practice Representing Powers of 10

Students will complete online practice problems. Then they will complete Practice Representing Powers of 10 from *Summit Math 5 Activity Book*.

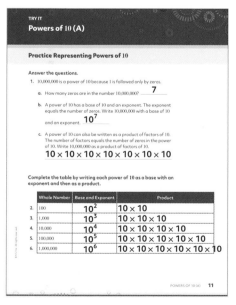

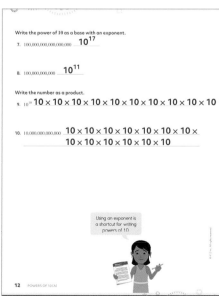

Represent Powers of 10

Students will solve a problem to show that they understand how to represent a power of 10 using an exponent.

Powers of 10 (B)

Lesson Overview

ACTIVITY	ACTIVITY TITLE	TIME	ONLINE/OFFLINE
GET READY	Introduction to Powers of 10 (B)	**2** minutes	🖥️
	Multiplying and Dividing by 2 Math Facts	**8** minutes	🖥️
LEARN AND **TRY IT**	Multiplying by a Power of 10	**15** minutes	🖥️
	Multiply by a Power of 10	**10** minutes	🖥️
	Practice Multiplying by a Power of 10	**20** minutes	🖥️ and 📄
WRAP-UP	Multiplying by a Power of 10	**5** minutes	🖥️

Content Background

In this lesson, students will learn how to use a pattern of zeros to multiply a number by a power of 10. When a number is multiplied by a power of 10, the number of zeros in the power of 10 are added after the last digit of the other number.

Here is an example of a number multiplied by a power of 10: $45 \times 100 = 4,500$. There are two zeros in 100. Add two zeros to the end of 45 to get 4,500. The number of zeros in the power of 10 does not always equal the number of zeros in the product if the other number already ends in one or more zeros. For example, $20 \times 100 = 2,000$ not 200. You must add two zeros to the end of 20 to get 2,000.

MATERIALS

Supplied
- *Summit Math 5 Activity Book:* Practice Multiplying by a Power of 10

Lesson Goals

- Describe the patterns in multiplying numbers by powers of 10.
- Multiply a number by a power of 10 by using patterns.

GET READY

Introduction to Powers of 10 (B)

Students will get a glimpse of what they will learn about in the lesson. They will also read the lesson goals.

Multiplying and Dividing by 2 Math Facts

Students will practice multiplying and dividing by 2.

LEARN AND TRY IT

LEARN   Multiplying by a Power of 10

Students will learn how to multiply a whole number by a power of 10 using a pattern of zeros. The number of zeros added after the last digit of the whole number equals the number of zeros in the power of 10. The pattern applies regardless of whether the power of 10 is the first or the second factor in the product. In other words, $23 \times 100 = 100 \times 23$. Powers of 10 will be given as whole numbers and using exponents.

TRY IT   Multiply by a Power of 10

Students will practice describing the pattern of zeros when multiplying by a power of 10. They will also practice multiplying by a power of 10. Support will be provided to help students overcome misconceptions.

TRY IT   Practice Multiplying by a Power of 10

Students will complete online practice problems. Then they will complete Practice Multiplying by a Power of 10 from *Summit Math 5 Activity Book*.

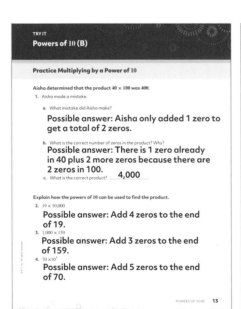

WRAP-UP

Multiplying by a Power of 10

Students will solve a problem to show that they understand how to multiply by a power of 10.

Powers of 10 (C)

Lesson Overview

ACTIVITY	ACTIVITY TITLE	TIME	ONLINE/OFFLINE
GET READY	Introduction to Powers of 10 (C)	**2** minutes	📶
TRY IT	Review Powers of 10	**18** minutes	📶
QUIZ	Powers of 10	**25** minutes	📶
WRAP-UP	More Math Practice	**15** minutes	📶

Lesson Goals

- Review representing powers of 10 and multiplying by powers of 10.

- Take a quiz.

> **MATERIALS**
>
> There are no materials to gather for this lesson.

GET READY

Introduction to Powers of 10 (C)

Students will read the lesson goals.

TRY IT

Review Powers of 10

Students will answer questions to review what they have learned about powers of 10.

QUIZ

Powers of 10

Students will complete the Powers of 10 quiz.

More Math Practice

Students will practice skills according to their individual needs.

Multidigit Whole Number Multiplication (A)

Lesson Overview

ACTIVITY	ACTIVITY TITLE	TIME	ONLINE/OFFLINE
GET READY	Introduction to Multidigit Whole Number Multiplication (A)	**2** minutes	🖥️
	Look Back at Describing Multidigit Multiplication	**8** minutes	🖥️
LEARN AND **TRY IT**	Multiplying Whole Numbers with Zeros	**7** minutes	🖥️
	Multiply Whole Numbers with Zeros	**7** minutes	🖥️
	Multiplying Whole Numbers	**7** minutes	🖥️
	Multiply Whole Numbers	**7** minutes	🖥️
	Practice Multiplying Whole Numbers	**20** minutes	🖥️ and 📄
WRAP-UP	Multiplying Whole Numbers	**2** minutes	🖥️

Content Background

In this lesson, students will learn how to multiply multidigit numbers. First, students will multiply numbers when one or both factors end in one or more zeros. To multiply these numbers, students will multiply the nonzero digits and then add the appropriate number of zeros. For example, to find 15×300, first multiply 15 by 3 to get 45. Then add two zeros to the end of 45 to get 4,500. Two zeros are added because there are two zeros in 300.

Students will also learn how to multiply two multidigit whole numbers using the standard algorithm. An emphasis is on understanding place value in the second factor. For example, in the product 34×48, the first step is to multiply 34 by 8 and record this partial product. The next step is to multiply 34 by 40. Notice that we don't say to multiply 34 by 4. The 4 is in the tens place, so it is more accurate to say that we are multiplying 34 by 40. This language helps students remember to record a 0 in the ones place when writing the partial products.

$$
\begin{array}{r}
\overset{\scriptstyle 1}{\overset{\scriptstyle \cancel{3}}{3}}4 \\
\times\ 48 \\
\hline
272 \\
+\ 1{,}360 \\
\hline
1{,}632
\end{array}
$$

Lesson Goals

- Multiply numbers with zeros using patterns.
- Multiply numbers using the algorithm.

Introduction to Multidigit Whole Number Multiplication (A)

Students will get a glimpse of what they will learn about in the lesson. They will also read the lesson goals and keywords. Have students select each keyword and preview its definition.

Look Back at Describing Multidigit Multiplication

Students will practice the prerequisite skill of describing multidigit multiplication using rectangular arrays or an area model.

LEARN AND TRY IT

LEARN   Multiplying Whole Numbers with Zeros

Students will learn how to multiply when one or both factors end in one or more zeros. They will be shown how to use a pattern of zeros to find the correct product.

SUPPORT   Students may struggle if the product of the nonzero numbers ends in zero. In the product $25 \times 2,000$, 25 times 2 is 50. Then, three zeros are added to the end of 50 to get the product 50,000. Notice that the product has four zeros even though 2,000 only has three zeros. This result happens because the product of 25 and 2 ends in a zero. Remind students that an answer can have more zeros than one of the factors.

Students also may struggle if they encounter a number that has a zero, but the zero is not the last digit—for example $205 \times 5,000$. Students should multiply 205 by 5 to get 1,025. Then, they should add three zeros to the end of 1,025 to get 1,025,000. The number 1,025,000 has three zeros at the end of the number. Remind students that we only count the number of zeros at the end of the number.

TRY IT   Multiply Whole Numbers with Zeros

Students will practice using patterns to multiply when one or both factors end in one or more zeros. Support will be provided to help students overcome misconceptions.

LEARN Multiplying Whole Numbers

Students will learn the standard algorithm for multiplying multidigit numbers. A rectangular array is used to support the idea of partial products and reinforce the importance of place value.

NOTE Models are used to complement the steps of the standard multiplication algorithm. When students understand that multiplying each digit results in an area, they can better visualize place value and remember to line up the digits of the partial products correctly.

TRY IT Multiply Whole Numbers

Students will practice multiplying multidigit whole numbers. Support will be provided to help students overcome misconceptions.

TIP It might help students to work the problems using paper and pencil first before entering the answers online.

TRY IT Practice Multiplying Whole Numbers

Students will complete online practice problems. Then they will complete Practice Multiplying Whole Numbers from *Summit Math 5 Activity Book*.

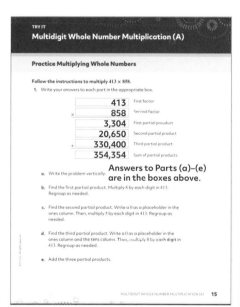

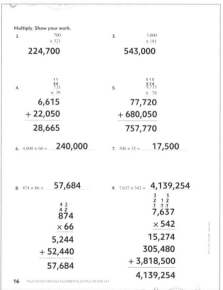

WRAP-UP

Multiplying Whole Numbers

Students will solve a problem to show that they understand how to multiply multidigit whole numbers using the standard algorithm.

Multidigit Whole Number Multiplication (B)

Lesson Overview

ACTIVITY	ACTIVITY TITLE	TIME	ONLINE/OFFLINE
GET READY	Introduction to Multidigit Whole Number Multiplication (B)	**2** minutes	🖥️
	Multiplying and Dividing by 2 with Instant Recall	**8** minutes	🖥️
LEARN AND **TRY IT**	Multiplying Whole Numbers in the Real World	**15** minutes	🖥️
	Multiply Whole Numbers in the Real World	**10** minutes	🖥️
	Practice Multiplying Whole Numbers in the Real World	**20** minutes	🖥️ and 📄
WRAP-UP	Multiplying Whole Numbers in the Real World	**5** minutes	🖥️

Content Background

In this lesson, students will use the multidigit multiplication algorithm to solve real-world problems. An emphasis is on understanding place value while using the algorithm. For example, in the product 254×137, the first step is to multiply 7 by each digit in 254 and record this partial product. The next step is to multiply 30 by each digit in 254. We do this by writing a placeholder 0 in the ones place and multiplying each digit in 254 by 3. Similarly, the final step is to multiply 100 by each digit in 254. This language helps students remember to record the correct number of placeholder zeros when writing the partial products.

$$
\begin{array}{r}
\overset{\times\ \times}{\underset{254}{\overset{\times\ \times}{}}} \\
\times\ 137 \\
\hline
1{,}778 \\
7{,}620 \\
+\ 25{,}400 \\
\hline
34{,}798
\end{array}
$$

Lesson Goals

- Solve real-world problems by using the multiplication algorithm.

Introduction to Multidigit Whole Number Multiplication (B)

Students will get a glimpse of what they will learn about in the lesson. They will also read the lesson goals.

Multiplying and Dividing by 2 with Instant Recall

Students will practice multiplying and dividing by 2.

LEARN AND **TRY IT**

LEARN Multiplying Whole Numbers in the Real World

Students will learn how to use the standard multiplication algorithm to solve real-world problems involving multiplication.

TRY IT Multiply Whole Numbers in the Real World

Students will practice using the standard multiplication algorithm to solve real-world problems. Support will be provided to help students overcome misconceptions.

TIP Remind students that the number with more digits should be written first when setting up the multiplication problem vertically.

TIP It might help students to solve the problems using paper and pencil before entering the answers online.

TRY IT Practice Multiplying Whole Numbers in the Real World

Students will complete online practice problems. Then they will complete Practice Multiplying Whole Numbers in the Real World from *Summit Math 5 Activity Book*.

TIP It might help students to solve the problems using paper and pencil before entering the answers online.

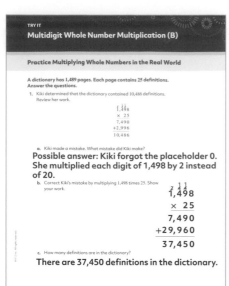

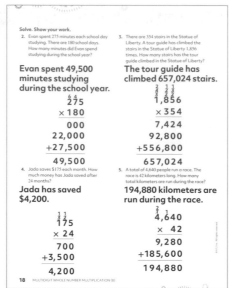

Multidigit Whole Number Multiplication (B)

Practice Multiplying Whole Numbers in the Real World

A dictionary has 1,489 pages. Each page contains 25 definitions. Answer the questions.

1. Kiki determined that the dictionary contained 10,486 definitions. Review her work.

$$
\begin{array}{r}
1,498 \\
\times\ 25 \\
\hline
7,490 \\
+2,996 \\
\hline
10,486
\end{array}
$$

a. Kiki made a mistake. What mistake did Kiki make?

Possible answer: Kiki forgot the placeholder 0. She multiplied each digit of 1,498 by 2 instead of 20.

b. Correct Kiki's mistake by multiplying 1,498 times 25. Show your work.

$$
\begin{array}{r}
1,498 \\
\times\ 25 \\
\hline
7,490 \\
+29,960 \\
\hline
37,450
\end{array}
$$

c. How many definitions are in the dictionary?

There are 37,450 definitions in the dictionary.

Solve. Show your work.

2. Evan spent 275 minutes each school day studying. There are 180 school days. How many minutes did Evan spend studying during the school year?

Evan spent 49,500 minutes studying during the school year.

$$
\begin{array}{r}
275 \\
\times\ 180 \\
\hline
000 \\
22,000 \\
+27,500 \\
\hline
49,500
\end{array}
$$

3. There are 354 stairs in the Statue of Liberty. A tour guide has climbed the stairs in the Statue of Liberty 1,856 times. How many stairs has the tour guide climbed in the Statue of Liberty?

The tour guide has climbed 657,024 stairs.

$$
\begin{array}{r}
1,856 \\
\times\ 354 \\
\hline
7,424 \\
92,800 \\
+556,800 \\
\hline
657,024
\end{array}
$$

4. Jada saves $175 each month. How much money has Jada saved after 24 months?

Jada has saved $4,200.

$$
\begin{array}{r}
175 \\
\times\ 24 \\
\hline
700 \\
+3,500 \\
\hline
4,200
\end{array}
$$

5. A total of 4,640 people run a race. The race is 42 kilometers long. How many total kilometers are run during the race?

194,880 kilometers are run during the race.

$$
\begin{array}{r}
4,640 \\
\times\ 42 \\
\hline
9,280 \\
+185,600 \\
\hline
194,880
\end{array}
$$

WRAP-UP

Multiplying Whole Numbers in the Real World

Students will solve a problem to show that they understand how to use the standard multiplication algorithm when solving a real-world problem.

Multidigit Whole Number Multiplication (C)

Lesson Overview

ACTIVITY	ACTIVITY TITLE	TIME	ONLINE/OFFLINE
GET READY	Introduction to Multidigit Whole Number Multiplication (C)	**2** minutes	📶
TRY IT	Review Multidigit Whole Number Multiplication	**18** minutes	📶
QUIZ	Multidigit Whole Number Multiplication	**25** minutes	📶
WRAP-UP	More Math Practice	**15** minutes	📶

Lesson Goals

- Review multiplying numbers using patterns of zero and using the algorithm.
- Take a quiz.

MATERIALS

There are no materials to gather for this lesson.

GET READY

Introduction to Multidigit Whole Number Multiplication (C)

Students will read the lesson goals.

TRY IT

Review Multidigit Whole Number Multiplication

Students will answer questions to review what they have learned about multiplying whole numbers with more than one digit.

QUIZ

Multidigit Whole Number Multiplication

Students will complete the Multidigit Whole Number Multiplication quiz.

More Math Practice

Students will practice skills according to their individual needs.

Multidigit Division Strategies (A)

Lesson Overview

ACTIVITY	ACTIVITY TITLE	TIME	ONLINE/OFFLINE
GET READY	Introduction to Multidigit Division Strategies (A)	**2** minutes	🖥
	Look Back at Multiplying by a Multiple of 10	**8** minutes	🖥
LEARN AND **TRY IT**	Dividing with No Remainder Using Models	**7** minutes	🖥
	Divide with No Remainder Using Models	**7** minutes	🖥
	Dividing with a Remainder Using Models	**7** minutes	🖥
	Divide with a Remainder Using Models	**7** minutes	🖥
	Practice Dividing Using Models	**20** minutes	🖥 and 📄
WRAP-UP	Dividing Using Models	**2** minutes	🖥

Content Background

In this lesson, students will learn how to use an area model to divide multidigit numbers. Students are familiar with using the area of a rectangle to model multiplication where the two factors are the length and width and the product is the area of the rectangle. To use an area model to divide, the dividend is the area of the rectangle, the divisor is the width of the rectangle, and the quotient is the length of the rectangle. The area of the rectangle is subdivided based on the digits of the quotient. Eventually, students will use the standard division algorithm to divide. Using this area model will help deepen students' understanding of the standard division algorithm. For example, compare the completed area model to the standard division algorithm for $324 \div 12$.

Lesson Goals

- Divide numbers by using area models.

Introduction to Multidigit Division Strategies (A)

Students will get a glimpse of what they will learn about in the lesson. They will also read the lesson goals and keywords. Have students select each keyword and preview its definition.

Look Back at Multiplying by a Multiple of 10

Students will practice the prerequisite skill of finding a product where one factor is a multiple of 10.

LEARN AND TRY IT

LEARN   Dividing with No Remainder Using Models

Students will learn how to use an area model to divide two numbers. The quotient will not have a remainder.

NOTE   Students may encounter a problem where the ones or tens digit is 0. For example, examine the area model representing $7,545 \div 15$. Notice that the quotient is 503, not 53.

$$
\begin{array}{c|c|c}
 & 500 & 3 \\
\hline
15 & 7,500 & 45 \\
\end{array}
$$

TRY IT   Divide with No Remainder Using Models

Students will practice using an area model to divide two numbers where the quotient does not have a remainder. Support will be provided to help students overcome misconceptions.

LEARN Dividing with a Remainder Using Models

Students will learn how to use an area model to divide two numbers where the quotient does have a remainder.

TIP The remainder should always be less than the divisor. If students work out a problem and the remainder is *greater* than the divisor, then the remainder contains at least one more factor of the divisor. Remind students that they need to get as close to the area as possible without going over.

TRY IT Divide with a Remainder Using Models

Students will practice dividing two numbers where the quotient has a remainder. Support will be provided to help students overcome misconceptions.

TRY IT Practice Dividing Using Models

Students will complete online practice problems. Then they will complete Practice Dividing Using Models from *Summit Math 5 Activity Book*.

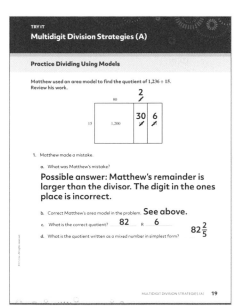

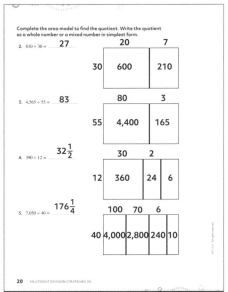

Dividing Using Models

Students will solve a problem to show that they understand how to use an area model to divide two numbers.

Multidigit Division Strategies (B)

Lesson Overview

ACTIVITY	ACTIVITY TITLE	TIME	ONLINE/OFFLINE
GET READY	Introduction to Multidigit Division Strategies (B)	**2** minutes	📶
	Multiplying and Dividing by 2 Math Facts Game	**8** minutes	📶
LEARN AND **TRY IT**	Writing Equations for Division Models	**15** minutes	📶
	Write Equations for Division Models	**10** minutes	📶
	Practice Writing Equations for Division Models	**20** minutes	📶 and 📄
WRAP-UP	Writing Equations for Division Models	**5** minutes	📶

Content Background

In this lesson, students will learn how to write division equations to describe division calculations. This step is important in building connections between an area model and the standard division algorithm.

It is important to notice that the calculations are directly related to area models that have been used to represent a division problem. A common misconception is that the divisor is used to divide each digit of the dividend. For example, consider $2{,}414 \div 34$. A student might incorrectly write $2{,}414 \div 34 = (2{,}000 \div 34) + (400 \div 34) + (10 \div 34) + (4 \div 34)$. In this equation, the dividend is expanded by place value. It is a true equation, but it is not helpful in finding the quotient because 34 does not divide evenly into $2{,}000$, 400, 10, and 4. The purpose of using equations is to partition the dividend into numbers that can be divided evenly by 34. Those numbers come from the area model. Notice that the numbers in the area model, the division equations, and the standard division algorithm are all related.

Area Model	Division Equations	Standard Division Algorithm
70 1 34 2,380 34	$2{,}414 \div 34 = (2{,}380 \div 34) + (34 \div 34)$ $2{,}414 \div 34 = 70 + 1$ $2{,}414 \div 34 = 71$	$\begin{array}{r} 71 \\ 34{\overline{)2{,}414}} \\ -2{,}380 \\ \hline 34 \\ -34 \\ \hline 0 \end{array}$

The area model and division equations prepare students to apply the standard algorithm with accuracy and understanding.

Lesson Goals

- Describe area models for division problems with equations.

Introduction to Multidigit Division Strategies (B)

Students will get a glimpse of what they will learn about in the lesson. They will also read the lesson goals.

Multiplying and Dividing by 2 Math Facts Game

Students will practice multiplying and dividing by 2.

LEARN AND TRY IT

LEARN   Writing Equations for Division Models

Students will learn how to write division equations to describe division calculations. Each number in each division equation is directly related to a number on the related area model.

TRY IT   Write Equations for Division Models

Students will practice writing division equations to describe division calculations. Support will be provided to help students overcome misconceptions.

TRY IT Practice Writing Equations for Division Models

Students will complete online practice problems. Then they will complete Practice Writing Equations for Division Models from *Summit Math 5 Activity Book.*

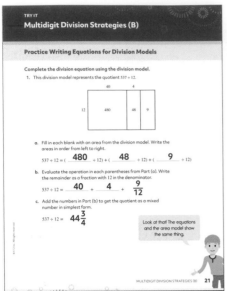

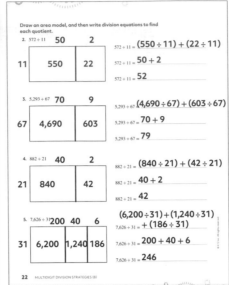

Writing Equations for Division Models

Students will solve a problem to show that they understand how to write division equations to represent division calculations.

Multidigit Division Strategies (C)

Lesson Overview

ACTIVITY	ACTIVITY TITLE	TIME	ONLINE/OFFLINE
GET READY	Introduction to Multidigit Division Strategies (C)	**2** minutes	🖥️
TRY IT	Review Multidigit Division Strategies	**18** minutes	🖥️
QUIZ	Multidigit Division Strategies	**25** minutes	🖥️
WRAP-UP	More Math Practice	**15** minutes	🖥️

Lesson Goals

- Review using an area model to find a quotient and writing equations for quotients from an area model.

- Take a quiz.

MATERIALS

There are no materials to gather for this lesson.

GET READY

Introduction to Multidigit Division Strategies (C)

Students will read the lesson goals.

TRY IT

Review Multidigit Division Strategies

Students will answer questions to review what they have learned about multidigit division strategies.

QUIZ

Multidigit Division Strategies

Students will complete the Multidigit Division Strategies quiz.

More Math Practice

Students will practice skills according to their individual needs.

Multidigit Division Algorithm (A)

Lesson Overview

ACTIVITY	ACTIVITY TITLE	TIME	ONLINE/OFFLINE
GET READY	Introduction to Multidigit Division Algorithm (A)	**2** minutes	📶
	Look Back at Products of 2-Digit and 1-Digit Numbers	**8** minutes	📶
LEARN AND **TRY IT**	Dividing 2-Digit Numbers by 2-Digit Numbers	**7** minutes	📶
	Divide 2-Digit Numbers by 2-Digit Numbers	**7** minutes	📶
	Dividing a 2-Digit Number in the Real World	**7** minutes	📶
	Divide a 2-Digit Number in the Real World	**7** minutes	📶
	Practice Dividing 2-Digit Numbers by 2-Digit Numbers	**20** minutes	📶 and 📄
WRAP-UP	Dividing 2-Digit Numbers by 2-Digit Numbers	**2** minutes	📶

Content Background

In this lesson, students will learn how to use a division house to represent division problems involving two two-digit numbers. In this lesson, remainders will only be represented using R or mixed numbers. Using decimals to represent remainders will not be used in this unit.

Lesson Goals

• Divide two-digit numbers by two-digit numbers.

• Solve real-world problems by dividing two-digit numbers by two-digit numbers.

GET READY

Introduction to Multidigit Division Strategies (A)
Students will get a glimpse of what they will learn about in the lesson. They will also read the lesson goals.

Look Back at Products of 2-Digit and 1-Digit Numbers

Students will practice the prerequisite skill of multiplying a two-digit number by a one-digit number.

LEARN AND TRY IT

LEARN   Dividing 2-Digit Numbers by 2-Digit Numbers

Students will learn how to use a division house to represent division problems involving two 2-digit numbers. Some problems will have a remainder and some will not.

TRY IT   Divide 2-Digit Numbers by 2-Digit Numbers

Students will practice using a division house to represent dividing a two-digit number by a two-digit number. Support will be provided to help students overcome misconceptions.

LEARN   Dividing a 2-Digit Number in the Real World

Students will solve real-world problems that involve dividing a two-digit number by a two-digit number. The answer to the problem is not always the entire quotient. It could be the remainder or just the whole-number part of the quotient.

TRY IT   Divide a 2-Digit Number in the Real World

Students will practice solving real-world division problems with two 2-digit numbers. Support will be provided to help students overcome misconceptions.

TRY IT   Practice Dividing 2-Digit Numbers by 2-Digit Numbers

Students will complete online practice problems. Then they will complete Practice Dividing 2-Digit Numbers by 2-Digit Numbers from *Summit Math 5 Activity Book*.

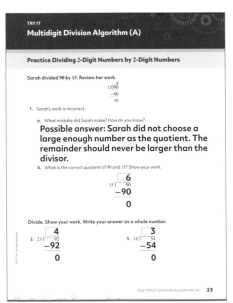

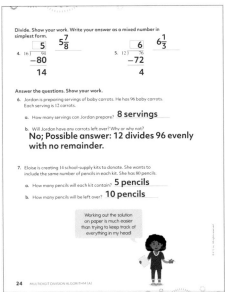

Dividing 2-Digit Numbers by 2-Digit Numbers

Students will solve a problem to show that they understand dividing two-digit numbers by two-digit numbers.

Multidigit Division Algorithm (B)

Lesson Overview

ACTIVITY	ACTIVITY TITLE	TIME	ONLINE/OFFLINE
GET READY	Introduction to Multidigit Division Algorithm (B)	**2** minutes	🖥️
	Multiplying and Dividing by 3 Math Facts	**8** minutes	🖥️
LEARN AND **TRY IT**	Dividing 3-Digit Numbers by 2-Digit Numbers	**7** minutes	🖥️
	Divide 3-Digit Numbers by 2-Digit Numbers	**7** minutes	🖥️
	Dividing a 3-Digit Number in the Real World	**7** minutes	🖥️
	Divide a 3-Digit Number in the Real World	**7** minutes	🖥️
	Practice Dividing 3-Digit Numbers by 2-Digit Numbers	**20** minutes	🖥️ and 📄
WRAP-UP	Dividing 3-Digit Numbers by 2-Digit Numbers	**2** minutes	🖥️

Content Background

In this lesson, students will learn how to apply the standard division algorithm to the quotient of a three-digit number and a two-digit number. You may have learned a slightly different version of this algorithm that involved bringing down a digit. This version of the algorithm does not require bringing down any digits because it continues to emphasize place value.

Standard Division Algorithm Steps

1. **Divide.** Determine how many times the divisor will divide into the dividend at the greatest place value.

2. **Write a digit in the quotient.** Write each digit above the matching place value in the dividend.

3. **Multiply it by the divisor.** For the digit in the tens place, multiply the divisor by that many tens, not by that many ones.

4. **Subtract.**

5. **Repeat for the next digit of the quotient.** If there is a remainder, write the remainder as a fraction where the remainder is the numerator and the denominator is the divisor. Simplify the fraction if possible.

> **MATERIALS**
>
> **Supplied**
> - *Summit Math 5 Activity Book:* Practice Dividing 3-Digit Numbers by 2-Digit Numbers

Lesson Goals

- Divide three-digit numbers by two-digit numbers.
- Solve real-world problems by dividing three-digit numbers by two-digit numbers.

GET READY

Introduction to Multidigit Division Algorithm (B)

Students will get a glimpse of what they will learn about in the lesson. They will also read the lesson goals.

Multiplying and Dividing by 3 Math Facts

Students will practice multiplying and dividing by 3.

LEARN AND TRY IT

LEARN   Dividing 3-Digit Numbers by 2-Digit Numbers

Students will learn how to apply the standard division algorithm to divide three-digit numbers by two-digit numbers.

TRY IT   Divide 3-Digit Numbers by 2-Digit Numbers

Students will practice dividing a three-digit number by a two-digit number using the standard division algorithm. Support will be provided to help students overcome misconceptions.

TIP   Multiplication and division are inverse operations. Remind students that they can use multiplication to check the answer to a division problem. To check, multiply the divisor by the whole-number portion of the quotient. Then add the remainder if there is one. The result should be the original dividend.

LEARN   Dividing a 3-Digit Number in the Real World

Students will solve real-world problems that involve dividing a three-digit number by a two-digit number. The answer to the problem is not always the entire quotient. It could be the remainder or just the whole-number part of the quotient.

TRY IT   Divide a 3-Digit Number in the Real World

Students will practice solving real-world division problems where a three-digit number must be divided by a two-digit number. Support will be provided to help students overcome misconceptions.

TRY IT   Practice Dividing 3-Digit Numbers by 2-Digit Numbers

Students will complete online practice problems. Then they will complete Practice Dividing 3-Digit Numbers by 2-Digit Numbers from *Summit Math 5 Activity Book*.

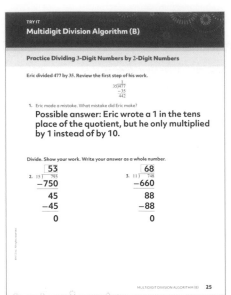

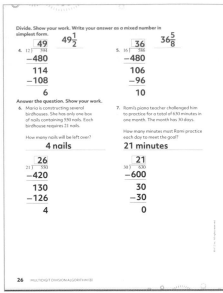

WRAP-UP

Dividing 3-Digit Numbers by 2-Digit Numbers

Students will solve a problem to show that they understand how to divide a three-digit number by a two-digit number using the standard division algorithm.

Multidigit Division Algorithm (C)

Lesson Overview

ACTIVITY	ACTIVITY TITLE	TIME	ONLINE/OFFLINE
GET READY	Introduction to Multidigit Division Algorithm (C)	**2** minutes	🖥️
	Multiplying and Dividing by 3 with Instant Recall	**8** minutes	🖥️
LEARN AND **TRY IT**	Dividing 4-Digit Numbers by 2-Digit Numbers	**7** minutes	🖥️
	Divide 4-Digit Numbers by 2-Digit Numbers	**7** minutes	🖥️
	Dividing a 4-Digit Number in the Real World	**7** minutes	🖥️
	Divide a 4-Digit Number in the Real World	**7** minutes	🖥️
	Practice Dividing 4-Digit Numbers by 2-Digit Numbers	**20** minutes	🖥️ and 📄
WRAP-UP	Dividing 4-Digit Numbers by 2-Digit Numbers	**2** minutes	🖥️

Content Background

In this lesson, students will learn how to apply the standard division algorithm to the quotient of a four-digit number and a two-digit number. Students will also encounter problems where the tens or ones digit of the quotient is zero. They may forget to record a digit and end up with an incorrect quotient. Remind students that they can check their answers using multiplication since multiplication and division are inverses. To check an answer, multiply the divisor by the whole-number portion of the quotient. Then add the remainder if there is one. The result should be the original dividend.

MATERIALS

Supplied
- *Summit Math 5 Activity Book:* Practice Dividing 4-Digit Numbers by 2-Digit Numbers

Lesson Goals

- Divide four-digit numbers by two-digit numbers.

- Solve real-world problems by dividing four-digit numbers by two-digit numbers.

GET READY

Introduction to Multidigit Division Algorithm (C)

Students will get a glimpse of what they will learn about in the lesson. They will also read the lesson goals.

Multiplying and Dividing by 3 with Instant Recall

Students will practice multiplying and dividing by 3 with instant recall.

LEARN Dividing 4-Digit Numbers by 2-Digit Numbers

Students will learn how to apply the standard division algorithm to divide four-digit numbers by two-digit numbers.

TRY IT Divide 4-Digit Numbers by 2-Digit Numbers

Students will practice dividing a four-digit number by a two-digit number using the standard division algorithm. Support will be provided to help students overcome misconceptions.

LEARN Dividing a 4-Digit Number in the Real World

Students will solve real-world problems that involve dividing a four-digit number by a two-digit number. The answer to the problem is not always the entire quotient. It could be the remainder or just the whole-number part of the quotient.

TRY IT Divide a 4-Digit Number in the Real World

Students will practice solving real-world division problems where a four-digit number must be divided by a two-digit number. Support will be provided to help students overcome misconceptions.

TRY IT Practice Dividing 4-Digit Numbers by 2-Digit Numbers

Students will complete online practice problems. Then they will complete Practice Dividing 4-Digit Numbers by 2-Digit Numbers from *Summit Math 5 Activity Book*.

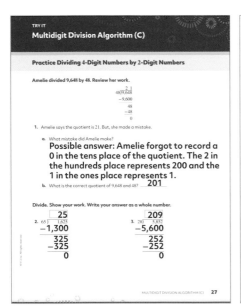

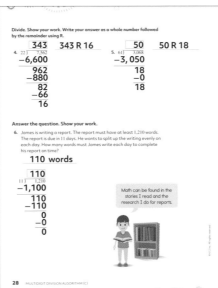

Dividing 4-Digit Numbers by 2-Digit Numbers

Students will solve a problem to show that they understand how to divide a four-digit number by a two-digit number using the standard division algorithm.

Multidigit Division Algorithm (D)

Lesson Overview

ACTIVITY	ACTIVITY TITLE	TIME	ONLINE/OFFLINE
GET READY	Introduction to Multidigit Division Algorithm (D)	**2** minutes	🖥️
TRY IT	Review Multidigit Division Algorithm	**18** minutes	🖥️
QUIZ	Multidigit Division Algorithm	**25** minutes	🖥️
WRAP-UP	More Math Practice	**15** minutes	🖥️

Lesson Goals

- Review dividing two-digit, three-digit, and four-digit numbers by two-digit numbers.

- Take a quiz.

MATERIALS

There are no materials to gather for this lesson.

GET READY

Introduction to Multidigit Division Algorithm (D)

Students will read the lesson goals.

TRY IT

Review Multidigit Division Algorithm (D)

Students will answer questions to review what they have learned about the multidigit division algorithm.

QUIZ

Multidigit Division Algorithm

Students will complete the Multidigit Division Algorithm quiz.

More Math Practice

Students will practice skills according to their individual needs.

Big Ideas: Extended Problems

Lesson Overview

Big Ideas lessons provide students the opportunity to further apply the knowledge and skills acquired throughout previous units. Each Big Ideas lesson consists of three parts:

1. **Cumulative Review:** Students keep their skills fresh by reviewing prior content.

2. **Preview:** Students practice answering the types of questions they will commonly find on standardized tests.

3. **Synthesis:** Students complete an assignment that allows them to interweave and apply what they've learned. These synthesis assignments will vary throughout the course.

   In the Synthesis portion of this Big Ideas lesson, students will complete multistep problems that go beyond the short answer and multiple choice problems they encounter in their regular lessons. These problems give students an opportunity to demonstrate problem solving, reasoning, communication, and modeling skills. Students will need to use pencil and paper and/or technology to show their work.

   LEARNING COACH CHECK-IN   This is a graded assessment. Make sure students complete, review, and submit the assignment to their teacher.

All materials needed for this lesson are linked online. The materials are not provided in this Lesson Guide or in the Activity Book.

Addition and Subtraction of Fractions

Addition of Fractions (A)

Lesson Overview

ACTIVITY	ACTIVITY TITLE	TIME	ONLINE/OFFLINE
GET READY	Introduction to Addition of Fractions (A)	**2** minutes	🖥️
	Addition and Subtraction of Fractions in 60 Seconds	**3** minutes	🖥️
	Look Back at Describing a Fraction	**5** minutes	🖥️
LEARN AND **TRY IT**	Adding Fractions with Like Denominators	**7** minutes	🖥️
	Add Fractions with Like Denominators	**7** minutes	🖥️
	Adding Fractions with Like Denominators in the Real World	**7** minutes	🖥️
	Add Fractions with Like Denominators in the Real World	**7** minutes	🖥️
	Practice Adding Fractions with Like Denominators	**20** minutes	🖥️ and 📄
WRAP-UP	Adding Fractions with Like Denominators	**2** minutes	🖥️

Content Background

In this lesson, students will learn how to add fractions with like denominators. At first, models will be used to help students understand the procedure for adding fractions. By the end of the lesson, students should be able to add fractions without using a model by following these steps:

1. Add the numerators.

2. Keep the like denominator.

3. Simplify if needed.

Sometimes, students continue to add the denominators instead of keeping the like denominator. The denominator represents how many equal-sized pieces students are working with. Adding the denominators changes the number of equal-sized pieces, which is not what happens when they add fractions with like denominators.

For example, this rectangle has been split into 10 equal-sized pieces. Each section represents $\frac{1}{10}$ of the whole.

MATERIALS

Supplied
- *Summit Math 5 Activity Book:* Practice Adding Fractions with Like Denominators

KEYWORDS

denominator – the number in a fraction that is below the fraction bar

like denominators – denominators that are exactly the same in two or more fractions

numerator – the number in a fraction that is above the fraction bar

simplest form – of fractions, a fraction with a numerator and denominator that have no common factor other than 1

It can be used to model $\frac{3}{10} + \frac{4}{10}$. First, shade $\frac{3}{10}$, or 3 smaller rectangles. Next, shade $\frac{4}{10}$, or 4 smaller rectangles.

There are 7 one-tenth pieces shaded, so $\frac{3}{10} + \frac{4}{10} = \frac{7}{10}$. Notice that the number of equal-sized pieces does not change. There are still 10. Only the number of *shaded* pieces has changed. Therefore, the numerator changes but the denominator stays the same.

Lesson Goals

- Add fractions with like denominators.

- Solve real-world problems by adding fractions with like denominators.

GET READY

Introduction to Addition of Fractions (A)

Students will get a glimpse of what they will learn about in the lesson. They will also read the lesson goals and keywords. Have students select each keyword and preview its definition.

Addition and Subtraction of Fractions in 60 Seconds

Students will watch a short video designed to spark their interest in upcoming topics.

Look Back at Describing a Fraction

Students will practice the prerequisite skill of describing a fraction.

LEARN AND TRY IT

LEARN   Adding Fractions with Like Denominators

Students will learn how to add fractions with like denominators.

SUPPORT   If students have difficulty adding fractions with like denominators, have them use fraction strips, number lines, or other models to solve problems.

TRY IT   Add Fractions with Like Denominators

Students will practice adding fractions with like denominators. Support will be provided to help students overcome misconceptions.

TIP   Answers should always be given in simplest form. Have students check to see if the numerator and denominator can both be divided by the same number.

LEARN Adding Fractions with Like Denominators in the Real World

Students will learn how to solve real-world problems by adding fractions with like denominators.

TRY IT Add Fractions with Like Denominators in the Real World

Students will practice solving real-world problems by adding fractions with like denominators. Support will be provided to help students overcome misconceptions.

TRY IT Practice Adding Fractions with Like Denominators

Students will complete online practice problems. Then they will complete Practice Adding Fractions with Like Denominators from *Summit Math 5 Activity Book.*

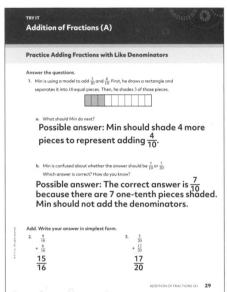
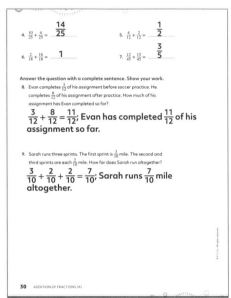

WRAP-UP

Adding Fractions with Like Denominators

Students will solve a problem to show that they understand how to add fractions with like denominators.

Addition of Fractions (B)

Lesson Overview

ACTIVITY	ACTIVITY TITLE	TIME	ONLINE/OFFLINE
GET READY	Introduction to Addition of Fractions (B)	**2** minutes	🖥
	Multiplying and Dividing by 3 Math Facts Game	**8** minutes	🖥
LEARN AND **TRY IT**	Generating Equivalent Fractions	**7** minutes	🖥
	Generate Equivalent Fractions	**7** minutes	🖥
	Generating Equivalent Fractions Using Greatest Common Factor	**7** minutes	🖥
	Generate Equivalent Fractions Using Greatest Common Factor	**7** minutes	🖥
	Practice Generating Equivalent Fractions	**20** minutes	🖥 and 📄
WRAP-UP	Generating Equivalent Fractions	**5** minutes	🖥

Content Background

In this lesson, students will learn how to generate equivalent fractions. By the end of the lesson, students should be able to generate equivalent fractions by multiplying or dividing both the numerator and the denominator by the same number.

Some students may try to generate equivalent fractions by adding to or subtracting from the numerator and denominator by the same amount. Doing so will not generate equivalent fractions. Students can use fraction strips to help visualize why this approach is incorrect. For example, students might add 3 to the numerator and denominator of $\frac{1}{2}$ to generate an equivalent fraction: $\frac{1+2}{2+2} = \frac{3}{4}$. Fraction strips show that $\frac{1}{2}$ and $\frac{3}{4}$ are not equivalent fractions.

1		

$\frac{1}{2}$	

$\frac{1}{4}$	$\frac{1}{4}$	$\frac{1}{4}$

Equivalent fractions are only generated by multiplying or dividing both the numerator and denominator by the same number.

> **MATERIALS**
>
> **Supplied**
> - *Summit Math 5 Activity Book:* Practice Generating Equivalent Fractions

> **KEYWORDS**
>
> **equivalent fractions –** fractions that name the same amount, such as $\frac{1}{2}$ and $\frac{3}{6}$

Lesson Goals

- Write a fraction that is equivalent to a given fraction.

Introduction to Addition of Fractions (B)

Students will get a glimpse of what they will learn about in the lesson. They will also read the lesson goals and keywords. Have students select each keyword and preview its definition.

Multiplying and Dividing by 3 Math Facts Game

Students will practice multiplying and dividing by 3.

LEARN AND TRY IT

LEARN Generating Equivalent Fractions

Students will learn how to generate equivalent fractions. At first, they will use fraction strips to model fractions that are equivalent to $\frac{1}{2}$, such as $\frac{2}{4}$ and $\frac{4}{8}$. Eventually, students should be able to generate equivalent fractions by multiplying or dividing both the numerator and the denominator by the same number.

TRY IT Generate Equivalent Fractions

Students will practice generating equivalent fractions. Support will be provided to help students overcome misconceptions.

TIP   Remind students that they can only use multiplication and division to generate equivalent fractions. Adding the same amount to the numerator and denominator will not generate an equivalent fraction. Subtracting the same amount from the numerator and denominator will not generate an equivalent fraction.

LEARN Generating Equivalent Fractions Using Greatest Common Factor

Students will learn to write the prime factorization of a number using a factor tree. The prime factorization of a number is an expression that shows a whole number as a product of its prime factors. For example, $18 = 2 \times 2 \times 2 \times 3$. Students will then use the prime factorization to find the greatest common factor (GCF) of two numbers so that they can use the GCF to write equivalent fractions.

TRY IT   Generate Equivalent Fractions Using Greatest Common Factor

Students will practice finding the prime factorization of two numbers to determine the GCF. They will then use the GCF to generate equivalent fractions. Support will be provided to help students overcome misconceptions.

TRY IT   Practice Generating Equivalent Fractions

Students will complete online practice problems. Then they will complete Practice Generating Equivalent Fractions from *Summit Math 5 Activity Book*.

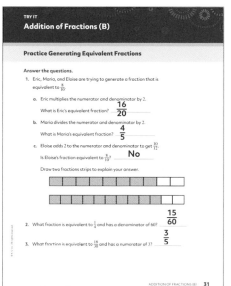

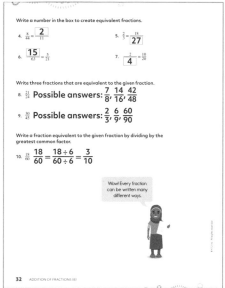

WRAP-UP

Generating Equivalent Fractions

Students will solve a problem to show that they understand how to generate equivalent fractions.

Addition of Fractions (C)

Lesson Overview

ACTIVITY	ACTIVITY TITLE	TIME	ONLINE/OFFLINE
GET READY	Introduction to Addition of Fractions (C)	**2** minutes	📶
	Multiplying and Dividing by 4 Math Facts	**8** minutes	📶
LEARN AND **TRY IT**	Writing Fractions in Simplest Form	**7** minutes	📶
	Write Fractions in Simplest Form	**7** minutes	📶
	Converting Improper Fractions to Mixed Numbers	**7** minutes	📶
	Convert Improper Fractions to Mixed Numbers	**7** minutes	📶
	Practice Writing Fractions in Different Forms	**20** minutes	📶 and 📄
WRAP-UP	Writing Fractions in Different Forms	**2** minutes	📶

Content Background

In this lesson, students will first learn how to write a fraction in simplest form. Then they will learn how to convert improper fractions to mixed numbers.

Lesson Goals

- Write a fraction in simplest form.
- Write an improper fraction as a mixed number.

MATERIALS

Supplied
- *Summit Math 5 Activity Book:* Practice Writing Fractions in Different Forms

KEYWORDS

improper fraction – a fraction whose numerator is greater than or equal to its denominator

mixed number – a whole number and a proper fraction that show a single amount

simplest form – of fractions, a fraction with a numerator and denominator that have no common factor other than 1

GET READY

Introduction to Addition of Fractions (C)

Students will get a glimpse of what they will learn about in the lesson. They will also read the lesson goals and keywords. Have students select each keyword and preview its definition.

Multiplying and Dividing by 4 Math Facts

Students will practice multiplying and dividing by 4.

LEARN   Writing Fractions in Simplest Form

Students will learn how to write fractions in simplest form. The most efficient way to write a fraction in simplest form is to divide both the numerator and the denominator by the greatest common factor of the numerator and denominator. However, it is not necessary to divide by the greatest common factor. Students can divide by common factors until the fraction is in simplest form.

TRY IT   Write Fractions in Simplest Form

Students will practice writing fractions in simplest form. Support will be provided to help students overcome misconceptions.

TIP   Answers should always be given in simplest form.

LEARN   Converting Improper Fractions to Mixed Numbers

Students will learn how to convert improper fractions into mixed numbers. They will divide the numerator of an improper fraction by its denominator to convert an improper fraction to a mixed number. Students can use long division or mental math to divide.

TIP   Remind students that they can check their answer by multiplying the whole number part of the mixed number by the denominator and then adding the numerator of the mixed number. The result should be the numerator of the improper fraction. The check must be completed before the fraction part is written in simplest form.

TRY IT   Convert Improper Fractions to Mixed Numbers

Students will practice converting improper fractions to mixed numbers. Support will be provided to help students overcome misconceptions.

TRY IT Practice Writing Fractions in Different Forms

Students will complete online practice problems. Then they will complete Practice Writing Fractions in Different Forms from *Summit Math 5 Activity Book*.

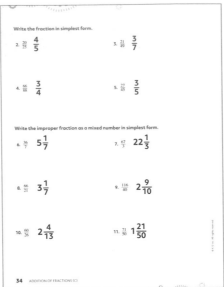

Writing Fractions in Different Forms

Students will solve a problem to show that they understand how to convert improper fractions to mixed numbers and write a fraction in simplest form.

Addition of Fractions (D)

Lesson Overview

ACTIVITY	ACTIVITY TITLE	TIME	ONLINE/OFFLINE
GET READY	Introduction to Addition of Fractions (D)	**2** minutes	🖥️
	Multiplying and Dividing by 4 with Instant Recall	**8** minutes	🖥️
LEARN AND **TRY IT**	Adding Fractions with Unlike Denominators	**7** minutes	🖥️
	Add Fractions with Unlike Denominators	**7** minutes	🖥️
	Determining the Reasonableness of a Fraction Sum	**7** minutes	🖥️
	Determine the Reasonableness of a Fraction Sum	**7** minutes	🖥️
	Practice Adding Fractions with Unlike Denominators	**20** minutes	🖥️ and 📄
WRAP-UP	Adding Fractions with Unlike Denominators	**2** minutes	🖥️

Content Background

In this lesson, students will first review how to find the least common multiple (LCM) of two numbers. Doing so will prepare them to learn how to add fractions with unlike denominators by finding and getting the least common denominator (LCD). Students will also learn how to determine how reasonable an answer is to an addition problem of fractions with unlike denominators.

Lesson Goals

- Add fractions with unlike denominators.
- Determine if a given sum for two fractions is reasonable.

MATERIALS

Supplied
- *Summit Math 5 Activity Book:* Practice Adding Fractions with Unlike Denominators

KEYWORDS

least common denominator (LCD) – the least common multiple of two or more denominators

least common multiple (LCM) – the least number, other than 0, that is a multiple of two or more given whole numbers; used for the least common denominator

unlike denominators – denominators that are different in two or more fractions

Introduction to Addition of Fractions (D)

Students will get a glimpse of what they will learn about in the lesson. They will also read the lesson goals and keywords. Have students select each keyword and preview its definition.

Multiplying and Dividing by 4 with Instant Recall

Students will practice multiplying and dividing by 4 with instant recall.

LEARN AND TRY IT

LEARN   Adding Fractions with Unlike Denominators

Students will learn how to add fractions with unlike denominators. First, students will review how to find the least common multiple of two numbers to find the least common denominator of two fractions. A least common multiple is not absolutely necessary to add fractions with unlike denominators. Any common multiple will do. However, they will have to work with larger numbers than are needed, and there will be additional simplifying after the fractions are added.

OPTIONAL   Students are taught to make two lists of multiples to find the least common multiple. Another strategy is to make a list of multiples for the bigger number and stop when they get a number that is also a multiple of the smaller number.

TRY IT   Add Fractions with Unlike Denominators

Students will practice finding a least common multiple and adding fractions with like denominators. Support will be provided to help students overcome misconceptions.

LEARN   Determining the Reasonableness of a Fraction Sum

Students will learn how to determine the reasonableness of the answer to an addition problem where fractions with unlike denominators are added. It is helpful to compare each fraction to benchmark numbers such as $\frac{1}{2}$ and 1.

TRY IT   Determine the Reasonableness of a Fraction Sum

Students will practice determining the reasonableness of an answer to an addition problem of fractions with unlike denominators. Support will be provided to help students overcome misconceptions.

TRY IT   Practice Adding Fractions with Unlike Denominators

Students will complete online practice problems. Then they will complete Practice Adding Fractions with Unlike Denominators from *Summit Math 5 Activity Book*.

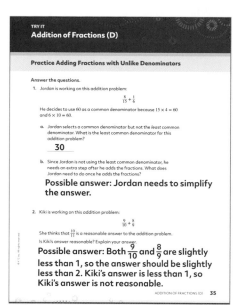

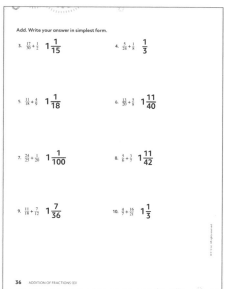

WRAP-UP

Adding Fractions with Unlike Denominators

Students will solve a problem to show that they understand how to add fractions with unlike denominators.

Addition of Fractions (E)

Lesson Overview

ACTIVITY	ACTIVITY TITLE	TIME	ONLINE/OFFLINE
GET READY	Introduction to Addition of Fractions (E)	**2** minutes	🖥️
	Multiplying and Dividing by 4 Math Facts Game	**8** minutes	🖥️
LEARN AND **TRY IT**	Adding Fractions in the Real World	**15** minutes	🖥️
	Add Fractions in the Real World	**10** minutes	🖥️
	Practice Adding Fractions in the Real World	**20** minutes	🖥️ and 📄
WRAP-UP	Adding Fractions in the Real World	**5** minutes	🖥️

Content Background

In this lesson, students will estimate and solve real-world fraction addition problems. They also will determine the reasonableness of a solution to a real-world fraction addition problem. Estimating is a skill that will help students in various situations throughout their lives. Look for opportunities to practice estimating fractions in daily activities. For example, you often need to add fractions when you are cooking in the kitchen. You could even ask students to compare fractional amounts using measuring cups. Repeated opportunities to estimate will help students develop a strong number sense.

MATERIALS

Supplied
- *Summit Math 5 Activity Book:* Practice Adding Fractions in the Real World

Lesson Goals

- Estimate answers to real-world problems involving the addition of fractions.

- Solve real-world problems by adding fractions.

- Determine if the answer given for the sum of two fractions with unlike denominators is reasonable.

Introduction to Addition of Fractions (E)

Students will get a glimpse of what they will learn about in the lesson. They will also read the lesson goals.

Multiplying and Dividing by 4 Math Facts Game

Students will practice multiplying and dividing by 4.

LEARN AND TRY IT

LEARN   Adding Fractions in the Real World

Students will learn how to estimate the answer to a real-world fraction addition problem. Then they will solve the addition problem and compare their answer to the estimated answer. Students will also determine the reasonableness of an answer to a real-world fraction addition problem.

TRY IT   Add Fractions in the Real World

Students will practice estimating the answer to a fraction addition problem, solving real-world fraction addition problems, and determining the reasonableness of an answer to a fraction addition problem. Support will be provided to help students overcome misconceptions.

TRY IT   Practice Adding Fractions in the Real World

Students will complete online practice problems. Then they will complete Practice Adding Fractions in the Real World from *Summit Math 5 Activity Book*.

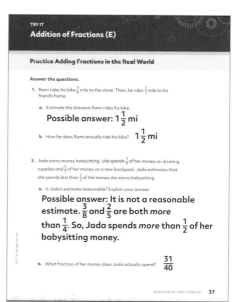

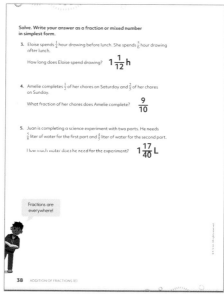

Adding Fractions in the Real World

Students will solve a problem to show that they understand how to add fractions with unlike denominators in a real-world problem.

Addition of Fractions (F)

Lesson Overview

ACTIVITY	ACTIVITY TITLE	TIME	ONLINE/OFFLINE
GET READY	Introduction to Addition of Fractions (F)	**2** minutes	🖥️
	Multiplying and Dividing by 6 Math Facts	**8** minutes	🖥️
LEARN AND **TRY IT**	Solving Multistep Problems by Adding Fractions	**15** minutes	🖥️
	Solve Multistep Problems by Adding Fractions	**10** minutes	🖥️
	Practice Solving Multistep Problems by Adding Fractions	**20** minutes	🖥️ and 📄
WRAP-UP	Solving Multistep Problems by Adding Fractions	**5** minutes	🖥️

Content Background

In this lesson, students will add fractions to solve multistep problems. These problems could be multistep because three or more fractions need to be added. Problems could also be multistep because fractions need to be added and then compared to solve a real-world problem.

Lesson Goals

- Add three or more fractions with unlike denominators.

- Solve real-world multistep problems by adding fractions with unlike denominators.

GET READY

Introduction to Addition of Fractions (F)

Students will get a glimpse of what they will learn about in the lesson. They will also read the lesson goals.

Multiplying and Dividing by 6 Math Facts

Students will practice multiplying and dividing by 6.

LEARN   Solving Multistep Problems by Adding Fractions

Students will learn how to solve problems involving three or more fractions. Sometimes, all three fractions are added. Other times, fractions must be added and compared to answer a real-world question.

TIP   Students can add three or more fractions using a couple of different methods. They can find a denominator that is common to all the fractions and add in one step. Or, students can find a common denominator for two of the fractions, add them, and then find a common denominator again and add again. The second method takes more steps, but it may be helpful for students who struggle to find a lowest common denominator for three or more fractions.

TRY IT   Solve Multistep Problems by Adding Fractions

Students will practice solving multistep problems by adding fractions. Support will be provided to help students overcome misconceptions.

TIP   Remind students that simplest form includes writing an improper fraction as a mixed number and simplifying the fraction part, if possible. They can use the floating keyboard to create fractions and mixed numbers.

TRY IT   Practice Solving Multistep Problems by Adding Fractions

Students will complete online practice problems. Then they will complete Practice Solving Multistep Problems by Adding Fractions from *Summit Math 5 Activity Book.*

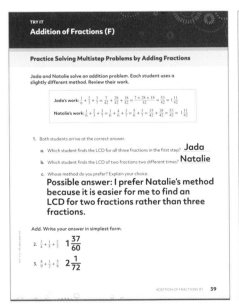

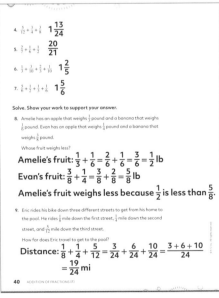

Solving Multistep Problems by Adding Fractions

Students will solve a problem to show that they understand how to solve real-world multistep problems by adding fractions.

Addition of Fractions (G)

Lesson Overview

ACTIVITY	ACTIVITY TITLE	TIME	ONLINE/OFFLINE
GET READY	Introduction to Addition of Fractions (G)	**2** minutes	🖥
TRY IT	Review Addition of Fractions	**18** minutes	🖥
QUIZ	Addition of Fractions	**25** minutes	🖥
WRAP-UP	More Math Practice	**15** minutes	🖥

Lesson Goals

- Review creating equivalent fractions, adding fractions with like and unlike denominators, and solving real-world problems by adding fractions.

- Take a quiz.

MATERIALS

There are no materials to gather for this lesson.

GET READY

Introduction to Addition of Fractions (G)

Students will read the lesson goals.

TRY IT

Review Addition of Fractions

Students will answer questions to review what they have learned about addition of fractions.

QUIZ

Addition of Fractions

Students will complete the Addition of Fractions quiz.

More Math Practice

Students will practice skills according to their individual needs.

Subtraction of Fractions (A)

Lesson Overview

ACTIVITY	ACTIVITY TITLE	TIME	ONLINE/OFFLINE
GET READY	Introduction to Subtraction of Fractions (A)	**2** minutes	🖥️
	Look Back at Adding Fractions with Like Denominators	**8** minutes	🖥️
LEARN AND **TRY IT**	Subtracting Fractions with Like Denominators	**7** minutes	🖥️
	Subtract Fractions with Like Denominators	**7** minutes	🖥️
	Subtracting Fractions with Like Denominators in the Real World	**7** minutes	🖥️
	Subtract Fractions with Like Denominators in the Real World	**7** minutes	🖥️
	Practice Subtracting Fractions with Like Denominators	**20** minutes	🖥️ and 📄
WRAP-UP	Subtracting Fractions with Like Denominators	**2** minutes	🖥️

Content Background

In this lesson, students will learn how to subtract fractions with like denominators. At first, models will be used to help students understand the procedure for subtracting fractions. By the end of the lesson, students should be able to subtract fractions without using a model by following these steps:

1. Subtract the numerators.

2. Keep the like denominator.

3. Simplify if needed.

Notice that the steps to subtract fractions with like denominators is almost exactly the same as the steps to add fractions with like denominators. The only difference is that the numerators must be subtracted instead of added.

Lesson Goals

- Subtract fractions with like denominators.

- Solve real-world problems by subtracting fractions with like denominators.

MATERIALS

Supplied

- *Summit Math 5 Activity Book:* Practice Subtracting Fractions with Like Denominators

Introduction to Subtraction of Fractions (A)

Students will get a glimpse of what they will learn about in the lesson. They will also read the lesson goals.

Look Back at Adding Fractions with Like Denominators

Students will practice the prerequisite skill of adding fractions with like denominators.

LEARN AND TRY IT

LEARN Subtracting Fractions with Like Denominators

Students will learn how to subtract fractions with like denominators.

TRY IT Subtract Fractions with Like Denominators

Students will practice subtracting fractions with like denominators. Support will be provided to help students overcome misconceptions.

TIP Answers should always be given in simplest form. Remind students to check to see if the numerator and denominator can both be divided by the same number.

LEARN Subtracting Fractions with Like Denominators in the Real World

Students will learn how to solve real-world problems by subtracting fractions with like denominators.

TRY IT Subtract Fractions with Like Denominators in the Real World

Students will practice solving real-world problems by subtracting fractions with like denominators. Support will be provided to help students overcome misconceptions.

TRY IT   Practice Subtracting Fractions with Like Denominators

Students will complete online practice problems. Then they will complete Practice Subtracting Fractions with Like Denominators from *Summit Math 5 Activity Book.*

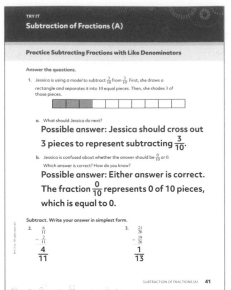

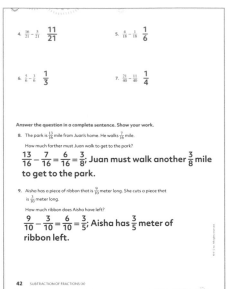

WRAP-UP

Subtracting Fractions with Like Denominators

Students will solve a problem to show that they understand how to subtract fractions with the same denominator.

Subtraction of Fractions (B)

Lesson Overview

ACTIVITY	ACTIVITY TITLE	TIME	ONLINE/OFFLINE
GET READY	Introduction to Subtraction of Fractions (B)	**2** minutes	🖥️
	Multiplying and Dividing by 6 with Instant Recall	**8** minutes	🖥️
LEARN AND **TRY IT**	Subtracting Fractions from One	**15** minutes	🖥️
	Subtract Fractions from One	**10** minutes	🖥️
	Practice Subtracting Fractions from One	**20** minutes	🖥️ and 📄
WRAP-UP	Subtracting Fractions from One	**5** minutes	🖥️

Content Background

In this lesson, students will learn how to subtract a fraction from 1. The key to solving this type of problem is rewriting 1 using the correct fraction. Students should always use the denominator of the second fraction as the number of parts. Once there are two fractions with like denominators, students can subtract the numerators and keep the like denominator.

MATERIALS

Supplied
- *Summit Math 5 Activity Book:* Practice Subtracting Fractions from One

Lesson Goals

- Subtract a fraction from 1.

GET READY

Introduction to Subtraction of Fractions (B)

Students will get a glimpse of what they will learn about in the lesson. They will also read the lesson goals.

Multiplying and Dividing by 6 with Instant Recall

Students will practice multiplying and dividing by 6.

LEARN Subtracting Fractions from One

Students will learn how to subtract a fraction from 1.

TRY IT Subtract Fractions from One

Students will practice subtracting a fraction from 1. Support will be provided to help students overcome misconceptions.

TRY IT Practice Subtracting Fractions from One

Students will complete online practice problems. Then they will complete Practice Subtracting Fractions from One from *Summit Math 5 Activity Book.*

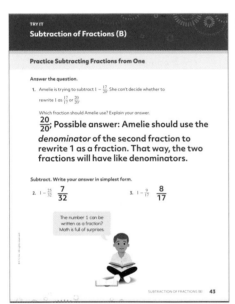

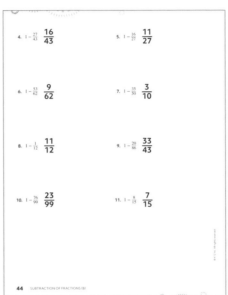

Subtracting Fractions from One

Students will solve a problem to show that they understand how to subtract a fraction from 1.

Subtraction of Fractions (C)

Lesson Overview

ACTIVITY	ACTIVITY TITLE	TIME	ONLINE/OFFLINE
GET READY	Introduction to Subtraction of Fractions (C)	**2** minutes	🖥️
	Multiplying and Dividing by 6 Math Facts Game	**8** minutes	🖥️
LEARN AND **TRY IT**	Subtracting Fractions with Unlike Denominators	**7** minutes	🖥️
	Subtract Fractions with Unlike Denominators	**7** minutes	🖥️
	Determining the Reasonableness of a Difference	**7** minutes	🖥️
	Determine the Reasonableness of a Difference	**7** minutes	🖥️
	Practice Subtracting Fractions with Unlike Denominators	**20** minutes	🖥️ and 📄
WRAP-UP	Subtracting Fractions with Unlike Denominators	**2** minutes	🖥️

Content Background

In this lesson, students will learn how to subtract fractions with unlike denominators. The process for subtracting fractions is very similar to the process students used to add fractions. The only difference is that they subtract the numerators instead of adding after they get the LCD. Students will also learn how to determine the reasonableness of an answer to a subtraction problem with unlike denominators.

> ### MATERIALS
>
> **Supplied**
> - *Summit Math 5 Activity Book:* Practice Subtracting Fractions with Unlike Denominators

Lesson Goals

- Subtract fractions with unlike denominators.
- Determine if a given difference of two fractions is reasonable.

GET READY

Introduction to Subtraction of Fractions (C)

Students will get a glimpse of what they will learn about in the lesson. They will also read the lesson goals.

Multiplying and Dividing by 6 Math Facts Game
Students will practice multiplying and dividing by 6.

LEARN AND TRY IT

LEARN   Subtracting Fractions with Unlike Denominators

Students will learn how to subtract fractions with unlike denominators. They will first review how to find the least common multiple of two numbers to find the least common denominator of two fractions.

TIP   A least common multiple is not absolutely necessary to subtract fractions with unlike denominators. Any common multiple will do. However, students will have to work with larger numbers than are needed, and there will be additional simplifying after the fractions are subtracted.

TRY IT   Subtract Fractions with Unlike Denominators

Students will practice subtracting fractions with unlike denominators. Support will be provided to help students overcome misconceptions.

TIP   Once students make equivalent fractions with a like denominator, the numerator of the first fraction should never be greater than the numerator of the second fraction at this level. If it is, students have made a mistake.

LEARN   Determining the Reasonableness of a Difference

Students will learn how to determine the reasonableness of the answer to a problem where fractions with unlike denominators are subtracted.

TIP   It is helpful to compare each fraction to benchmark numbers such as $\frac{1}{2}$ and 1.

TRY IT   Determine the Reasonableness of a Difference

Students will practice determining the reasonableness of an answer to a subtraction problem of fractions with unlike denominators. Support will be provided to help students overcome misconceptions.

TRY IT Practice Subtracting Fractions with Unlike Denominators

Students will complete online practice problems. Then they will complete Practice Subtracting Fractions with Unlike Denominators from *Summit Math 5 Activity Book.*

TRY IT

Subtraction of Fractions (C)

Practice Subtracting Fractions with Unlike Denominators

Answer the questions.

1. Maria is working on the problem $\frac{13}{14} - \frac{3}{7}$. Why is $\frac{1}{2}$ a reasonable estimate? Fill in the blanks on each part to help Maria explain.

   a. $\frac{13}{14}$ is __13__ out of __14__ equal parts. It is close to __1__

   b. $\frac{3}{7}$ is __3__ out of __7__ equal parts. It is close to __$\frac{1}{2}$__

   c. $\frac{1}{2}$ __is__ a reasonable estimate of $\frac{13}{14} - \frac{3}{7}$.

2. Nick is working on the problem $\frac{2}{3} - \frac{3}{5}$. He thinks that $\frac{6}{15}$ is a reasonable answer to the subtraction problem.

   Is Nick's estimate reasonable? Explain your answer.

   Possible answer: Both $\frac{2}{3}$ and $\frac{3}{5}$ are *more* **than $\frac{1}{2}$, so the answer should be close to 0. Nick's estimate is not very close to 0. So, his answer is not reasonable.**

SUBTRACTION OF FRACTIONS (C) **45**

Subtract. Write your answer in simplest form.

3. $\frac{7}{9} - \frac{4}{27}$ $\frac{17}{27}$

4. $\frac{4}{5} - \frac{3}{7}$ $\frac{13}{35}$

5. $\frac{1}{2} - \frac{4}{13}$ $\frac{5}{26}$

6. $\frac{3}{5} - \frac{2}{6}$ $\frac{4}{15}$

7. $\frac{11}{12} - \frac{12}{15}$ $\frac{7}{60}$

8. $\frac{5}{8} - \frac{1}{6}$ $\frac{11}{24}$

46 SUBTRACTION OF FRACTIONS (C)

WRAP-UP

Subtracting Fractions with Unlike Denominators

Students will solve a problem to show that they understand how to subtract fractions with unlike denominators.

Subtraction of Fractions (D)

Lesson Overview

ACTIVITY	ACTIVITY TITLE	TIME	ONLINE/OFFLINE
GET READY	Introduction to Subtraction of Fractions (D)	**2** minutes	📶
	Multiplying and Dividing by 7 Math Facts	**8** minutes	📶
LEARN AND **TRY IT**	Subtracting Fractions in the Real World	**15** minutes	📶
	Subtract Fractions in the Real World	**10** minutes	📶
	Practice Subtracting Fractions in the Real World	**20** minutes	📶 and 📄
WRAP-UP	Subtracting Fractions in the Real World	**5** minutes	📶

Content Background

In this lesson, students will estimate and solve real-world fraction subtraction problems. They will also determine the reasonableness of a solution to a real-world fraction subtraction problem. Estimating is a skill that will help students in various situations throughout their lives. Look for opportunities to practice estimating fractions in daily activities. Repeated opportunities to estimate will help students develop a strong number sense.

MATERIALS

Supplied
- *Summit Math 5 Activity Book:* Practice Subtracting Fractions in the Real World

Lesson Goals

- Estimate answers to real-world problems involving the subtraction of fractions.

- Solve real-world problems by subtracting fractions.

- Determine if the answer given for the difference of two fractions with unlike denominators is reasonable.

GET READY

Introduction to Subtraction of Fractions (D)

Students will get a glimpse of what they will learn about in the lesson. They will also read the lesson goals.

Multiplying and Dividing by 7 Math Facts

Students will practice multiplying and dividing by 7.

LEARN AND TRY IT

LEARN   Subtracting Fractions in the Real World

Students will learn how to estimate the answer to a real-world fraction subtraction problem. They will then solve the subtraction problem and compare their answer to the estimated answer. Students will also determine the reasonableness of an answer to a real-world fraction subtraction problem.

TRY IT   Subtract Fractions in the Real World

Students will practice estimating the answer to a fraction subtraction problem, solving real-world fraction subtraction problems, and determining the reasonableness of an answer to a fraction subtraction problem. Support will be provided to help students overcome misconceptions.

TRY IT   Practice Subtracting Fractions in the Real World

Students will complete online practice problems. Then they will complete Practice Subtracting Fractions in the Real World from *Summit Math 5 Activity Book*.

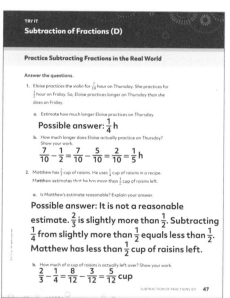

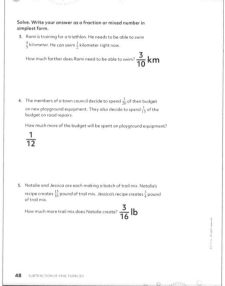

WRAP-UP

Subtracting Fractions in the Real World

Students will solve a problem to show that they understand how to solve fraction subtraction problems in the real world.

Subtraction of Fractions (E)

Lesson Overview

ACTIVITY	ACTIVITY TITLE	TIME	ONLINE/OFFLINE
GET READY	Introduction to Subtraction of Fractions (E)	**2** minutes	📶
	Multiplying and Dividing by 7 with Instant Recall	**8** minutes	📶
LEARN AND **TRY IT**	Solving Multistep Fraction Problems	**15** minutes	📶
	Solve Multistep Fraction Problems	**10** minutes	📶
	Practice Solving Multistep Fraction Problems	**20** minutes	📶 and 📄
WRAP-UP	Solving Multistep Fraction Problems	**5** minutes	📶

Content Background

In this lesson, students will add and subtract fractions to solve multistep problems. These problems could be multistep because three or more fractions need to be subtracted and/or added. Some problems require students to use the order of operations to solve. Students will also solve real-world multistep problems that involve subtraction or subtraction and addition.

MATERIALS

Supplied
- *Summit Math 5 Activity Book:* Practice Solving Multistep Fraction Problems

Lesson Goals

- Solve multistep computations using addition and subtraction of fractions and mixed numbers.

- Solve multistep, real-world problems involving the addition and/or subtraction of fractions and mixed numbers.

GET READY

Introduction to Subtraction of Fractions (E)

Students will get a glimpse of what they will learn about in the lesson. They will also read the lesson goals.

Multiplying and Dividing by 7 with Instant Recall

Students will practice multiplying and dividing by 7.

LEARN AND TRY IT

LEARN   Solving Multistep Fraction Problems

Students will learn how to solve problems involving three or more fractions. Each problem will include at least two operations. Fractions could be subtracted twice or added and subtracted. Sometimes, a problem will include parentheses. Students must apply the order of operations to solve all problems. They will also learn how to solve real-world problems that require them to subtract, add, and/or compare fractions.

NOTE   Students must correctly apply the order of operations to solve problems with multiple steps. First, they add or subtract to eliminate parentheses. Next, they add or subtract in order from left to right.

TRY IT   Solve Multistep Fraction Problems

Students will practice solving multistep fraction problems and real-world multistep fraction problems. Support will be provided to help students overcome misconceptions.

TIP   Remind students that simplest form includes writing an improper fraction as a mixed number and simplifying the fraction part, if possible. They can use the floating keyboard to create fractions and mixed numbers.

TRY IT   Practice Solving Multistep Fraction Problems

Students will complete online practice problems. Then they will complete Practice Solving Multistep Fraction Problems from *Summit Math 5 Activity Book*.

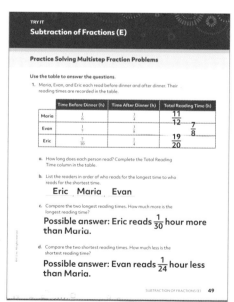

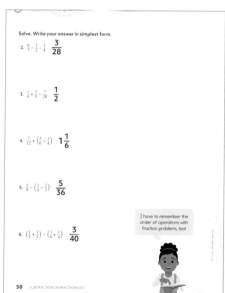

Solving Multistep Fraction Problems

Students will solve a problem to show that they understand how to solve real-world multistep problems by subtracting and adding fractions.

Subtraction of Fractions (F)

Lesson Overview

ACTIVITY	ACTIVITY TITLE	TIME	ONLINE/OFFLINE
GET READY	Introduction to Subtraction of Fractions (F)	**2** minutes	🖥️
TRY IT	Review Subtraction of Fractions	**18** minutes	🖥️
QUIZ	Subtraction of Fractions	**25** minutes	🖥️
WRAP-UP	More Math Practice	**15** minutes	🖥️

Lesson Goals

- Review subtracting fractions, solving real-world problems by subtracting fractions, and solving multistep fraction problems.

- Take a quiz.

MATERIALS

There are no materials to gather for this lesson.

GET READY

Introduction to Subtraction of Fractions (F)

Students will read the lesson goals.

TRY IT

Review Subtraction of Fractions

Students will answer questions to review what they have learned about subtraction of fractions.

QUIZ

Subtraction of Fractions

Students will complete the Subtraction of Fractions quiz.

More Math Practice

Students will practice skills according to their individual needs.

Big Ideas: Mini-Project

Lesson Overview

Big Ideas lessons provide students the opportunity to further apply the knowledge and skills acquired throughout previous units. Each Big Ideas lesson consists of three parts:

1. **Cumulative Review:** Students keep their skills fresh by reviewing prior content.

2. **Preview:** Students practice answering the types of questions they will commonly find on standardized tests.

3. **Synthesis:** Students complete an assignment that allows them to interweave and apply what they've learned. These synthesis assignments will vary throughout the course.

In the Synthesis portion of this Big Ideas lesson, students will complete a small, creative project designed to tie together concepts and skills that students have encountered across units. These small projects are designed to emphasize a real-world application that connects mathematics to other subjects, including science, technology, engineering, art, and history. Students will need to use pencil and paper and/or technology to show their work.

LEARNING COACH CHECK-IN Make sure students complete, review, and submit the assignment to their teacher.

All materials needed for this lesson are linked online. The materials are not provided in this Lesson Guide or in the Activity Book.

Addition and Subtraction of Mixed Numbers

Addition of Mixed Numbers (A)

Lesson Overview

ACTIVITY	ACTIVITY TITLE	TIME	ONLINE/OFFLINE
GET READY	Introduction to Addition of Mixed Numbers (A)	**2** minutes	🖥️
	Addition and Subtraction of Mixed Numbers in 60 Seconds	**3** minutes	🖥️
	Look Back at Adding Fractions with Like Denominators	**5** minutes	🖥️
LEARN AND **TRY IT**	Adding Mixed Numbers with Like Denominators	**7** minutes	🖥️
	Add Mixed Numbers with Like Denominators	**7** minutes	🖥️
	Writing Sums of Mixed Numbers in Simplest Form	**7** minutes	🖥️
	Write Sums of Mixed Numbers in Simplest Form	**7** minutes	🖥️
	Practice Adding Mixed Numbers with Like Denominators	**20** minutes	🖥️ and 📄
WRAP-UP	Adding Mixed Numbers with Like Denominators	**2** minutes	🖥️

Content Background

In this lesson, students will add mixed numbers and fractions that have like denominators. Each sum will include at least one mixed number. Most sums will require students to add two numbers. However, there are some instances where students will need to add three numbers. The process is the same regardless of how many numbers are being added.

To find the sum of two mixed numbers, add the whole number parts and fraction parts separately. Then, combine the whole number sum with the fraction sum. In some cases, the fraction portion will be an improper fraction. When this happens, students should convert the improper fraction to a mixed number. The whole numbers can be added again to find the sum. Students should continue to give their answers in simplest form.

For example, to add $3\frac{5}{6}$ and $4\frac{5}{6}$, first add the fraction parts and the whole number parts: $3\frac{5}{6} + 4\frac{5}{6} = 7\frac{10}{6}$. Because $\frac{10}{6}$ is an improper fraction, convert it to a mixed number and add to 7: $\frac{10}{6} = \frac{6}{6} + \frac{4}{6} = 1\frac{4}{6}$, so $7\frac{10}{6} = 7 + 1\frac{4}{6} = 8\frac{4}{6}$. The last step in this problem is to give the answer in simplest form: $8\frac{4}{6} = 8\frac{4 \div 2}{6 \div 2} = 8\frac{2}{3}$.

MATERIALS

Supplied
- *Summit Math 5 Activity Book:* Practice Adding Mixed Numbers with Like Denominators

KEYWORDS

improper fraction – a fraction whose numerator is greater than or equal to its denominator

mixed number – a whole number and a proper fraction that show a single amount

simplest form – of fractions, a fraction with a numerator and denominator that have no common factor other than 1

Lesson Goals

- Add fractions and mixed numbers with like denominators.

GET READY

Introduction to Addition of Mixed Numbers (A)

Students will get a glimpse of what they will learn about in the lesson. They will also read the lesson goals and keywords. Have students select each keyword and preview its definition.

Addition and Subtraction of Mixed Numbers in 60 Seconds

Students will watch a short video designed to spark their interest in upcoming topics.

Look Back at Adding Fractions with Like Denominators

Students will practice the prerequisite skill of adding fractions that have like denominators.

LEARN AND TRY IT

LEARN   Adding Mixed Numbers with Like Denominators

Students will add two mixed numbers with like denominators. They will learn to add the fraction parts and whole number parts separately, and then combine the two parts.

TRY IT   Add Mixed Numbers with Like Denominators

Students will practice adding two mixed numbers. Support will be provided to help students overcome misconceptions.

LEARN   Writing Sums of Mixed Numbers in Simplest Form

Students will find sums of mixed numbers that are not initially in simplest form. Some problems require rewriting the fraction sum as a mixed number and continuing to add. Other problems require dividing out a common factor from the numerator and denominator of the fraction part. Some problems require both additional steps.

TRY IT   Write Sums of Mixed Numbers in Simplest Form

Students will practice finding the sum of mixed numbers that require simplifying. Support will be provided to help students overcome misconceptions.

SUPPORT   For students having difficulty when the fraction sum is an improper fraction, encourage them to draw or use fraction strips to model the problem.

TRY IT Practice Adding Mixed Numbers with Like Denominators

Students will complete online practice problems. Then they will complete Practice Adding Mixed Numbers with Like Denominators from *Summit Math 5 Activity Book*.

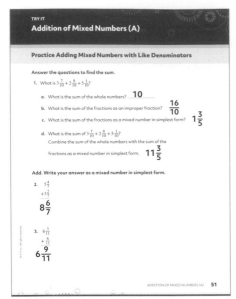

Adding Mixed Numbers with Like Denominators

Students will solve a problem to show that they understand how to find the sum of mixed numbers or a fraction and a mixed number.

Addition of Mixed Numbers (B)

Lesson Overview

ACTIVITY	ACTIVITY TITLE	TIME	ONLINE/OFFLINE
GET READY	Introduction to Addition of Mixed Numbers (B)	**2** minutes	🖥️
	Multiplying and Dividing by 7 Math Facts Game	**8** minutes	🖥️
LEARN AND **TRY IT**	Adding Mixed Numbers with Unlike Denominators	**15** minutes	🖥️
	Add Mixed Numbers with Unlike Denominators	**10** minutes	🖥️
	Practice Adding Mixed Numbers with Unlike Denominators	**20** minutes	🖥️ and 📄
WRAP-UP	Adding Mixed Numbers with Unlike Denominators	**5** minutes	🖥️

Content Background

In this lesson, students will add fractions and mixed numbers with unlike denominators. Each sum will continue to include at least one mixed number. Adding fractions or mixed numbers with unlike denominators is similar to adding fractions with like denominators. There is an additional first step to rewrite the fraction portions of each mixed number as equivalent fractions with like denominators.

Students should continue to give answers as mixed numbers in simplest form. Improper fractions must be rewritten as a mixed number in simplest form and then combined with the whole number part of the sum.

> ### Lesson Goals
> - Add fractions and mixed numbers with unlike denominators.

GET READY

Introduction to Addition of Mixed Numbers (B)
Students will get a glimpse of what they will learn about in the lesson. They will also read the lesson goals.

Multiplying and Dividing by 7 Math Facts Game
Students will practice multiplying and dividing by 7.

LEARN Adding Mixed Numbers with Unlike Denominators

Students will learn how to add mixed numbers or a mixed number and a fraction with unlike denominators. Some problems will result in a fraction sum that is a mixed number. Students should continue to write answers as mixed numbers in simplest form. Improper fractions must be rewritten as a mixed number and combined with the whole number sum.

NOTE   Adding mixed numbers with unlike denominators requires two different skills:

- Finding a common denominator to add fractions with unlike denominators

- Adding mixed numbers with like denominators.

If students struggle with either of these skills, it may help to use fractions strips to model the sum.

TRY IT Add Mixed Numbers with Unlike Denominators

Students will practice finding sums involving mixed numbers and fractions with unlike denominators. Support will be provided to help students overcome misconceptions.

TRY IT Practice Adding Mixed Numbers with Unlike Denominators

Students will complete online practice problems. Then they will complete Practice Adding Mixed Numbers with Unlike Denominators from *Summit Math 5 Activity Book*.

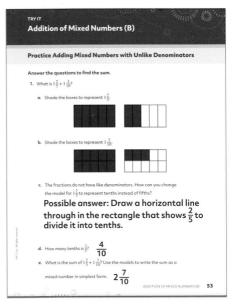

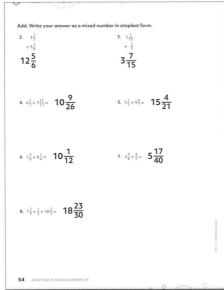

WRAP-UP

Adding Mixed Numbers with Unlike Denominators

Students will solve a problem to show that they understand how to add mixed numbers with unlike denominators.

Addition of Mixed Numbers (C)

Lesson Overview

ACTIVITY	ACTIVITY TITLE	TIME	ONLINE/OFFLINE
GET READY	Introduction to Addition of Mixed Numbers (C)	**2** minutes	🖥
	Multiplying and Dividing by 8 Math Facts	**8** minutes	🖥
LEARN AND **TRY IT**	Adding Mixed Numbers in the Real World	**15** minutes	🖥
	Add Mixed Numbers in the Real World	**10** minutes	🖥
	Practice Adding Mixed Numbers in the Real World	**20** minutes	📶 and 📄
WRAP-UP	Adding Mixed Numbers in the Real World	**5** minutes	🖥

Content Background

In this lesson, students will apply their knowledge and skills of adding fractions and mixed numbers to solve practical problems. Each sum contains at least one mixed number. Two numbers or three numbers must be added to solve. The process is the same regardless of how many numbers are being added. Answers should continue to be given as mixed numbers in simplest form.

NOTE One reason students learn computations in math is so they can apply that understanding to solve actual problems in everyday life.

MATERIALS

Supplied
- *Summit Math 5 Activity Book:* Practice Adding Mixed Numbers in the Real World

Lesson Goals

- Solve real-world problems by adding fractions and mixed numbers.

GET READY

Introduction to Addition of Mixed Numbers (C)
Students will get a glimpse of what they will learn about in the lesson. They will also read the lesson goals.

Multiplying and Dividing by 8 Math Facts
Students will practice multiplying and dividing by 8.

LEARN   Adding Mixed Numbers in the Real World

Students will solve real-world problems involving the addition of fractions and mixed numbers.

TRY IT   Add Mixed Numbers in the Real World

Students will practice solving real-world problems involving the addition of fractions and mixed numbers. Support will be provided to help students overcome misconceptions.

TRY IT   Practice Adding Mixed Numbers in the Real World

Students will complete online practice problems. Then they will complete Practice Adding Mixed Numbers in the Real World from *Summit Math 5 Activity Book*.

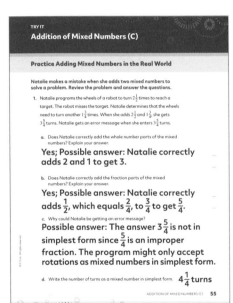

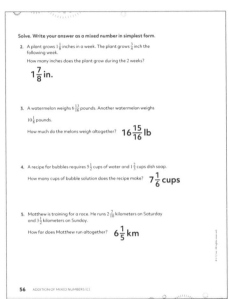

WRAP-UP

Adding Mixed Numbers in the Real World

Students will solve a problem to show that they understand how to solve a real-world problem by adding fractions and mixed numbers.

Addition of Mixed Numbers (D)

Lesson Overview

ACTIVITY	ACTIVITY TITLE	TIME	ONLINE/OFFLINE
GET READY	Introduction to Addition of Mixed Numbers (D)	**2** minutes	🖥️
TRY IT	Review Addition of Mixed Numbers	**18** minutes	🖥️
QUIZ	Addition of Mixed Numbers	**25** minutes	🖥️
WRAP-UP	More Math Practice	**15** minutes	🖥️

Lesson Goals

- Review adding fractions and mixed numbers with like or unlike denominators and solving real-world problems by adding fractions and mixed numbers.

- Take a quiz.

MATERIALS

There are no materials to gather for this lesson.

GET READY

Introduction to Addition of Mixed Numbers (D)

Students will read the lesson goals.

TRY IT

Review Addition of Mixed Numbers

Students will answer questions to review what they have learned about the addition of mixed numbers.

QUIZ

Addition of Mixed Numbers

Students will complete the Addition of Mixed Numbers quiz.

More Math Practice

Students will practice skills according to their individual needs.

Subtraction of Mixed Numbers (A)

Lesson Overview

ACTIVITY	ACTIVITY TITLE	TIME	ONLINE/OFFLINE
GET READY	Introduction to Subtraction of Mixed Numbers (A)	**2** minutes	🖥️
	Look Back at Subtracting Fractions with Like Denominators	**8** minutes	🖥️
LEARN AND **TRY IT**	Subtracting Mixed Numbers with Like Denominators	**7** minutes	🖥️
	Subtract Mixed Numbers with Like Denominators	**7** minutes	🖥️
	Renaming When Subtracting Mixed Numbers	**7** minutes	🖥️
	Rename When Subtracting Mixed Numbers	**7** minutes	🖥️
	Practice Subtracting Mixed Numbers with Like Denominators	**20** minutes	🖥️ and 📄
WRAP-UP	Subtracting Mixed Numbers with Like Denominators	**2** minutes	🖥️

Content Background

In this lesson, students will subtract fractions and mixed numbers with like denominators. Each difference will include at least one mixed number. To subtract with mixed numbers, subtract the whole number parts and fraction parts separately, and then combine the parts to give the difference.

Students will encounter differences that require them to rename or regroup the first number. For example, in the difference $3\frac{1}{4} - 1\frac{3}{4}$, they will not be able to subtract $\frac{3}{4}$ from $\frac{1}{4}$ without regrouping. Take 1 whole from 3, rewrite it as $\frac{4}{4}$, and combine it with $\frac{1}{4}$ to get $2\frac{5}{4}$. Once the first number is renamed, the second number can be subtracted.

> ## MATERIALS
>
> **Supplied**
> - *Summit Math 5 Activity Book:* Practice Subtracting Mixed Numbers with Like Denominators

> ## Lesson Goals
> - Subtract fractions and mixed numbers with like denominators.

Introduction to Subtraction of Mixed Numbers (A)

Students will get a glimpse of what they will learn about in the lesson. They will also read the lesson goals.

Look Back at Subtracting Fractions with Like Denominators

Students will practice the prerequisite skill of subtracting fractions with like denominators.

LEARN AND TRY IT

LEARN   Subtracting Mixed Numbers with Like Denominators

Students will subtract two numbers with like denominators. In this activity, they will not need to regroup to subtract. They will simply subtract the whole number parts and fraction parts separately, and then combine the parts to give the difference.

TRY IT   Subtract Mixed Numbers with Like Denominators

Students will practice subtracting mixed numbers and fractions with like denominators. Support will be provided to help students overcome misconceptions.

LEARN   Renaming When Subtracting Mixed Numbers

Students will learn how to rename a number to subtract fractions and mixed numbers with like denominators. Sometimes renaming is referred to as regrouping. When the fraction part of the first number is smaller than the fraction part of the second number, students must rename or regroup the first number to subtract. For example, $5\frac{1}{3}$ might need to be changed to $4\frac{4}{3}$ to subtract.

SUPPORT   For students having difficulty renaming or regrouping a fraction, encourage them to write out the steps shown in the video. They can also use fraction tiles to model the regrouping.

TRY IT   Rename When Subtracting Mixed Numbers

Students will practice renaming a number to subtract fractions and mixed numbers with like denominators. Support will be provided to help students overcome misconceptions.

TRY IT   Practice Subtracting Mixed Numbers with Like Denominators

Students will complete online practice problems. Then they will complete Practice Subtracting Mixed Numbers with Like Denominators from *Summit Math 5 Activity Book*.

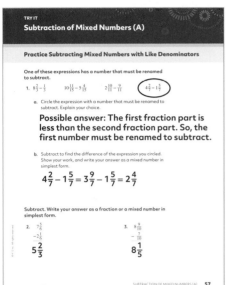

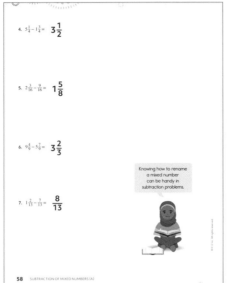

Subtracting Mixed Numbers with Like Denominators

Students will solve a problem to show that they understand how to rename to subtract mixed numbers.

Subtraction of Mixed Numbers (B)

Lesson Overview

ACTIVITY	ACTIVITY TITLE	TIME	ONLINE/OFFLINE
GET READY	Introduction to Subtraction of Mixed Numbers (B)	**2** minutes	🖥
	Multiplying and Dividing by 8 with Instant Recall	**8** minutes	🖥
LEARN AND **TRY IT**	Subtracting Mixed Numbers with Unlike Denominators	**15** minutes	🖥
	Subtract Mixed Numbers with Unlike Denominators	**10** minutes	🖥
	Practice Subtracting Mixed Numbers with Unlike Denominators	**20** minutes	🖥 and 📄
WRAP-UP	Subtracting Mixed Numbers with Unlike Denominators	**5** minutes	🖥

Content Background

In this lesson, students will subtract fractions and mixed numbers with unlike denominators. Each difference includes at least one mixed number. Subtracting fractions or mixed numbers with unlike denominators is similar to subtracting fractions with like denominators. There is just an additional first step to rewrite the fraction portions of each mixed number as equivalent fractions with like denominators. In some cases, students must rename or regroup the first number to subtract.

MATERIALS

Supplied
- *Summit Math 5 Activity Book:* Practice Subtracting Mixed Numbers with Unlike Denominators

Lesson Goals

- Subtract mixed numbers with unlike denominators.

GET READY

Introduction to Subtraction of Mixed Numbers (B)
Students will get a glimpse of what they will learn about in the lesson. They will also read the lesson goals.

Multiplying and Dividing by 8 with Instant Recall
Students will practice multiplying and dividing by 8 with instant recall.

LEARN   Subtracting Mixed Numbers with Unlike Denominators

Students will subtract fractions and mixed numbers with unlike denominators. Some differences require renaming or regrouping the first number to subtract. Students should always rewrite the fraction part of each number as equivalent fractions using the LCD *before* renaming or regrouping.

NOTE   Subtracting mixed numbers with unlike denominators requires two different skills:

- Finding the LCD and using it to rewrite fractions

- Renaming or regrouping a mixed number

If students struggle with either of these skills, it may help for them to use fraction strips to model the sum.

TRY IT   Subtract Mixed Numbers with Unlike Denominators

Students will practice subtracting fractions and mixed numbers with unlike denominators. Support will be provided to help students overcome misconceptions.

TRY IT   Practice Subtracting Mixed Numbers with Unlike Denominators

Students will complete online practice problems. Then they will complete Practice Subtracting Mixed Numbers with Unlike Denominators from *Summit Math 5 Activity Book.*

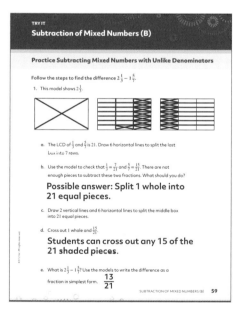

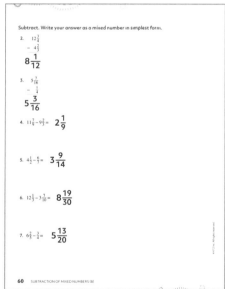

WRAP-UP

Subtracting Mixed Numbers with Unlike Denominators

Students will solve a problem to show that they understand how to subtract mixed numbers with unlike denominators.

Subtraction of Mixed Numbers (C)

Lesson Overview

ACTIVITY	ACTIVITY TITLE	TIME	ONLINE/OFFLINE
GET READY	Introduction to Subtraction of Mixed Numbers (C)	**2** minutes	🖥️
	Multiplying and Dividing by 8 Math Facts Game	**8** minutes	🖥️
LEARN AND TRY IT	Subtracting Mixed Numbers in the Real World	**15** minutes	🖥️
	Subtract Mixed Numbers in the Real World	**10** minutes	🖥️
	Practice Subtracting Mixed Numbers in the Real World	**20** minutes	🖥️ and 📄
WRAP-UP	Subtracting Mixed Numbers in the Real World	**5** minutes	🖥️

Content Background

In this lesson, students will apply their knowledge and skills of subtracting fractions and mixed numbers to solve practical problems. Each difference includes at least one mixed number. Most problems require rewriting the fraction parts with an LCD. Some problems require renaming or regrouping the first number to subtract. Answers should be given as mixed numbers in simplest form.

> ### MATERIALS
>
> **Supplied**
> - *Summit Math 5 Activity Book:* Practice Subtracting Mixed Numbers in the Real World

Lesson Goals

- Solve real-world problems by subtracting mixed numbers.

GET READY

Introduction to Subtraction of Mixed Numbers (C)

Students will get a glimpse of what they will learn about in the lesson. They will also read the lesson goals.

Multiplying and Dividing by 8 Math Facts Game

Students will practice multiplying and dividing by 8.

LEARN   Subtracting Mixed Numbers in the Real World

Students will solve real-world problems involving the subtraction of fractions and mixed numbers.

SUPPORT   Students may struggle when the first number is a whole number with no fraction part, such as $10 - 4\frac{1}{5}$. Remind students to think of the first number as a mixed number with a fraction part that has a numerator of 0. The first number must be renamed to subtract: $10 - 4\frac{1}{5} = 9\frac{5}{5} - 4\frac{1}{5} = 5\frac{4}{5}$.

TRY IT   Subtract Mixed Numbers in the Real World

Students will practice solving real-world problems involving the subtraction of fractions and mixed numbers. Support will be provided to help students overcome misconceptions.

TRY IT   Practice Subtracting Mixed Numbers in the Real World

Students will complete online practice problems. Then they will complete Practice Subtracting Mixed Numbers in the Real World from *Summit Math 5 Activity Book*.

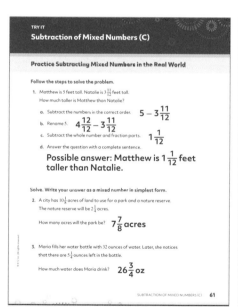

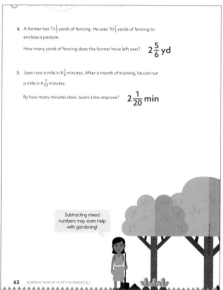

Subtracting Mixed Numbers in the Real World

Students will solve a problem to show that they understand how to solve real-world problems involving the subtraction of mixed numbers.

Subtraction of Mixed Numbers (D)

Lesson Overview

ACTIVITY	ACTIVITY TITLE	TIME	ONLINE/OFFLINE
GET READY	Introduction to Subtraction of Mixed Numbers (D)	**2** minutes	📶
TRY IT	Review Subtraction of Mixed Numbers	**18** minutes	📶
QUIZ	Subtraction of Mixed Numbers	**25** minutes	📶
WRAP-UP	More Math Practice	**15** minutes	📶

Lesson Goals

- Review subtracting fractions and mixed numbers with like denominators, with unlike denominators, and in real-world problems.

- Take a quiz.

MATERIALS

There are no materials to gather for this lesson.

GET READY

Introduction to Subtraction of Mixed Numbers (D)

Students will read the lesson goals.

TRY IT

Review Subtraction of Mixed Numbers

Students will answer questions to review what they have learned about the subtraction of mixed numbers.

QUIZ

Subtraction of Mixed Numbers

Students will complete the Subtraction of Mixed Numbers quiz.

More Math Practice

Students will practice skills according to their individual needs.

Addition and Subtraction of Mixed Numbers (A)

Lesson Overview

ACTIVITY	ACTIVITY TITLE	TIME	ONLINE/OFFLINE
GET READY	Introduction to Addition and Subtraction of Mixed Numbers (A)	**2** minutes	🖥️
	Look Back at Multistep Problems with Fractions	**8** minutes	📶
LEARN AND TRY IT	Evaluating Multistep Expressions with Mixed Numbers	**15** minutes	🖥️
	Evaluate Multistep Expressions with Mixed Numbers	**10** minutes	🖥️
	Practice Evaluating Multistep Expressions with Mixed Numbers	**20** minutes	📶 and 📄
WRAP-UP	Evaluating Multistep Expressions with Mixed Numbers	**5** minutes	📶

Content Background

In this lesson, students will add and subtract fractions and mixed numbers to evaluate expressions with multiple steps. These expressions require multiple steps because three or more fractions or mixed numbers need to be subtracted and/or added. Some problems include grouping symbols and require students to use the order of operations to solve.

> **MATERIALS**
>
> **Supplied**
> - *Summit Math 5 Activity Book:* Practice Evaluating Multistep Expressions with Mixed Numbers

Lesson Goals

- Solve multistep problems by adding and subtracting fractions and mixed numbers.

GET READY

Introduction to Addition and Subtraction of Mixed Numbers (A)

Students will get a glimpse of what they will learn about in the lesson. They will also read the lesson goals.

Look Back at Multistep Problems with Fractions

Students will practice the prerequisite skill of solving a multistep fraction problem with adding and subtracting.

LEARN   Evaluating Multistep Expressions with Mixed Numbers

Students will learn how to evaluate expressions in which three or more fractions and mixed numbers are added and/or subtracted. Each problem includes at least two operations. Often, expressions include parentheses, so students must apply the order of operations to evaluate.

NOTE   Students must correctly apply the order of operations to solve problems with multiple steps. First, add or subtract to eliminate parentheses. Next, add or subtract in order from left to right.

TRY IT   Evaluate Multistep Expressions with Mixed Numbers

Students will practice evaluating expressions with multiple steps by adding and subtracting mixed numbers. Support will be provided to help students overcome misconceptions.

TRY IT   Practice Evaluating Multistep Expressions with Mixed Numbers

Students will complete online practice problems. Then they will complete Practice Evaluating Multistep Expressions with Mixed Numbers from *Summit Math 5 Activity Book*.

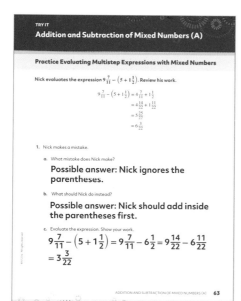

TRY IT
Addition and Subtraction of Mixed Numbers (A)

Practice Evaluating Multistep Expressions with Mixed Numbers

Nick evaluates the expression $9\frac{7}{11} - \left(5 + 1\frac{1}{2}\right)$. Review his work.

$$9\frac{7}{11} - \left(5 + 1\frac{1}{2}\right) = 4\frac{7}{11} + 1\frac{1}{2}$$
$$= 4\frac{14}{22} + 1\frac{11}{22}$$
$$= 5\frac{25}{22}$$
$$= 6\frac{3}{22}$$

1. Nick makes a mistake.

   a. What mistake does Nick make?

   Possible answer: Nick ignores the parentheses.

   b. What should Nick do instead?

   Possible answer: Nick should add inside the parentheses first.

   c. Evaluate the expression. Show your work.

   $$9\frac{7}{11} - \left(5 + 1\frac{1}{2}\right) = 9\frac{7}{11} - 6\frac{1}{2} = 9\frac{14}{22} - 6\frac{11}{22}$$
   $$= 3\frac{3}{22}$$

ADDITION AND SUBTRACTION OF MIXED NUMBERS (A)   **63**

Find the value of the expression. Write your answer as a mixed number or fraction in simplest form.

2. $11\frac{1}{3} + 10\frac{5}{9} - 7\frac{10}{27} =$ **$14\frac{14}{27}$**

3. $15\frac{1}{4} - 9\frac{3}{5} + 2\frac{3}{10} =$ **$8\frac{13}{20}$**

4. $4\frac{5}{8} + \left(10\frac{7}{10} - 3\frac{3}{5}\right) =$ **$11\frac{37}{40}$**

5. $2\frac{1}{6} - \left(1\frac{1}{2} - \frac{7}{9}\right) =$ **$1\frac{4}{9}$**

6. $\left(11\frac{1}{3} - 2\frac{1}{5}\right) - \left(8\frac{4}{5} - 6\frac{16}{25}\right) =$ **$6\frac{73}{75}$**

64   ADDITION AND SUBTRACTION OF MIXED NUMBERS (A)

WRAP-UP

Evaluating Multistep Expressions with Mixed Numbers

Students will solve a problem to show that they understand how to add and subtract fractions and mixed numbers in multiple steps.

Addition and Subtraction of Mixed Numbers (B)

Lesson Overview

ACTIVITY	ACTIVITY TITLE	TIME	ONLINE/OFFLINE
GET READY	Introduction to Addition and Subtraction of Mixed Numbers (B)	**2** minutes	🖥️
	Multiplying and Dividing by 9 Math Facts	**8** minutes	🖥️
LEARN AND **TRY IT**	Solving Multistep Problems with Mixed Numbers	**7** minutes	🖥️
	Solve Multistep Problems with Mixed Numbers	**7** minutes	🖥️
	Solving Time Problems with Mixed Numbers	**7** minutes	🖥️
	Solve Time Problems with Mixed Numbers	**7** minutes	🖥️
	Practice Solving Multistep Problems with Mixed Numbers	**20** minutes	🖥️ and 📄
WRAP-UP	Solving Multistep Problems with Mixed Numbers	**2** minutes	🖥️

Content Background

In this lesson, students will apply their knowledge of evaluating expressions with multiple steps to solve real-world problems.

Lesson Goals

- Solve real-world multistep problems by adding and subtracting fractions and mixed numbers.

GET READY

Introduction to Addition and Subtraction of Mixed Numbers (B)

Students will get a glimpse of what they will learn about in the lesson. They will also read the lesson goals.

Multiplying and Dividing by 9 Math Facts

Students will practice multiplying and dividing by 9.

LEARN Solving Multistep Problems with Mixed Numbers

Students will learn how to solve problems that require adding and/or subtracting fractions and mixed numbers in multiple steps.

TRY IT Solve Multistep Problems with Mixed Numbers

Students will practice solving real-world problems in which fractions and mixed numbers are added and/or subtracted in multiple steps. Support will be provided to help students overcome misconceptions.

NOTE Answers must always be given in simplest form. An improper fraction by itself or as the fraction part of a mixed number is not simplest form. Convert improper fractions to mixed numbers, and divide out common factors in the fraction part of a mixed number.

LEARN Solving Time Problems with Mixed Numbers

Students will learn how to solve problems involving times zones around the world using mixed numbers. These problems will involve multiple steps.

TRY IT Solve Time Problems with Mixed Numbers

Students will practice solving problems involving times zones around the world using mixed numbers.

TRY IT Practice Solving Multistep Problems with Mixed Numbers

Students will complete online practice problems. Then they will complete Practice Solving Multistep Problems with Mixed Numbers from *Summit Math 5 Activity Book*.

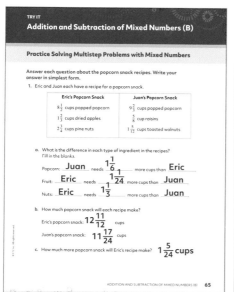

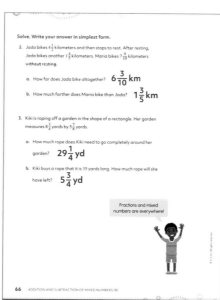

Solving Multistep Problems with Mixed Numbers

Students will solve a problem to show that they understand how to solve a real-world problem in which fractions and mixed numbers must be added and/or subtracted in multiple steps.

Addition and Subtraction of Mixed Numbers (C)

Lesson Overview

ACTIVITY	ACTIVITY TITLE	TIME	ONLINE/OFFLINE
GET READY	Introduction to Addition and Subtraction of Mixed Numbers (C)	**2** minutes	🖥
TRY IT	Review Addition and Subtraction of Mixed Numbers	**18** minutes	🖥
QUIZ	Addition and Subtraction of Mixed Numbers	**25** minutes	🛜
WRAP-UP	More Math Practice	**15** minutes	🖥

Lesson Goals

- Review evaluating multistep expressions and solving multistep problems with fractions and mixed numbers.

- Take a quiz.

MATERIALS

There are no materials to gather for this lesson.

GET READY

Introduction to Addition and Subtraction of Mixed Numbers (C)

Students will read the lesson goals.

TRY IT

Review Addition and Subtraction of Mixed Numbers

Students will answer questions to review what they have learned about the addition and subtraction of mixed numbers.

QUIZ

Addition and Subtraction of Mixed Numbers

Students will complete the Addition and Subtraction of Mixed Numbers quiz.

More Math Practice

Students will practice skills according to their individual needs.

Big Ideas: Extended Problems

Lesson Overview

Big Ideas lessons provide students the opportunity to further apply the knowledge and skills acquired throughout previous units. Each Big Ideas lesson consists of three parts:

1. **Cumulative Review:** Students keep their skills fresh by reviewing prior content.

2. **Preview:** Students practice answering the types of questions they will commonly find on standardized tests.

3. **Synthesis:** Students complete an assignment that allows them to interweave and apply what they've learned. These synthesis assignments will vary throughout the course.

In the Synthesis portion of this Big Ideas lesson, students will complete multistep problems that go beyond the short answer and multiple choice problems they encounter in their regular lessons. These problems give students an opportunity to demonstrate problem solving, reasoning, communication, and modeling skills. Students will need to use pencil and paper and/or technology to show their work.

LEARNING COACH CHECK-IN   This is a graded assessment. Make sure students complete, review, and submit the assignment to their teacher.

All materials needed for this lesson are linked online. The materials are not provided in this Lesson Guide or in the Activity Book.

MATERIALS

Supplied
- Extended Problems Instructions (printout)

Multiplication with Fractions and Mixed Numbers

Multiplying with Fractions (A)

Lesson Overview

ACTIVITY	ACTIVITY TITLE	TIME	ONLINE/OFFLINE
GET READY	Introduction to Multiplying with Fractions (A)	**2** minutes	🖥️
	Multiplication with Fractions and Mixed Numbers in 60 Seconds	**3** minutes	🖥️
	Look Back at Writing an Improper Fraction as a Mixed Number	**5** minutes	🖥️
LEARN AND **TRY IT**	Describing Division Problems	**15** minutes	🖥️
	Describe Division Problems	**10** minutes	🖥️
	Practice Describing Division Problems	**20** minutes	🖥️ and 📄
WRAP-UP	Describing Division Problems	**5** minutes	🖥️

Content Background

In this lesson, students will learn how to use models and equations to divide one whole number by another whole number. The quotient of two whole numbers can be another whole number: $6 \div 3 = 2$. However, the quotient also can be a fraction or an improper fraction, which should be rewritten as a mixed number: $2 \div 7 = \frac{2}{7}$ or $8 \div 3 = \frac{8}{3} = 2\frac{2}{3}$.

Lesson Goals

- Solve real-world division problems using models and multiplication equations.

MATERIALS

Supplied
- *Summit Math 5 Activity Book:* Practice Describing Division Problems

KEYWORDS

improper fraction – a fraction whose numerator is greater than or equal to its denominator

mixed number – a whole number and a proper fraction that show a single amount

simplest form – of fractions, a fraction with a numerator and denominator that have no common factor other than 1

GET READY

Introduction to Multiplying with Fractions (A)

Students will get a glimpse of what they will learn about in the lesson. They will also read the lesson goals.

Multiplication with Fractions and Mixed Numbers in 60 Seconds

Students will watch a short video designed to spark their interest in upcoming topics.

Look Back at Writing an Improper Fraction as a Mixed Number

Students will practice the prerequisite skill of writing an improper fraction as a mixed number.

LEARN AND TRY IT

LEARN   Describing Division Problems

Students will learn how to use models and equations to divide one whole number by another whole number when the result is a fraction.

TRY IT   Describe Division Problems

Students will practice dividing whole numbers using models and equations. Support will be provided to help students overcome misconceptions.

TIP   When drawing a model for a fraction, remind students to draw 1 line fewer than the number of parts. For example, dividing a rectangle into fourths requires drawing 3 lines inside the rectangle.

TRY IT   Practice Describing Division Problems

Students will complete online practice problems. Then they will complete Practice Describing Division Problems from *Summit Math 5 Activity Book*.

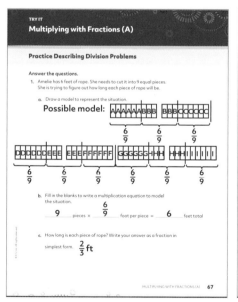

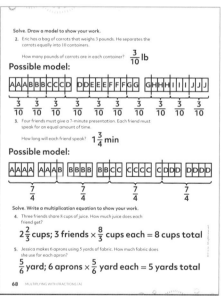

TIP   Some students benefit from labeling the rectangles when they model a problem. For example, if they are dividing 2 pounds of sand into 3 buckets, the rectangles can each be labeled "pound of sand." Otherwise, they might start to think that the rectangles represent buckets instead of sand.

Describing Division Problems

Students will solve a problem to show that they understand how to use a model to divide whole numbers that result in a fraction.

Multiplying with Fractions (B)

Lesson Overview

ACTIVITY	ACTIVITY TITLE	TIME	ONLINE/OFFLINE
GET READY	Introduction to Multiplying with Fractions (B)	**2** minutes	🖥️
	Multiplying and Dividing by 9 with Instant Recall	**8** minutes	🖥️
LEARN AND **TRY IT**	Modeling a Fraction Times a Whole	**7** minutes	🖥️
	Model a Fraction Times a Whole	**7** minutes	🖥️
	Using an Area Model	**7** minutes	🖥️
	Use an Area Model	**7** minutes	🖥️
	Practice Using a Model to Multiply a Fraction Times a Whole	**20** minutes	🖥️ and 📄
WRAP-UP	Using a Model to Multiply a Fraction Times a Whole	**2** minutes	🖥️

Content Background

In this lesson, students will use models to "see" how fraction multiplication works. Although the traditional algorithm of multiplying numerators and denominators certainly works to find the product of fractions, the rule gives students an answer that they often do not understand. They struggle to know if their answers make sense. By modeling several problems, students begin acquiring an intuitive sense about the correctness of their answers when they begin using the algorithm.

Lesson Goals

- Use models and equations to show the multiplication of a fraction and a whole number.

- Explain why the product of a fraction and a whole number is less than the whole number.

MATERIALS

Supplied
- *Summit Math 5 Activity Book:* Practice Using a Model to Multiply a Fraction Times a Whole

KEYWORDS

area model – a model for multiplication that shows the product of two factors as the total number of squares on a rectangular grid; one factor is the number of rows and the other factor is the number of columns

factor – one of two or more numbers that are multiplied

Introduction to Multiplying with Fractions (B)

Students will get a glimpse of what they will learn about in the lesson. They will also read the lesson goals and keywords. Have students select each keyword and preview its definition.

Multiplying and Dividing by 9 with Instant Recall

Students will practice multiplying and dividing by 9 with instant recall.

LEARN AND TRY IT

LEARN   Modeling a Fraction Times a Whole

Students will learn how to multiply a fraction by a whole number using models such as number lines and arrays. They also will write an equation from a model. In the model, the factors can be listed in any order.

TRY IT   Model a Fraction Times a Whole

Students will practice using a model to multiply a fraction by a whole number. Support will be provided to help students overcome misconceptions.

LEARN   Using an Area Model

Students will learn how to use an area model to represent the product of a whole number and a fraction. They also will learn that when a number is multiplied by a fraction less than 1, the product is less than the original number.

TRY IT   Use an Area Model

Students will practice using an area model to multiply a whole number by a fraction. They also will explain the product of a whole number and a fraction less than 1. Support will be provided to help students overcome misconceptions.

TRY IT   Practice Using a Model to Multiply a Fraction Times a Whole

Students will complete online practice problems. Then they will complete Practice Using a Model to Multiply a Fraction Times a Whole from *Summit Math 5 Activity Book.*

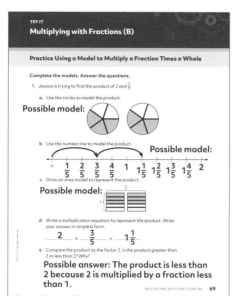

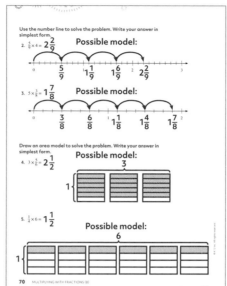

NOTE   When checking equation answers, the factors can be in any order. For example, both $3 \times \frac{2}{7} = \frac{6}{7}$ and $\frac{2}{7} \times 3 = \frac{6}{7}$ are correct answers. Both correct answers are not listed in the answer key.

WRAP-UP

Using a Model to Multiply a Fraction Times a Whole

Students will solve a problem to show that they understand how to use an area problem to multiply a whole number by a fraction.

Multiplying with Fractions (C)

Lesson Overview

ACTIVITY	ACTIVITY TITLE	TIME	ONLINE/OFFLINE
GET READY	Introduction to Multiplying with Fractions (C)	**2** minutes	🖥️
	Multiplying and Dividing by 9 Math Facts Game	**8** minutes	🖥️
LEARN AND **TRY IT**	Multiplying Whole Numbers by Fractions	**7** minutes	🖥️
	Multiply Whole Numbers by Fractions	**7** minutes	🖥️
	Multiplying Whole Numbers by Fractions in the Real World	**7** minutes	🖥️
	Multiply Whole Numbers by Fractions in the Real World	**7** minutes	🖥️
	Practice Multiplying Whole Numbers by Fractions	**20** minutes	🖥️ and 📄
WRAP-UP	Multiplying Whole Numbers by Fractions	**2** minutes	🖥️

Content Background

In this lesson, students will learn how to multiply a whole number by a fraction using an algorithm instead of a model. They also will solve real-world problems that involve giving a fraction of a number and using a fraction to make a comparison.

Here is the algorithm:

1. Multiply the whole number by the numerator of the fraction.

2. Keep the denominator of the fraction.

3. Simplify if needed. Simplifying includes dividing out common factors from the numerator and denominator and/or writing an improper fraction as a mixed number.

In some problems, the whole number and the denominator of the fraction have a common factor. In these cases, divide the greatest common factor (GCF) out of the denominator of the fraction and the whole number before the multiplication step. Dividing the GCF from the denominator and the whole number means multiplying smaller numbers and not having to simplify a fraction at the end. This shortcut is optional.

NOTE   Sometimes the informal term *canceling* is used instead of *dividing out*. However, it is more correct to use the term *dividing out*.

MATERIALS

Supplied
- *Summit Math 5 Activity Book:* Practice Multiplying Whole Numbers by Fractions

---

KEYWORDS

greatest common factor (GCF) – the greatest whole number that is a factor of two or more given whole numbers

---

Lesson Goals

- Multiply a fraction and a whole number.

- Solve real-world problems by multiplying a fraction and a whole number.

- Determine a real-world story to match the product of a fraction and a whole number.

Introduction to Multiplying with Fractions (C)

Students will get a glimpse of what they will learn about in the lesson. They will also read the lesson goals and keywords. Have students select each keyword and preview its definition.

Multiplying and Dividing by 9 Math Facts Game

Students will practice multiplying and dividing by 9.

LEARN AND TRY IT

LEARN   Multiplying Whole Numbers by Fractions

Students will learn how to use an algorithm to multiply a fraction and a whole number.

TRY IT   Multiply Whole Numbers by Fractions

Students will practice multiplying a whole number and a fraction without using a model. Support will be provided to help students overcome misconceptions.

SUPPORT   For students who struggle to know if their answer makes sense, they can use a model to check their work.

LEARN   Multiplying Whole Numbers by Fractions in the Real World

Students will solve real-world problems that involve multiplying a whole number and a fraction without using a model. They also will learn how to represent the product of a fraction and a whole number in a story context.

TRY IT   Multiply Whole Numbers by Fractions in the Real World

Students will practice solving and writing real-world problems involving the product of a whole number and a fraction. Support will be provided to help students overcome misconceptions.

TRY IT Practice Multiplying Whole Numbers by Fractions

Students will complete online practice problems. Then they will complete Practice Multiplying Whole Numbers by Fractions from *Summit Math 5 Activity Book*.

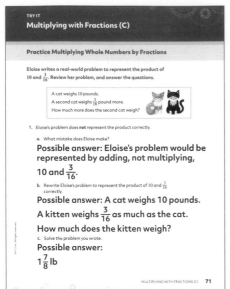
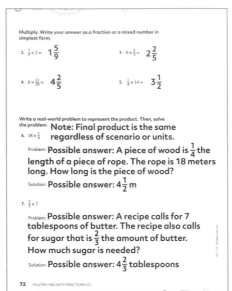

NOTE Students will write their own real-world problems to represent a product. An answer is correct as long as the story describes finding a fraction of a whole number quantity.

WRAP-UP

Multiplying Whole Numbers by Fractions

Students will solve a problem to show that they understand how to multiply a whole number and a fraction without using a model.

Multiplying with Fractions (D)

Lesson Overview

ACTIVITY	ACTIVITY TITLE	TIME	ONLINE/OFFLINE
GET READY	Introduction to Multiplying with Fractions (D)	**2** minutes	🖥️
	Multiplying and Dividing by 11 Math Facts	**8** minutes	🖥️
LEARN AND **TRY IT**	Multiplying Two Fractions Using Models	**7** minutes	🖥️
	Multiply Two Fractions Using Models	**7** minutes	🖥️
	Determining the Area of a Rectangle	**7** minutes	🖥️
	Determine the Area of a Rectangle	**7** minutes	🖥️
	Practice Multiplying Two Fractions and Determining Area	**20** minutes	🖥️ and 📄
WRAP-UP	Multiplying Two Fractions and Determining Area	**2** minutes	🖥️

Content Background

In this lesson, students will use models, including area models, to "see" how fraction multiplication works. Each product includes two fractions less than 1. When building an area model, it is important to divide the square along the length for one fraction and the width for the other fraction. It doesn't matter which side corresponds to which fraction, as long as *both* fractions do not both divide the length or both divide the width.

Although the traditional algorithm of multiplying numerators and denominators certainly works to find the product of fractions, the rule gives students answers that they often do not understand. They struggle to know if their answers make sense. By modeling several problems, students begin to get an intuitive sense about the correctness of their answers. Drawing models is also a helpful way to check the results when students start using the traditional algorithm.

> ### MATERIALS
>
> **Supplied**
> - *Summit Math 5 Activity Book:* Practice Multiplying Two Fractions and Determining Area

Lesson Goals

- Represent the product of two fractions with models.
- Solve real-world problems, including the area of a rectangle, by modeling the product of two fractions.

Introduction to Multiplying with Fractions (D)

Students will get a glimpse of what they will learn about in the lesson. They will also read the lesson goals.

Multiplying and Dividing by 11 Math Facts

Students will practice multiplying and dividing by 11.

LEARN AND TRY IT

LEARN   Multiplying Two Fractions Using Models

Students will learn how to multiply two fractions using models. They also will use an equation to represent a product given as a model.

TRY IT   Multiply Two Fractions Using Models

Students will practice multiplying two fractions using models. Support will be provided to help students overcome misconceptions.

LEARN   Determining the Area of a Rectangle

Students will use area models to solve real-world problems involving the product of two fractions. The area models look very similar to the rectangular models used earlier in the lesson.

TRY IT   Determine the Area of a Rectangle

Students will practice using area models to solve real-world problems involving the product of two fractions. Support will be provided to help students overcome misconceptions.

TRY IT   Practice Multiplying Two Fractions and Determining Area

Students will complete online practice problems. Then they will complete Practice Multiplying Two Fractions and Determining Area from *Summit Math 5 Activity Book*.

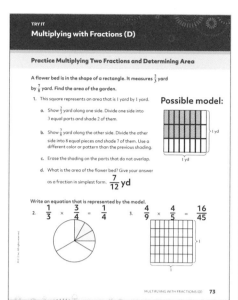
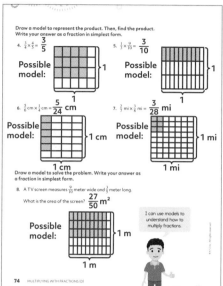

Multiplying Two Fractions and Determining Area

Students will solve a problem to show that they understand how to use an area model to solve real-world problems involving the product of two fractions.

Multiplying with Fractions (E)

Lesson Overview

ACTIVITY	ACTIVITY TITLE	TIME	ONLINE/OFFLINE
GET READY	Introduction to Multiplying with Fractions (E)	**2** minutes	📶
	Multiplying and Dividing by 11 with Instant Recall	**8** minutes	📶
LEARN AND TRY IT	Multiplying Fractions	**7** minutes	📶
	Multiply Fractions	**7** minutes	📶
	Solving Real-World Problems by Multiplying Fractions	**7** minutes	📶
	Solve Real-World Problems by Multiplying Fractions	**7** minutes	📶
	Practice Multiplying Fractions	**20** minutes	📶 and 📄
WRAP-UP	Multiplying Fractions	**2** minutes	📶

Content Background

In this lesson, students will extend their knowledge of models of fraction multiplication to apply the standard algorithm. When using the algorithm, students will learn to divide out common factors in the original problem. This step is an optional first step. However, it does make fractions easier to multiply; the answer already will be in simplest form.

Students will also solve real-world problems that involve multiplying fractions, including area of squares and rectangles with fractional side lengths, and represent the product of two fractions in a story context.

Additionally, students will learn what happens when a fraction is multiplied by a fraction whose numerator and denominator are the same, such as $\frac{5}{5}$.

A fraction in this form is equal to 1, and multiplying by 1 does not change the value of a number. This property is used to generate equivalent fractions. For example, $\frac{2}{3} = \frac{2 \times 5}{3 \times 5} = \frac{10}{15}$, which can also be written $\frac{2}{3} = \frac{2}{3} \times \frac{5}{5} = \frac{10}{15}$.

Lesson Goals

- Multiply fractions without using models.

- Solve real-world problems by multiplying fractions.

- Explain how fraction multiplication relates to rectangular area models and to writing equivalent fractions.

GET READY

Introduction to Multiplying with Fractions (E)

Students will get a glimpse of what they will learn about in the lesson. They will also read the lesson goals.

Multiplying and Dividing by 11 with Instant Recall

Students will practice multiplying and dividing by 11 with instant recall.

LEARN AND TRY IT

LEARN   Multiplying Fractions

Students will learn how to apply the standard algorithm for multiplying fractions, which is to multiply the numerators, and then multiply the denominators. Students should always give their answer in simplest form. They can divide out common factors after they multiply, or they can divide out a common factor first. Students also will discover that multiplying a fraction by a fraction that equals 1 does not change the value of the original fraction.

NOTE   The process for multiplying two fractions extends to multiplying a fraction and a whole if you first write the whole number over 1.

TRY IT   Multiply Fractions

Students will practice multiplying fractions using the standard algorithm. Support will be provided to help students overcome misconceptions.

LEARN   Solving Real-World Problems by Multiplying Fractions

Students will learn how to solve real-world problems by multiplying fractions using the standard algorithm.

TRY IT   Solve Real-World Problems by Multiplying Fractions

Students will practice solving real-world problems by multiplying fractions using the standard algorithm. Support will be provided to help students overcome misconceptions.

TRY IT   Practice Multiplying Fractions

Students will complete online practice problems. Then they will complete Practice Multiplying Fractions from *Summit Math 5 Activity Book*.

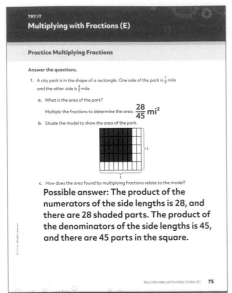

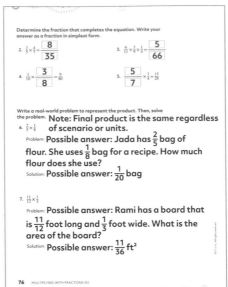

WRAP-UP

Multiplying Fractions

Students will solve a problem to show that they understand how to multiply two fractions using the standard algorithm.

Multiplying with Fractions (F)

Lesson Overview

ACTIVITY	ACTIVITY TITLE	TIME	ONLINE/OFFLINE
GET READY	Introduction to Multiplying with Fractions (F)	**2** minutes	🖥️
TRY IT	Review Multiplying with Fractions	**18** minutes	🖥️
QUIZ	Multiplying with Fractions	**25** minutes	🖥️
WRAP-UP	More Math Practice	**15** minutes	🖥️

Lesson Goals

- Review solving a division problem with a model, multiplying a fraction and whole number with and without a model, and multiplying a fraction and a fraction with and without a model.

- Take a quiz.

MATERIALS

There are no materials to gather for this lesson.

GET READY

Introduction to Multiplying with Fractions (F)

Students will read the lesson goals.

TRY IT

Review Multiplying with Fractions

Students will answer questions to review what they have learned about multiplying with fractions.

QUIZ

Multiplying with Fractions

Students will complete the Multiplying with Fractions quiz.

More Math Practice

Students will practice skills according to their individual needs.

Multiplying with Mixed Numbers (A)

Lesson Overview

ACTIVITY	ACTIVITY TITLE	TIME	ONLINE/OFFLINE
GET READY	Introduction to Multiplying with Mixed Numbers (A)	**2** minutes	🖥️
	Look Back at Using a Model to Multiply Fractions	**8** minutes	🖥️
LEARN AND **TRY IT**	Multiplying Mixed Numbers and Fractions with Models	**7** minutes	🖥️
	Multiply Mixed Numbers and Fractions with Models	**7** minutes	🖥️
	Multiplying Mixed Numbers with Models	**7** minutes	🖥️
	Multiply Mixed Numbers with Models	**7** minutes	🖥️
	Practice Multiplying with Mixed Numbers	**20** minutes	🖥️ and 📄
WRAP-UP	Multiplying with Mixed Numbers Using Models	**2** minutes	🖥️

Content Background

In this lesson, students will use models to represent products where at least one factor is a mixed number greater than 1. Adults often find the models cumbersome and irrelevant, especially models involving mixed numbers. However, many adults struggled with fractions when they were students and still do because they learned the algorithm without truly understanding the concept. Encourage students to understand the models before moving directly into the algorithm.

MATERIALS

Supplied

- *Summit Math 5 Activity Book:* Practice Multiplying with Mixed Numbers

Lesson Goals

- Solve problems involving the product of a fraction and a mixed number by using a model.

- Solve problems involving the product of two mixed numbers by using a model.

- Determine the size of a product, compared to a given factor, based on the size of the other factor.

Introduction to Multiplying with Mixed Numbers (A)

Students will get a glimpse of what they will learn about in the lesson. They will also read the lesson goals.

Look Back at Using a Model to Multiply Fractions

Students will practice the prerequisite skill of using a model to multiply fractions.

LEARN AND TRY IT

LEARN Multiplying Mixed Numbers and Fractions with Models

Students will learn how to solve a real-world problem by modeling the product of a fraction and a mixed number. They always should begin by modeling the mixed number.

TIP   Remind students that the length of the model is 1 and the width equals the mixed number. To model the fraction, the side length that represents 1 is divided into equal rows and the correct number of rows are shaded.

NOTE   Any time a mixed number is multiplied by a fraction less than 1, the product will be less than the original mixed number. This concept is illustrated in the model when the length of 1 is split into equivalent parts and only some of those parts are shaded in the model.

TRY IT Multiply Mixed Numbers and Fractions with Models

Students will practice solving real-world problems by modeling the product of a fraction and a mixed number. They will also practice determining the size of the product of a mixed number and a fraction less than 1. Support will be provided to help students overcome misconceptions.

LEARN Multiplying Mixed Numbers with Models

Students will learn how to solve a real-world problem by modeling the product of two mixed numbers.

TIP   When two mixed numbers are multiplied, it doesn't matter which number is modeled first. The length of the model begins as 1. Since the mixed number is greater than 1, rows that are identical to the first row are added.

NOTE   Any time two mixed numbers are multiplied, the product will be greater than either factor. This concept is illustrated in the model when the length of 1 is duplicated.

TRY IT Multiply Mixed Numbers with Models

Students will practice solving real-world problems by modeling the product of two mixed numbers. Support will be provided to help students overcome misconceptions.

TRY IT Practice Multiplying with Mixed Numbers

Students will complete online practice problems. Then they will complete Practice Multiplying with Mixed Numbers from *Summit Math 5 Activity Book*.

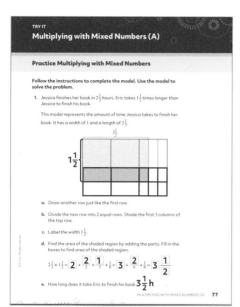

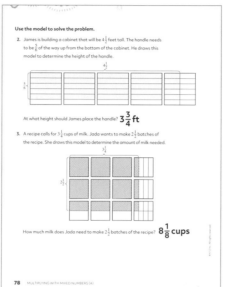

WRAP-UP

Multiplying with Mixed Numbers Using Models

Students will solve a problem to show that they understand how to solve a real-world problem by modeling the product of two mixed numbers.

Multiplying with Mixed Numbers (B)

Lesson Overview

ACTIVITY	ACTIVITY TITLE	TIME	ONLINE/OFFLINE
GET READY	Introduction to Multiplying with Mixed Numbers (B)	**2** minutes	🖥
	Multiplying and Dividing by 11 Math Facts Game	**8** minutes	🖥
LEARN AND **TRY IT**	Multiplying Mixed Numbers	**15** minutes	🖥
	Multiply Mixed Numbers	**10** minutes	🖥
	Practice Multiplying Mixed Numbers	**20** minutes	🖥 and 📄
WRAP-UP	Multiplying Mixed Numbers	**5** minutes	🖥

Content Background

In this lesson, students will extend their knowledge of models of fraction multiplication to apply the standard algorithm. They will begin by rewriting any mixed number factors as improper fractions. Once all factors are written as fractions, students can multiply numerators and denominators. The product always should be given in simplest form. Usually that means rewriting an improper fraction as a mixed number and/or dividing out any common factors in the fraction part of the mixed number.

Lesson Goals

- Multiply a fraction by a mixed number.
- Multiply a mixed number by a mixed number.

GET READY

Introduction to Multiplying with Mixed Numbers (B)
Students will get a glimpse of what they will learn about in the lesson. They will also read the lesson goals.

Multiplying and Dividing by 11 Math Facts Game
Students will practice multiplying and dividing by 11.

LEARN   Multiplying Mixed Numbers

Students will learn how to multiply mixed numbers using the standard algorithm instead of a model.

NOTE   Students may divide out common factors before multiplying. By dividing out common factors, students are simplifying the original problem and making the fractions simpler to multiply. Also, if they have in fact divided out all the common factors possible in the original problem, they will only need to rewrite the product as a mixed number. There should be no additional common factors left to simplify.

TRY IT   Multiply Mixed Numbers

Students will practice multiplying fractions and mixed numbers without using models. Support will be provided to help students overcome misconceptions.

TRY IT   Practice Multiplying Mixed Numbers

Students will complete online practice problems. Then they will complete Practice Multiplying Mixed Numbers from *Summit Math 5 Activity Book*.

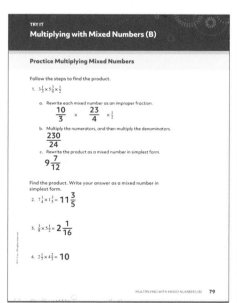

SUPPORT   Students can estimate a product to check for a reasonable answer.

For example, the product of $6\frac{1}{4} \times 2\frac{3}{4}$ should be fairly close to $6 \times 3 = 18$.

WRAP-UP

Multiplying Mixed Numbers

Students will solve a problem to show that they understand how to multiply mixed numbers without using a model.

Multiplying with Mixed Numbers (C)

Lesson Overview

ACTIVITY	ACTIVITY TITLE	TIME	ONLINE/OFFLINE
GET READY	Introduction to Multiplying with Mixed Numbers (C)	**2** minutes	🖥️
	Multiplying and Dividing by 12 Math Facts	**8** minutes	🖥️
LEARN AND **TRY IT**	Multiplying with Mixed Numbers in the Real World	**15** minutes	🖥️
	Multiply with Mixed Numbers in the Real World	**10** minutes	🖥️
	Practice Multiplying with Mixed Numbers in the Real World	**20** minutes	🖥️ and 📄
WRAP-UP	Multiplying with Mixed Numbers in the Real World	**5** minutes	🖥️

Content Background

In this lesson, students will apply their knowledge of mixed number multiplication to solve real-world problems. Each problem requires students to multiply a mixed number by a fraction or by another mixed number. Some problems require multiple steps to solve.

Lesson Goals

- Solve real-world problems by multiplying fractions and mixed numbers.

GET READY

Introduction to Multiplying with Mixed Numbers (C)

Students will get a glimpse of what they will learn about in the lesson. They will also read the lesson goals.

Multiplying and Dividing by 12 Math Facts

Students will practice math facts for multiplying and dividing by 12.

LEARN   Multiplying with Mixed Numbers in the Real World

Students will solve real-world problems that involve multiplying mixed numbers and fractions.

TRY IT   Multiply with Mixed Numbers in the Real World

Students will practice solving real-world problems that involve multiplying mixed numbers and fractions. Support will be provided to help students overcome misconceptions.

TRY IT   Practice Multiplying with Mixed Numbers in the Real World

Students will complete online practice problems. Then they will complete Practice Multiplying with Mixed Numbers in the Real World from *Summit Math 5 Activity Book*.

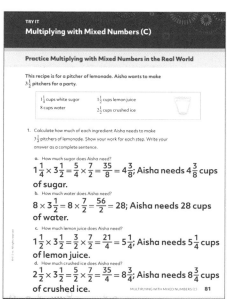
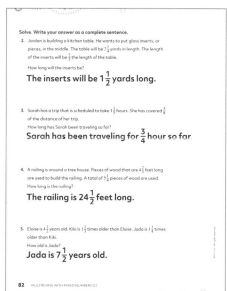

NOTE   When solving a real-world problem, students should write the answer to the question in a complete sentence.

Multiplying with Mixed Numbers in the Real World

Students will solve a problem to show that they understand how to solve real-world problems by multiplying mixed numbers and fractions.

Multiplying with Mixed Numbers (D)

Lesson Overview

ACTIVITY	ACTIVITY TITLE	TIME	ONLINE/OFFLINE
GET READY	Introduction to Multiplying with Mixed Numbers (D)	**2** minutes	🖥️
TRY IT	Review Multiplying with Mixed Numbers	**18** minutes	🖥️
QUIZ	Multiplying with Mixed Numbers	**25** minutes	🖥️
WRAP-UP	More Math Practice	**15** minutes	🖥️

Lesson Goals

- Review multiplying mixed numbers with models, multiplying mixed numbers without models, and solving real-world problems by multiplying with mixed numbers.

- Take a quiz.

MATERIALS

There are no materials to gather for this lesson.

GET READY

Introduction to Multiplying with Mixed Numbers (D)

Students will read the lesson goals.

TRY IT

Review Multiplying with Mixed Numbers

Students will answer questions to review what they have learned about multiplying with mixed numbers.

QUIZ

Multiplying with Mixed Numbers

Students will complete the Multiplying with Mixed Numbers quiz.

More Math Practice

Students will practice skills according to their individual needs.

Big Ideas: Mini-Project

Lesson Overview

Big Ideas lessons provide students the opportunity to further apply the knowledge and skills acquired throughout previous units. Each Big Ideas lesson consists of three parts:

1. **Cumulative Review:** Students keep their skills fresh by reviewing prior content.

2. **Preview:** Students practice answering the types of questions they will commonly find on standardized tests.

3. **Synthesis:** Students complete an assignment that allows them to interweave and apply what they've learned. These synthesis assignments will vary throughout the course.

    In the Synthesis portion of this Big Ideas lesson, students will complete a small, creative project designed to tie together concepts and skills that students have encountered across units. These small projects are designed to emphasize a real-world application that connects mathematics to other subjects, including science, technology, engineering, art, and history. Students will need to use pencil and paper and/or technology to show their work.

    LEARNING COACH CHECK-IN Make sure students complete, review, and submit the assignment to their teacher.

All materials needed for this lesson are linked online. The materials are not provided in this Lesson Guide or in the Activity Book.

MATERIALS

Supplied
- Mini-Project Instructions (printout)

Division with
Unit Fractions

Unit Fractions Divided by Whole Numbers (A)

Lesson Overview

ACTIVITY	ACTIVITY TITLE	TIME	ONLINE/OFFLINE
GET READY	Introduction to Unit Fractions Divided by Whole Numbers (A)	**2** minutes	🖥
	Division with Unit Fractions in 60 Seconds	**3** minutes	🖥
	Look Back at Representing Unit Fractions	**5** minutes	🖥
LEARN AND **TRY IT**	Dividing Unit Fractions Using Models	**15** minutes	🖥
	Divide Unit Fractions Using Models	**10** minutes	🖥
	Practice Dividing Unit Fractions Using Models	**20** minutes	🖥 and 📄
WRAP-UP	Dividing Unit Fractions Using Models	**5** minutes	🖥

Content Background

In this lesson, students will learn how to model the division of a unit fraction by a whole number. The division of fractions often has been taught as a rote manipulation of numbers. As a result, it is one of the mathematical concepts that is easily forgotten, even by adults. For this reason, it is very important to provide students with a variety of ways to model how a fraction can be divided by a number and to delay the introduction of specific steps for dividing fractions until students can observe and understand the underlying concepts. Students usually know $12 \div 4$ as, "How many groups of 4 are in 12," or "What is 12 shared 4 ways?" But,

they do not as easily view $\frac{1}{3} \div 4$ as "What fraction of 4 is in $\frac{1}{3}$," or "What is $\frac{1}{3}$ shared 4 ways?" It is important for students to gain this understanding before they learn division algorithms, or step-by-step procedures.

Lesson Goals

- Represent the quotient of a unit fraction and a whole number with a model.

- Determine the quotient of a unit fraction and a whole number by using a model.

MATERIALS

Supplied
- *Summit Math 5 Activity Book:* Practice Dividing Unit Fractions Using Models

KEYWORDS

unit fraction – a fraction with a numerator of 1, such as $\frac{1}{3}$ or $\frac{1}{7}$

Introduction to Unit Fractions Divided by Whole Numbers (A)

Students will get a glimpse of what they will learn about in the lesson. They will also read the lesson goals and keywords. Have students select each keyword and preview its definition.

Division with Unit Fractions in 60 Seconds

Students will watch a short video designed to spark their interest in upcoming topics.

Look Back at Representing Unit Fractions

Students will practice the prerequisite skill of representing unit fractions on a number line.

LEARN AND TRY IT

LEARN   Dividing Unit Fractions Using Models

Students will learn how to divide a unit fraction by a whole number using different models. They will use area models, number lines, and fraction strips to investigate and model each division problem.

NOTE   An area model and fraction strips are similar when drawn by hand. An area model usually appears as a square, whereas a fraction strip usually appears as a rectangle. Both models are divided into an equal number of columns to represent the unit fraction. In an area model, the square is divided into an equal number of rows to represent division by the whole number. In a fraction strip model, one of the columns is divided again into an equal number of columns to represent division by a whole number.

TRY IT   Divide Unit Fractions Using Models

Students will practice dividing a unit fraction by a whole number using models. Support will be provided to help students overcome misconceptions.

TRY IT Practice Dividing Unit Fractions Using Models

Students will complete online practice problems. Then they will complete Practice Dividing Unit Fractions Using Models from *Summit Math 5 Activity Book*.

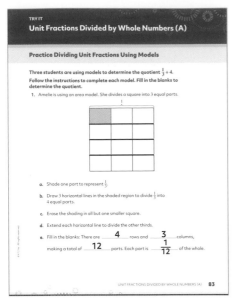

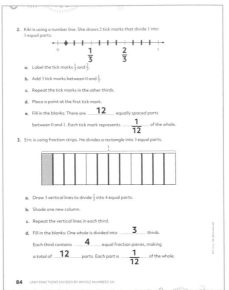

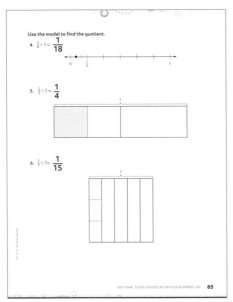

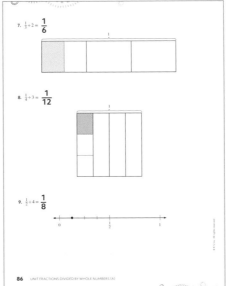

WRAP-UP

Dividing Unit Fractions Using Models

Students will solve a problem to show that they understand how to use a model to divide a unit fraction by a whole number.

Unit Fractions Divided by Whole Numbers (B)

Lesson Overview

ACTIVITY	ACTIVITY TITLE	TIME	ONLINE/OFFLINE
GET READY	Introduction to Unit Fractions Divided by Whole Numbers (B)	**2** minutes	🖥️
	Multiplying and Dividing by 12 with Instant Recall	**8** minutes	🖥️
LEARN AND **TRY IT**	Dividing Unit Fractions with Stories	**15** minutes	🖥️
	Divide Unit Fractions with Stories	**10** minutes	🖥️
	Practice Dividing Unit Fractions with Stories	**20** minutes	🖥️ and 📄
WRAP-UP	Dividing Unit Fractions with Stories	**5** minutes	🖥️

Content Background

In this lesson, students will write and solve real-world problems that involve the division of a unit fraction by a whole number. They will continue to use models to find the quotient of a unit fraction and a whole number.

Lesson Goals

- Write a story for the division of a unit fraction and a whole number.

- Solve real-world problems involving the division of a unit fraction and a whole number using stories and models.

GET READY

Introduction to Unit Fractions Divided by Whole Numbers (B)

Students will get a glimpse of what they will learn about in the lesson. They will also read the lesson goals.

Multiplying and Dividing by 12 with Instant Recall

Students will practice multiplying and dividing by 12 with instant recall.

LEARN   Dividing Unit Fractions with Stories

Students will learn how to write and solve real-world problems where a unit fraction is divided by a whole number.

TRY IT   Divide Unit Fractions with Stories

Students will practice writing and solving real-world problems where a unit fraction is divided by a whole number. Support will be provided to help students overcome misconceptions.

NOTE   Sometimes a situation seems to describe division twice. For example, a bag of pretzels is split equally into 4 bowls and each bowl of pretzels is shared equally between 3 friends. Students should use a unit fraction to represent the first division phrase. This situation would be represented by the expression $\frac{1}{4} \div 3$.

TRY IT   Practice Dividing Unit Fractions with Stories

Students will complete online practice problems. Then they will complete Practice Dividing Unit Fractions with Stories from *Summit Math 5 Activity Book.*

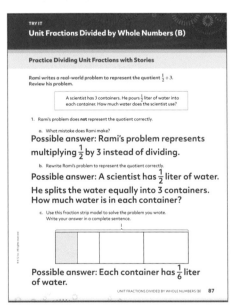

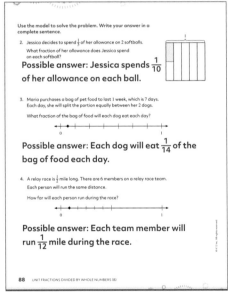

Dividing Unit Fractions with Stories

Students will solve a problem to show that they understand how to solve a real-world problem where a unit fraction is divided by a whole number.

Unit Fractions Divided by Whole Numbers (C)

Lesson Overview

ACTIVITY	ACTIVITY TITLE	TIME	ONLINE/OFFLINE
GET READY	Introduction to Unit Fractions Divided by Whole Numbers (C)	**2** minutes	🖥️
	Multiplying and Dividing by 12 Math Facts Game	**8** minutes	🖥️
LEARN AND **TRY IT**	Dividing Unit Fractions Using Multiplication	**15** minutes	🖥️
	Divide Unit Fractions Using Multiplication	**10** minutes	🖥️
	Practice Dividing Unit Fractions Using Multiplication	**20** minutes	🖥️ and 📄
WRAP-UP	Dividing Unit Fractions Using Multiplication	**5** minutes	🖥️

Content Background

In this lesson, students will use the inverse relationship between multiplication and division to divide a unit fraction by a whole number. Here is the process they will follow:

1. Write a multiplication problem that is related to the division problem. A question mark or other symbol can stand for the missing quotient and factor.

2. Rewrite the fraction in the multiplication problem as an equivalent fraction. The numerator of the fraction must be the same as the known factor.

3. Determine the missing factor. The numerator is 1, and the denominator is the same as the denominator of the equivalent fraction.

4. Determine the quotient. The quotient is the same as the missing factor.

This lesson is a bridge between using models to divide a unit fraction by a whole number and using a rule. As students progress through the lesson, they may notice a pattern in the quotients. The denominator of the quotient is the product of the whole number and the denominator of the unit fraction. The reason for the pattern is explained once the rule is introduced in the next lesson. Allow students to notice the pattern without immediately explaining the rule. Using the relationship between multiplication and division is an important step in helping students develop an intuitive sense about the correctness of their answers.

MATERIALS

Supplied
- *Summit Math 5 Activity Book:* Practice Dividing Unit Fractions Using Multiplication

KEYWORDS

equivalent fractions – fractions that name the same amount, such as $\frac{1}{2}$ and $\frac{3}{6}$

inverse relationship – the relationship between operations that reverse or undo each other; addition and subtraction have an inverse relationship; multiplication and division have an inverse relationship

Lesson Goals

- Divide a unit fraction by a whole number by using the relationship between multiplication and division.

Introduction to Unit Fractions Divided by Whole Numbers (C)

Students will get a glimpse of what they will learn about in the lesson. They will also read the lesson goals and keywords. Have students select each keyword and preview its definition.

Multiplying and Dividing by 12 Math Facts Game

Students will practice multiplying and dividing by 12.

LEARN   Dividing Unit Fractions Using Multiplication

Students will learn how to use the inverse relationship between multiplication and division to divide a unit fraction by a whole number.

SUPPORT   For students to be successful in this lesson, they must have mastered two important skills. First, they must be able to multiply a fraction by a whole number. Second, they must be able to write equivalent fractions. If students are struggling, it may help to review these two skills.

TRY IT   Divide Unit Fractions Using Multiplication

Students will practice using the relationship between multiplication and division to divide a unit fraction by a whole number. Support will be provided to help students overcome misconceptions.

TRY IT   Practice Dividing Unit Fractions Using Multiplication

Students will complete online practice problems. Then they will complete Practice Dividing Unit Fractions Using Multiplication from *Summit Math 5 Activity Book*.

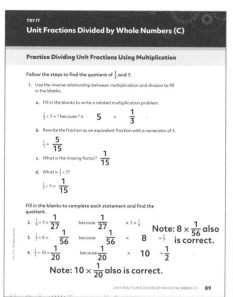

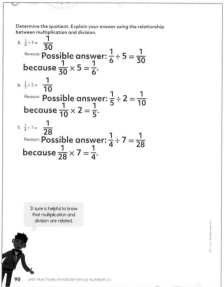

WRAP-UP

Dividing Unit Fractions Using Multiplication

Students will solve a problem to show that they understand how to use the relationship between multiplication and division to divide a unit fraction by a whole number.

Unit Fractions Divided by Whole Numbers (D)

Lesson Overview

ACTIVITY	ACTIVITY TITLE	TIME	ONLINE/OFFLINE
GET READY	Introduction to Unit Fractions Divided by Whole Numbers (D)	**2** minutes	📶
	Multiplying and Dividing by 20 Math Facts	**8** minutes	📶
LEARN AND **TRY IT**	Dividing Unit Fractions by Using the Rule	**15** minutes	📶
	Divide Unit Fractions by Using the Rule	**10** minutes	📶
	Practice Dividing Unit Fractions by Using the Rule	**20** minutes	📶 and 📄
WRAP-UP	Dividing Unit Fractions by Using the Rule	**5** minutes	📶

Content Background

In this lesson, students will learn the rule for dividing a unit fraction by a whole number. They will learn how to change dividing by the whole number to multiplying by the reciprocal. You may have learned to "flip and multiply." That strategy works as long as students are taught to write the whole number as a fraction over 1. Otherwise, students might make a mistake by flipping the unit fraction instead of flipping the whole number.

Lesson Goals

- Divide a unit fraction by a whole number using the rule.

GET READY

Introduction to Unit Fractions Divided by Whole Numbers (D)

Students will get a glimpse of what they will learn about in the lesson. They will also read the lesson goals and keywords. Have students select each keyword and preview its definition.

Multiplying and Dividing by 20 Math Facts

Students will practice multiplying and dividing by 20.

LEARN Dividing Unit Fractions by Using the Rule

Students will learn how divide a unit fraction by a whole number using the rule. The rule is to multiply the unit fraction by the reciprocal of the whole number.

TIP It is important to emphasize that the unit fraction (dividend) remains the same. The operation is changed from division to multiplication in the same step that the whole number is replaced by its reciprocal. Then students can multiply the two fractions.

TRY IT Divide Unit Fractions by Using the Rule

Students will practice using the rule to divide a unit fraction by a whole number. Support will be provided to help students overcome misconceptions.

SUPPORT For students having difficulty understanding their answers, encourage them to use a model, such as an area model, a number line, or fractions strips, to check their answer. Students could also use the inverse relationship between multiplication and division to check their answer.

TRY IT Practice Dividing Unit Fractions by Using the Rule

Students will complete online practice problems. Then they will complete Practice Dividing Unit Fractions by Using the Rule from *Summit Math 5 Activity Book*.

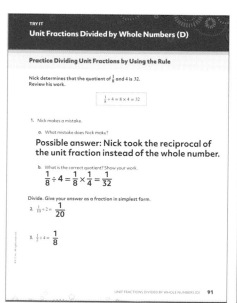

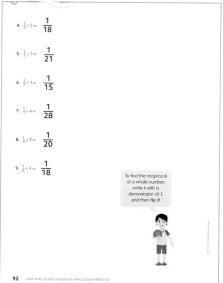

Dividing Unit Fractions by Using the Rule

Students will solve a problem to show that they understand how to divide a unit fraction by a whole number using the rule.

Unit Fractions Divided by Whole Numbers (E)

Lesson Overview

ACTIVITY	ACTIVITY TITLE	TIME	ONLINE/OFFLINE
GET READY	Introduction to Unit Fractions Divided by Whole Numbers (E)	**2** minutes	🖥️
	Multiplying and Dividing by 20 with Instant Recall	**8** minutes	🖥️
LEARN AND **TRY IT**	Dividing Unit Fractions to Solve Real-World Problems	**15** minutes	🖥️
	Divide Unit Fractions to Solve Real-World Problems	**10** minutes	🖥️
	Practice Dividing Unit Fractions to Solve Real-World Problems	**20** minutes	🖥️ and 📄
WRAP-UP	Dividing Unit Fractions to Solve Real-World Problems	**5** minutes	🖥️

Content Background

In this lesson, students will apply their knowledge of the rule for dividing a unit fraction by a whole number to solving real-world problems. They can continue to use models and multiplication equations to help make sense of division problems even though they are encouraged to apply the rule to solve problems in this lesson.

MATERIALS

Supplied
- *Summit Math 5 Activity Book:* Practice Dividing Unit Fractions to Solve Real-World Problems

Lesson Goals

- Solve real-world problems by dividing a unit fraction by a whole number.

GET READY

Introduction to Unit Fractions Divided by Whole Numbers (E)

Students will get a glimpse of what they will learn about in the lesson. They will also read the lesson goals.

Multiplying and Dividing by 20 with Instant Recall

Students will practice multiplying and dividing by 20 with instant recall.

LEARN Dividing Unit Fractions to Solve Real-World Problems

Students will solve real-world problems by using the rule to divide a unit fraction by a whole number.

TRY IT Divide Unit Fractions to Solve Real-World Problems

Students will practice dividing a unit fraction by a whole number using a rule to solve real-world problems. Support will be provided to help students overcome misconceptions.

TIP   Division problems are designed *only* include unit fractions in this lesson. However, some problems require students to add or subtract to find the unit fraction. Encourage students to read each problem carefully to determine the whole number in the division problem. For example, a fraction of a pizza might be split equally between Min and 3 friends. In this case, students might mistakenly try to divide by 3 instead of 4.

TRY IT Practice Dividing Unit Fractions to Solve Real-World Problems

Students will complete online practice problems. Then they will complete Practice Dividing Unit Fractions to Solve Real-World Problems from *Summit Math 5 Activity Book*.

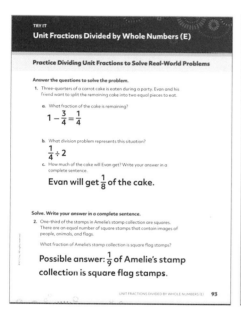

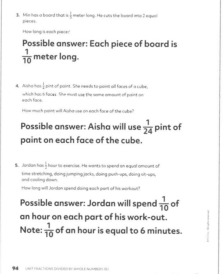

WRAP-UP

Dividing Unit Fractions to Solve Real-World Problems

Students will solve a problem to show that they understand how to divide a unit fraction by a whole number using the rule to solve a real-world problem.

Unit Fractions Divided by Whole Numbers (F)

Lesson Overview

ACTIVITY	ACTIVITY TITLE	TIME	ONLINE/OFFLINE
GET READY	Introduction to Unit Fractions Divided by Whole Numbers (F)	**2** minutes	🖥️
TRY IT	Review Unit Fractions Divided by Whole Numbers	**18** minutes	🖥️
QUIZ	Unit Fractions Divided by Whole Numbers	**25** minutes	🖥️
WRAP-UP	More Math Practice	**15** minutes	🖥️

Lesson Goals

- Review dividing unit fractions by whole numbers using models, stories, inverse relationships, and the rule.

- Take a quiz.

MATERIALS

There are no materials to gather for this lesson.

GET READY

Introduction to Unit Fractions Divided by Whole Numbers (F)

Students will read the lesson goals.

TRY IT

Review Unit Fractions Divided by Whole Numbers

Students will answer questions to review what they have learned about unit fractions divided by whole numbers.

QUIZ

Unit Fractions Divided by Whole Numbers

Students will complete the Unit Fractions Divided by Whole Numbers quiz.

More Math Practice

Students will practice skills according to their individual needs.

Whole Numbers Divided by Unit Fractions (A)

Lesson Overview

ACTIVITY	ACTIVITY TITLE	TIME	ONLINE/OFFLINE
GET READY	Introduction to Whole Numbers Divided by Unit Fractions (A)	**2** minutes	🖥️
	Look Back at Describing a Whole Number Division Problem	**8** minutes	🖥️
LEARN AND **TRY IT**	Dividing by Unit Fractions Using Models	**15** minutes	🖥️
	Divide by Unit Fractions Using Models	**10** minutes	🖥️
	Practice Dividing by Unit Fractions Using Models	**20** minutes	🖥️ and 📄
WRAP-UP	Dividing by Unit Fractions Using Models	**5** minutes	🖥️

Content Background

In this lesson, students will learn to understand division of fractions by studying examples of whole numbers divided by unit fractions. They will use area models and fractions strips as well as number lines to gain a deeper understanding of the meaning of division by a unit fraction.

Although the traditional algorithm of changing fraction division problems to multiplication by the reciprocal certainly works, the rule gives students answers that they often do not understand. They struggle to know if their answers make sense. By modeling several problems, students begin to get an intuitive sense about the correctness of their answers. Encourage them to understand the models before moving directly into the algorithm.

Lesson Goals

- Represent the quotient of a whole number and a unit fraction with a model.

- Determine the quotient of a whole number and a unit fraction by using a model.

MATERIALS

Supplied
- *Summit Math 5 Activity Book:* Practice Dividing by Unit Fractions Using Models

GET READY

Introduction to Whole Numbers Divided by Unit Fractions (A)

Students will get a glimpse of what they will learn about in the lesson. They will also read the lesson goals.

Look Back at Describing a Whole Number Division Problem

Students will practice the prerequisite skill of describing a whole number division problem.

LEARN   Dividing by Unit Fractions Using Models

Students will learn how to divide a whole number by a unit fraction using different models. They will use area models, number lines, and fraction strips to investigate and model each division problem.

NOTE   Students usually know $6 \div 3$ as, "How many groups of 3 are in 6?" They have learned that $\frac{1}{3} \div 6$ means, "What is $\frac{1}{3}$ shared 6 ways?" Similar language can be used to describe $6 \div \frac{1}{3}$. Help students make sense of a quotient by asking them, "How many thirds are in 6?" about an area model or fraction strip model. For a number line, you can tell them to "Count the number of one-third jumps between 0 and 6."

TRY IT   Divide by Unit Fractions Using Models

Students will practice dividing a whole number by a unit fraction using models. Support will be provided to help students overcome misconceptions.

TRY IT   Practice Dividing by Unit Fractions Using Models

Students will complete online practice problems. Then they will complete Practice Dividing by Unit Fractions Using Models from *Summit Math 5 Activity Book*.

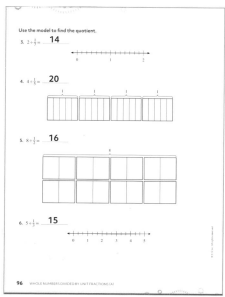

Dividing by Unit Fractions Using Models

Students will solve a problem to show that they understand how to use a model to divide a whole number by a unit fraction.

Whole Numbers Divided by Unit Fractions (B)

Lesson Overview

ACTIVITY	ACTIVITY TITLE	TIME	ONLINE/OFFLINE
GET READY	Introduction to Whole Numbers Divided by Unit Fractions (B)	**2** minutes	🖥
	Multiplying and Dividing by 20 Math Facts Game	**8** minutes	🖥
LEARN AND **TRY IT**	Dividing by Unit Fractions with Stories	**15** minutes	🖥
	Divide by Unit Fractions with Stories	**10** minutes	🖥
	Practice Dividing by Unit Fractions with Stories	**20** minutes	🖥 and 📄
WRAP-UP	Dividing by Unit Fractions with Stories	**5** minutes	🖥

Content Background

In this lesson, students will write and solve real-world problems that involve the division of a whole number by a unit fraction. They will continue to use models to find the quotient of a whole number and a unit fraction.

Lesson Goals

- Write a story for the division of a whole number and a unit fraction.
- Solve real-world problems involving the division of a whole number and a unit fraction using stories and models.

GET READY

Introduction to Whole Numbers Divided by Unit Fractions (B)
Students will get a glimpse of what they will learn about in the lesson. They will also read the lesson goals.

Multiplying and Dividing by 20 Math Facts Game
Students will practice multiplying and dividing by 20.

LEARN   Dividing by Unit Fractions with Stories

Students will practice writing and solving real-world problems where a whole number is divided by a unit fraction.

TRY IT   Divide by Unit Fractions with Stories

Students will practice writing and solving real-world problems where a whole number is divided by a unit fraction. Support will be provided to help students overcome misconceptions.

NOTE   Students are not limited to using area models, fraction strips, or number lines to make sense of a problem. For example, they could draw a measuring cup for a problem about measuring ingredients or a clock for a problem about time.

TRY IT   Practice Dividing by Unit Fractions with Stories

Students will complete online practice problems. Then they will complete Practice Dividing by Unit Fractions with Stories from *Summit Math 5 Activity Book*.

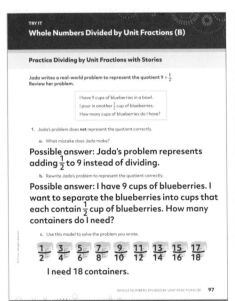

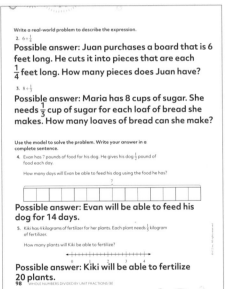

Dividing by Unit Fractions with Stories

Students will solve a problem to show that they understand how to solve a real-world problem where a story and model are used to divide a whole number by a unit fraction.

Whole Numbers Divided by Unit Fractions (C)

Lesson Overview

ACTIVITY	ACTIVITY TITLE	TIME	ONLINE/OFFLINE
GET READY	Introduction to Whole Numbers Divided by Unit Fractions (C)	**2** minutes	🖥
	Multiplying and Dividing by 30 Math Facts	**8** minutes	🖥
LEARN AND **TRY IT**	Dividing by Unit Fractions Using Multiplication	**15** minutes	🖥
	Divide by Unit Fractions Using Multiplication	**10** minutes	🖥
	Practice Dividing by Unit Fractions Using Multiplication	**20** minutes	🖥 and 📄
WRAP-UP	Dividing by Unit Fractions Using Multiplication	**5** minutes	🖥

Content Background

In this lesson, students will use the inverse relationship between multiplication and division to divide a whole number by a unit fraction. Here is the process they will follow:

1. Write a multiplication problem that is related to the division problem. A question mark or other symbol can stand for the missing quotient and factor.

2. Rewrite the whole number in the multiplication problem as a fraction with a denominator of 1. Then, rewrite this fraction an equivalent fraction. The denominator of the fraction must be the same as the unit fraction.

3. Determine the missing factor. It is the numerator of the equivalent fraction written in the previous step.

4. Determine the quotient. The quotient is the same as the missing factor.

This lesson is a bridge between using models to divide a whole number by a unit fraction and using a rule. As students progress throughout the lesson, they may begin to notice a pattern in the quotients. The quotient is the product of the whole number and the denominator of the unit fraction. The reason for the pattern is explained once the rule is introduced in the next lesson. Allow students to notice the pattern without immediately explaining the rule. Using the relationship between multiplication and division is an important step in helping students develop an intuitive sense about the correctness of their answers.

MATERIALS

Supplied
- *Summit Math 5 Activity Book:* Practice Dividing by Unit Fractions Using Multiplication

KEYWORDS

equivalent fractions – fractions that name the same amount, such as $\frac{1}{2}$ and $\frac{3}{6}$

inverse relationship – the relationship between operations that reverse or undo each other; addition and subtraction have an inverse relationship; multiplication and division have an inverse relationship

Lesson Goals

- Divide a whole number by a unit fraction using the relationship between multiplication and division.

Introduction to Whole Numbers Divided by Unit Fractions (C)

Students will get a glimpse of what they will learn about in the lesson. They will also read the lesson goals and keywords. Have students select each keyword and preview its definition.

Multiplying and Dividing by 30 Math Facts

Students will practice multiplying and dividing by 30.

LEARN AND TRY IT

LEARN   Dividing by Unit Fractions Using Multiplication

Students will learn how to use the inverse relationship between multiplication and division to divide a whole number by a unit fraction.

SUPPORT   For students to be successful in this lesson, they must be able to write equivalent fractions. If students are struggling, it may help to review this skill.

TRY IT   Divide by Unit Fractions Using Multiplication

Students will practice using the relationship between multiplication and division to divide a whole number by a unit fraction. Support will be provided to help students overcome misconceptions.

TRY IT   Practice Dividing by Unit Fractions Using Multiplication

Students will complete online practice problems. Then they will complete Practice Dividing by Unit Fractions Using Multiplication from *Summit Math 5 Activity Book*.

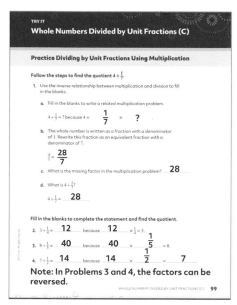

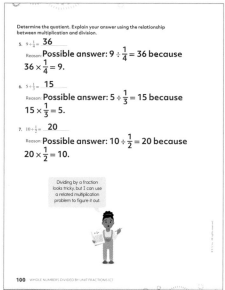

Dividing by Unit Fractions Using Multiplication

Students will solve a problem to show that they understand how to determine the quotient of a whole number and a unit fraction using the relationship between multiplication and division.

Whole Numbers Divided by Unit Fractions (D)

Lesson Overview

ACTIVITY	ACTIVITY TITLE	TIME	ONLINE/OFFLINE
GET READY	Introduction to Whole Numbers Divided by Unit Fractions (D)	**2** minutes	🖥
	Multiplying and Dividing by 30 with Instant Recall	**8** minutes	🖥
LEARN AND **TRY IT**	Dividing by Unit Fractions Using the Rule	**15** minutes	🖥
	Divide by Unit Fractions Using the Rule	**10** minutes	🖥
	Practice Dividing by Unit Fractions Using the Rule	**20** minutes	🖥 and 📄
WRAP-UP	Dividing by Unit Fractions Using the Rule	**5** minutes	🖥

Content Background

In this lesson, students will learn the rule for dividing a whole number by a unit fraction. They will learn how to change dividing by the unit fraction to multiplying by the reciprocal. You may have learned this as the "flip and multiply" algorithm. Each quotient becomes the product of two whole numbers using this rule.

Lesson Goals

- Divide a whole number by a unit fraction using the rule.

Introduction to Whole Numbers Divided by Unit Fractions (D)

Students will get a glimpse of what they will learn about in the lesson. They will also read the lesson goals and keywords. Have students select each keyword and preview its definition.

Multiplying and Dividing by 30 with Instant Recall

Students will practice multiplying and dividing by 30 with instant recall.

MATERIALS

Supplied

- *Summit Math 5 Activity Book:* Practice Dividing by Unit Fractions Using the Rule

KEYWORDS

dividend – the number to be divided; the dividend divided by the divisor equals the quotient

divisor – the number that divides the dividend; the dividend divided by the divisor equals the quotient

reciprocal – two numbers whose product is 1

LEARN   Dividing by Unit Fractions Using the Rule

Students will learn how to divide a whole number by a unit fraction using the rule. The rule is to multiply the whole by the reciprocal of the unit fraction. The operation is changed from division to multiplication in the same step that the unit fraction is replaced by its reciprocal. Then students can multiply the two whole numbers.

SUPPORT   For students having difficulty understanding their answers, encourage them to use a model or the relationship between multiplication and division to check their answers.

TRY IT   Divide by Unit Fractions Using the Rule

Students will practice using the rule to divide a whole number by a unit fraction. Support will be provided to help students overcome misconceptions.

TRY IT   Practice Dividing by Unit Fractions Using the Rule

Students will complete online practice problems. Then they will complete Practice Dividing by Unit Fractions Using the Rule from *Summit Math 5 Activity Book*.

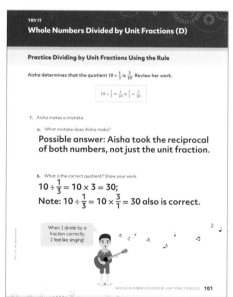

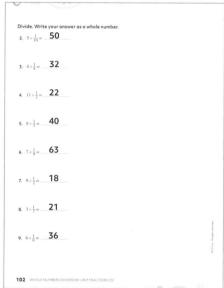

Dividing by Unit Fractions Using the Rule

Students will solve a problem to show that they understand how to divide a whole number by a unit fraction using the rule.

Whole Numbers Divided by Unit Fractions (E)

Lesson Overview

ACTIVITY	ACTIVITY TITLE	TIME	ONLINE/OFFLINE
GET READY	Introduction to Whole Numbers Divided by Unit Fractions (E)	**2** minutes	🖥
	Multiplying and Dividing by 30 Math Facts Game	**8** minutes	🖥
LEARN AND **TRY IT**	Dividing by Unit Fractions in the Real World	**15** minutes	🖥
	Divide by Unit Fractions in the Real World	**10** minutes	🖥
	Practice Dividing by Unit Fractions in the Real World	**20** minutes	🖥 and 📄
WRAP-UP	Dividing by Unit Fractions in the Real World	**5** minutes	🖥

Content Background

In this lesson, students will apply their knowledge of the rule for dividing a whole number by a unit fraction to solve real-world problems. They can continue to use models and multiplication equations to help make sense of division problems even though they are encouraged to apply the rule to solve problems in this lesson.

Lesson Goals

- Solve real-world problems by dividing a whole number by a unit fraction.

GET READY

Introduction to Whole Numbers Divided by Unit Fractions (E)

Students will get a glimpse of what they will learn about in the lesson. They will also read the lesson.

Multiplying and Dividing by 30 Math Facts Game

Students will practice multiplying and dividing by 30.

LEARN   Dividing by Unit Fractions in the Real World

Students will solve real-world problems by using the rule to divide a whole number by a unit fraction.

TRY IT   Divide by Unit Fractions in the Real World

Students will practice solving real-world problems by dividing a whole number by a unit fraction using the rule. Support will be provided to help students overcome misconceptions.

TRY IT   Practice Dividing by Unit Fractions in the Real World

Students will complete online practice problems. Then they will complete Practice Dividing by Unit Fractions in the Real World from *Summit Math 5 Activity Book*.

TIP   Each problem requires students to divide a whole number by a unit fraction. However, some problems require additional steps. Students may need to add, subtract, or multiply to find the whole number. Or, a quotient may need to be multiplied by or compared to another number. Encourage students to read each problem and question carefully to solve.

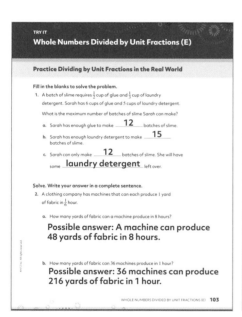

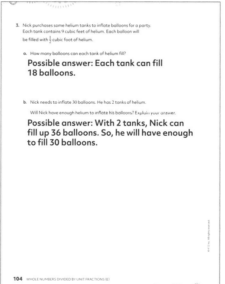

Dividing by Unit Fractions in the Real World

Students will solve a problem to show that they understand how to solve a real-world problem that requires division of a whole number by a unit fraction using the rule.

Whole Numbers Divided by Unit Fractions (F)

Lesson Overview

ACTIVITY	ACTIVITY TITLE	TIME	ONLINE/OFFLINE
GET READY	Introduction to Whole Numbers Divided by Unit Fractions (F)	**2** minutes	🖥️
TRY IT	Review Whole Numbers Divided by Unit Fractions	**18** minutes	🖥️
QUIZ	Whole Numbers Divided by Unit Fractions	**25** minutes	🖥️
WRAP-UP	More Math Practice	**15** minutes	🖥️

Lesson Goals

- Review dividing whole numbers by unit fractions using models, stories, inverse relationships, and the rule.

- Take a quiz.

GET READY

Introduction to Whole Numbers Divided by Unit Fractions (F)

Students will read the lesson goals.

TRY IT

Review Whole Numbers Divided by Unit Fractions

Students will answer questions to review what they have learned about whole numbers divided by unit fractions.

QUIZ

Whole Numbers Divided by Unit Fractions

Students will complete the Whole Numbers Divided by Unit Fractions quiz.

More Math Practice

Students will practice skills according to their individual needs.

Big Ideas: Challenge Problems

Lesson Overview

Big Ideas lessons provide students the opportunity to apply the knowledge and skills acquired throughout previous units. Each Big Ideas lesson consists of three parts:

1. **Cumulative Review:** Students keep their skills fresh by reviewing prior content.

2. **Preview:** Students practice answering the types of questions they will commonly find on standardized tests.

3. **Synthesis:** Students complete an assignment that allows them to interweave and apply what they've learned. These synthesis assignments will vary throughout the course.

   In the Synthesis portion of this Big Ideas lesson, students will complete one or more challenge problems that will guide them to discover new concepts. Through hard work and perseverance, students will learn that they can use the math they already know combined with logical thinking to solve problems about new concepts. Students will need to use pencil and paper and/or technology to show their work.

   LEARNING COACH CHECK-IN   Make sure students complete, review, and submit the assignment to their teacher

All materials needed for this lesson are linked online. The materials are not provided in this Lesson Guide or in the Activity Book.

MATERIALS

Supplied
- Challenge Problems Instructions (printout)

Geometric Measurement: Volume

Measuring Volume (A)

Lesson Overview

ACTIVITY	ACTIVITY TITLE	TIME	ONLINE/OFFLINE
GET READY	Introduction to Measuring Volume (A)	**2** minutes	🖥️
	Geometric Measurement: Volume in 60 Seconds	**3** minutes	🖥️
	Look Back at Understanding Area and Unit Squares	**5** minutes	🖥️
LEARN AND **TRY IT**	Understanding Volume	**7** minutes	🖥️
	Understand Volume	**7** minutes	🖥️
	Measuring Volume by Counting Unit Cubes	**7** minutes	🖥️
	Measure Volume by Counting Unit Cubes	**7** minutes	🖥️
	Practice Understanding and Measuring Volume	**20** minutes	🖥️ and 📄
WRAP-UP	Understanding and Measuring Volume	**2** minutes	🖥️

Content Background

In this lesson, students will learn about the volume of rectangular solids by finding how many unit cubes are needed to fill a solid figure.

Volume is measured in cubic units such as cubic centimeters, cubic inches, or just cubic units when the cubes are not a standard measure. Students will not use a rule or formula to find the volume of objects yet, but they will be encouraged to count cubes or find their own strategy to determine volume.

Students will explore solids in which not every cube is visible and will use their knowledge of three-dimensional shapes to figure out how many cubes will fill the solid. Some solids are irregular and others are rectangular prisms.

Students may recognize that when finding the volume of rectangular prisms, they can find the number of cubes on the bottom layer and then repeatedly add that amount for each layer. They may even realize that they can use multiplication instead of repeated addition. Allow students to use whatever strategy they come up with at this stage. Eventually, they will be taught how to use multiplication and then formulas to calculate volume.

MATERIALS

Supplied

- *Summit Math 5 Activity Book:* Practice Understanding and Measuring Volume

Lesson Goals

- Explain unit cubes and volume.

- Determine the volumes of figures by counting unit cubes.

KEYWORDS

cubed – the result of the operation where a number has been multiplied by itself two times, such as 5 cubed $= 5^3 = 5 \times 5 \times 5 = 125$; when the volume of a cube is found, the dimensions are cubed, and the volume is expressed in units cubed

cubic unit – a cube that is 1 unit on each side; a measure of volume

rectangular prism – a solid figure with 6 faces that are rectangles

solid figure – a figure with three dimensions: length, width, and height or depth

volume – the amount of space taken up by a three-dimensional object; measured in cubic units

GET READY

Introduction to Measuring Volume (A)

Students will get a glimpse of what they will learn about in the lesson. They will also read the lesson goals and keywords. Have students select each keyword and preview its definition.

Geometric Measurement: Volume in 60 Seconds

Students will watch a short video designed to spark their interest in upcoming topics.

Look Back at Understanding Area and Unit Squares

Students will practice the prerequisite skill of describing area and unit squares.

LEARN AND TRY IT

LEARN Understanding Volume

Students will learn how to recognize a unit cube and describe the concept of volume.

NOTE   In previous grades, students most likely learned about area of two-dimensional shapes by using unit *squares*, which are squares that measure 1 unit along each side, to fill the space inside a rectangle without any gaps or overlaps. A similar approach applies to finding the volume of three-dimensional shapes. Unit *cubes*, which are cubes that measure 1 unit along each side, are used to fill the space inside a rectangular prism without any gaps or overlaps.

TRY IT Understand Volume

Students will practice defining unit cubes and volume. Support will be provided to help students overcome misconceptions.

LEARN Measuring Volume by Counting Unit Cubes

Students will learn how to count unit cubes to measure the volume of solid figures, including rectangular prisms.

TRY IT   Measure Volume by Counting Unit Cubes

Students will practice counting unit cubes to measure the volume of solid figures. Support will be provided to help students overcome misconceptions.

TRY IT   Practice Understanding and Measuring Volume

Students will complete online practice problems. Then they will complete Practice Understanding and Measuring Volume from *Summit Math 5 Activity Book*.

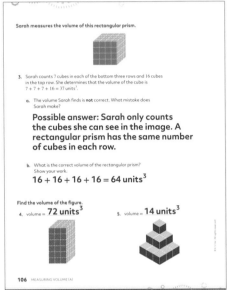

Understanding and Measuring Volume

Students will solve a problem to show that they understand how to measure the volume of a rectangular prism by counting unit cubes.

Measuring Volume (B)

Lesson Overview

ACTIVITY	ACTIVITY TITLE	TIME	ONLINE/OFFLINE
GET READY	Introduction to Measuring Volume (B)	**2** minutes	🖥️
	Multiplying and Dividing by 40 Math Facts	**8** minutes	🖥️
LEARN AND **TRY IT**	Measuring Volume with Various Cubic Units	**7** minutes	🖥️
	Measure Volume with Various Cubic Units	**7** minutes	🖥️
	Measuring Volume with Improvised Cubic Units	**7** minutes	🖥️
	Measure Volume with Improvised Cubic Units	**7** minutes	🖥️
	Practice Measuring Volume with Various Cubic Units	**20** minutes	🖥️ and 📄
WRAP-UP	Measuring Volume with Various Cubic Units	**2** minutes	🖥️

Content Background

In this lesson, students will measure the volume of solids, including rectangular prisms, by counting unit cubes with given measurements. They will also measure volume using solids that are made up of unit cubes such as bricks, toy chests, or other rectangular prisms.

Volume is the measure of the number of cubic units that a space occupies. It is a cubic-unit measurement since it measures the three dimensions of length, width, and height. The units used to measure volume have an exponent of 3. For example, you might see volume measured in cubic meters (m^3), cubic inches (in^3), cubic feet (ft^3), or cubic centimeters (cm^3).

Lesson Goals

- Determine the volume of a figure by counting unit cubes or other shapes made up of unit cubes.

MATERIALS

Supplied
- *Summit Math 5 Activity Book:* Practice Measuring Volume with Various Cubic Units

KEYWORDS

cubic centimeter – a cube that is 1 cm on each side; a measure of volume

cubic foot – a cube that is 1 ft on each side; a measure of volume

cubic inch – a cube that is 1 in. on each side; a measure of volume

Introduction to Measuring Volume (B)

Students will get a glimpse of what they will learn about in the lesson. They will also read the lesson goals and keywords. Have students select each keyword and preview its definition.

Multiplying and Dividing by 40 Math Facts

Students will practice multiplying and dividing by 40.

LEARN AND TRY IT

LEARN   Measuring Volume with Various Cubic Units

Students will learn how to measure the volume of solids by counting unit cubes that are cubic centimeters, cubic inches, or cubic feet.

TRY IT   Measure Volume with Various Cubic Units

Students will practice measuring volume by counting unit cubes with various units. Support will be provided to help students overcome misconceptions.

LEARN   Measuring Volume with Improvised Cubic Units

Students will learn how to measure volume with improvised cubic units. Improvised cubic units are solids that are made up of unit cubes. For example, students will find the number of toy boxes that fit into a crate, and each toy box is 2 unit cubes.

TRY IT   Measure Volume with Improvised Cubic Units

Students will practice measuring volume with improvised cubic units. Support will be provided to help students overcome misconceptions.

TRY IT Practice Measuring Volume with Various Cubic Units

Students will complete online practice problems. Then they will complete Practice Measuring Volume with Various Cubic Units from *Summit Math 5 Activity Book*.

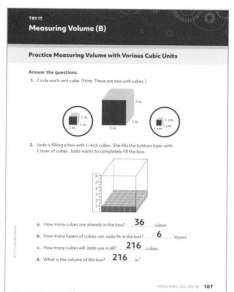

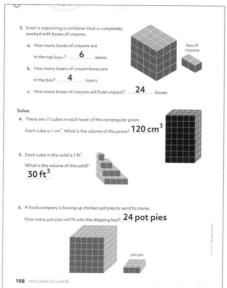

Measuring Volume with Various Cubic Units

Students will solve problems to show that they understand how to measure volume with cubic centimeters and with improvised units.

Measuring Volume (C)

Lesson Overview

ACTIVITY	ACTIVITY TITLE	TIME	ONLINE/OFFLINE
GET READY	Introduction to Measuring Volume (C)	**2** minutes	📶
TRY IT	Review Measuring Volume	**18** minutes	📶
QUIZ	Measuring Volume	**25** minutes	📶
WRAP-UP	More Math Practice	**15** minutes	📶

Lesson Goals

- Review measuring volume.
- Take a quiz.

MATERIALS

There are no materials to gather for this lesson.

GET READY

Introduction to Measuring Volume (C)

Students will read the lesson goals.

TRY IT

Review Measuring Volume

Students will answer questions to review what they have learned about measuring volume.

QUIZ

Measuring Volume

Students will complete the Measuring Volume quiz.

More Math Practice

Students will practice skills according to their individual needs.

Calculating Volume (A)

Lesson Overview

ACTIVITY	ACTIVITY TITLE	TIME	ONLINE/OFFLINE
GET READY	Introduction to Calculating Volume (A)	**2** minutes	🖥️
	Look Back at Multiplying Side Lengths to Find Area	**8** minutes	🖥️
LEARN AND **TRY IT**	Representing Volume Using Products	**15** minutes	🖥️
	Represent Volume Using Products	**10** minutes	🖥️
	Practice Representing Volume Using Products	**20** minutes	🖥️ and 📄
WRAP-UP	Representing Volume Using Products	**5** minutes	🖥️

Content Background

In this lesson, students will represent volumes of rectangular prisms using the products *length* × *width* × *height* and *base* × *height*. The connection between counting unit cubes and products is emphasized in this lesson to lead students to using formulas to find the volume in the next lesson. However, most problems in this lesson do not require students to actually find the volume. Emphasizing the connection between counting unit cubes and multiplying dimensions helps students develop an intuitive understanding of the volume formulas.

MATERIALS

Supplied
- *Summit Math 5 Activity Book:* Practice Representing Volume Using Products

Lesson Goals

- Represent the volume of a rectangular prism as the product of its three dimensions.

- Represent the volume of a rectangular prism as the product of its height and the area of the base.

GET READY

Introduction to Calculating Volume (A)

Students will get a glimpse of what they will learn about in the lesson. They will also read the lesson goals.

Look Back at Multiplying Side Lengths to Find Area

Students will practice the prerequisite skill of multiplying side lengths to find the area of rectangles.

LEARN AND TRY IT

LEARN   Representing Volume Using Products

Students will represent the volume of rectangular prisms using products. They will also discover that finding the volume by counting unit cubes gives the same result as multiplying the length, width, and height or multiplying the area of the base and the height of the prism.

TRY IT   Represent Volume Using Products

Students will practice representing volume using products. Support will be provided to help students overcome misconceptions.

TRY IT   Practice Representing Volume Using Products

Students will complete online practice problems. Then they will complete Practice Representing Volume Using Products from *Summit Math 5 Activity Book*.

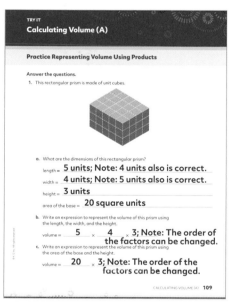

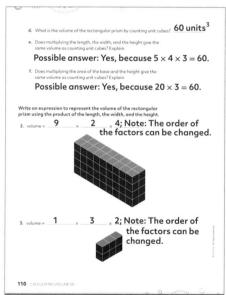

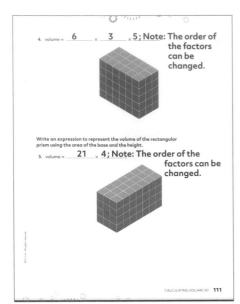

4. volume = __6__ × __3__ × 5; Note: The order of the factors can be changed.

Write an expression to represent the volume of the rectangular prism using the area of the base and the height.

5. volume = __21__ × 4; Note: The order of the factors can be changed.

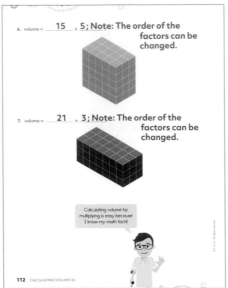

6. volume = __15__ × 5; Note: Note: The order of the factors can be changed.

7. volume = __21__ × 3; Note: Note: The order of the factors can be changed.

Calculating volume by multiplying is easy because I know my math facts!

TIP   If a practice problem has three blanks, students should write the length, the width, and the height of the prism. If a practice problem has two blanks, students should write the area of the base and the height of the prism.

WRAP-UP

Representing Volume Using Products

Students will solve problems to show that they understand how to represent the volume of a rectangular prism using products.

Calculating Volume (B)

Lesson Overview

ACTIVITY	ACTIVITY TITLE	TIME	ONLINE/OFFLINE
GET READY	Introduction to Calculating Volume (B)	**2** minutes	🖥️
	Multiplying and Dividing by 40 with Instant Recall	**8** minutes	📶
LEARN AND **TRY IT**	Calculating Volume Using a Formula	**15** minutes	📶
	Calculate Volume Using a Formula	**10** minutes	🖥️
	Practice Calculating Volume Using a Formula	**20** minutes	📶 and 📄
WRAP-UP	Calculating Volume Using a Formula	**5** minutes	📶

Content Background

In this lesson, students will use formulas to calculate volumes of rectangular prisms. They will learn to use both volume formulas: *volume = length × width × height* and *volume = area of the base × height*. Students have progressed from counting unit cubes to representing volume as a product, and they are now ready to use formulas to calculate volume.

MATERIALS

Supplied

- *Summit Math 5 Activity Book:* Practice Calculating Volume Using a Formula

Lesson Goals

- Use a formula to find the volume of a rectangular prism.

GET READY

Introduction to Calculating Volume (B)

Students will get a glimpse of what they will learn about in the lesson. They will also read the lesson goals.

Multiplying and Dividing by 40 with Instant Recall

Students will practice multiplying and dividing by 40 with instant recall.

LEARN   Calculating Volume Using a Formula

Students will calculate the volume of rectangular prisms using the two volume formulas.

TRY IT   Calculate Volume Using a Formula

Students will practice calculating the volume of rectangular prisms using formulas. They will also represent volume in multiple ways. Support will be provided to help students overcome misconceptions.

TRY IT   Practice Calculating Volume Using a Formula

Students will complete online practice problems. Then they will complete Practice Calculating Volume Using a Formula from *Summit Math 5 Activity Book*.

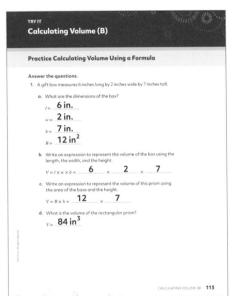
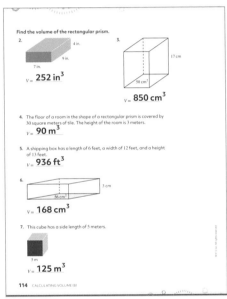

TIP   If students have difficulty understanding how to substitute measurements for variables in the formula for volume, have them write each variable and the corresponding measurement.

WRAP-UP

Calculating Volume Using a Formula

Students will solve a problem to show that they understand how to calculate volume using a formula.

Calculating Volume (C)

Lesson Overview

ACTIVITY	ACTIVITY TITLE	TIME	ONLINE/OFFLINE
GET READY	Introduction to Calculating Volume (C)	**2** minutes	🖥
	Multiplying and Dividing by 40 Math Facts Game	**8** minutes	🖥
LEARN AND **TRY IT**	Finding Missing Measurements in Volume Problems	**15** minutes	🖥
	Find Missing Measurements in Volume Problems	**10** minutes	🖥
	Practice Finding Missing Measurements in Volume Problems	**20** minutes	🖥 and 📄
WRAP-UP	Finding Missing Measurements in Volume Problems	**5** minutes	🖥

Content Background

In this lesson, students will find missing measurements of rectangular prisms using volume formulas. Each problem begins by giving the volume of a rectangular prism and one or more of its dimensions. Students will learn to use both volume formulas to determine the missing measurement.

Lesson Goals

- Use the volume of a rectangular prism to find a missing dimension.

GET READY

Introduction to Calculating Volume (C)

Students will get a glimpse of what they will learn about in the lesson. They will also read the lesson goals.

Multiplying and Dividing by 40 Math Facts Game

Students will practice multiplying and dividing by 40.

LEARN Finding Missing Measurements in Volume Problems

Students will find missing measurements of rectangular prisms given the volume and at least one dimension. They will experiment with the connection among unit cubes, the dimensions of a rectangular prism, and its volume using a volume tool.

SUPPORT To be successful in finding the missing measurement, students must be able to substitute values into the correct volume formula and be able to write a related division equation for a multiplication equation. It may help to review each of these skills.

TRY IT Find Missing Measurements in Volume Problems

Students will practice finding missing measurements of rectangular prisms using volume formulas. Support will be provided to help students overcome misconceptions.

TRY IT Practice Finding Missing Measurements in Volume Problems

Students will complete online practice problems. Then they will complete Practice Finding Missing Measurements in Volume Problems from *Summit Math 5 Activity Book*.

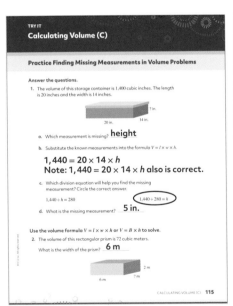

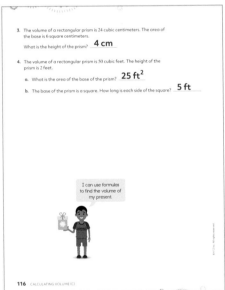

WRAP-UP

Finding Missing Measurements in Volume Problems

Students will solve problems to show that they understand how to find missing measurements of rectangular prisms using volume formulas.

Calculating Volume (D)

Lesson Overview

ACTIVITY	ACTIVITY TITLE	TIME	ONLINE/OFFLINE
GET READY	Introduction to Calculating Volume (D)	**2** minutes	🖥️
TRY IT	Review Calculating Volume	**18** minutes	🖥️
QUIZ	Calculating Volume	**25** minutes	🖥️
WRAP-UP	More Math Practice	**15** minutes	🖥️

Lesson Goals

- Review representing volume as the product of its dimensions, using a formula to calculate volume, and finding a missing dimension in a volume problem.

- Take a quiz.

MATERIALS

There are no materials to gather for this lesson.

GET READY

Introduction to Calculating Volume (D)

Students will read the lesson goals.

TRY IT

Review Calculating Volume

Students will answer questions to review what they have learned about calculating volume.

QUIZ

Calculating Volume

Students will complete the Calculating Volume quiz.

More Math Practice

Students will practice skills according to their individual needs.

Volume and Problem Solving (A)

Lesson Overview

ACTIVITY	ACTIVITY TITLE	TIME	ONLINE/OFFLINE
GET READY	Introduction to Volume and Problem Solving (A)	**2** minutes	🖥️
	Look Back at Finding the Volume of a Right Rectangular Prism	**8** minutes	🖥️
LEARN AND **TRY IT**	Calculating Volume in the Real World	**15** minutes	🖥️
	Calculate Volume in the Real World	**10** minutes	🖥️
	Practice Calculating Volume in the Real World	**20** minutes	🖥️ and 📄
WRAP-UP	Calculating Volume in the Real World	**5** minutes	🖥️

Content Background

In this lesson, students will apply what they have learned about volume and using volume formulas to solve real-world problems. This lesson includes various types of problems. Some problems require students to find volume, while others give students the volume and ask them to find a specific measurement. Other problems may require students to find and then compare volumes. They should also read problems carefully to determine which of the two volume formulas to use.

MATERIALS

Supplied
- *Summit Math 5 Activity Book:* Practice Calculating Volume in the Real World

Lesson Goals

- Solve real-world problems involving volume of rectangular prisms.

GET READY

Introduction to Volume and Problem Solving (A)

Students will get a glimpse of what they will learn about in the lesson. They will also read the lesson goals.

Look Back at Finding the Volume of a Right Rectangular Prism

Students will practice the prerequisite skill of solving mathematical problems involving the volume of a right rectangular prism using the volume formula $V = l \times w \times h$.

LEARN   Calculating Volume in the Real World

Students will solve real-world problems involving the volume of rectangular prisms. Encourage students to read the problems carefully to determine whether they are solving for the volume of a prism or one of the prism's missing dimensions.

TRY IT   Calculate Volume in the Real World

Students will practice solving real-world problems involving the volume of rectangular prisms. Support will be provided to help students overcome misconceptions.

SUPPORT   For students having difficulty knowing where to start, suggest listing the known and unknown measurements given in a problem. Use the labels V, l, w, h, and/or B. After the amounts are listed, you can ask students which formula should be used: $V = l \times w \times h$ or $V = B \times h$.

TRY IT   Practice Calculating Volume in the Real World

Students will complete online practice problems. Then they will complete Practice Calculating Volume in the Real World from *Summit Math 5 Activity Book*.

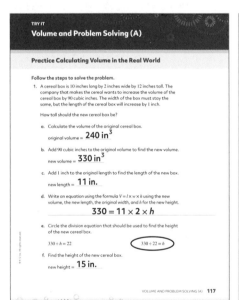

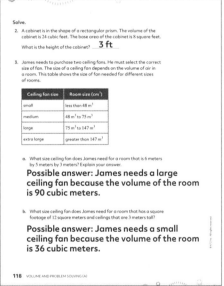

Calculating Volume in the Real World

Students will solve a problem to show that they understand how to solve problems involving the volume of rectangular prisms.

Volume and Problem Solving (B)

Lesson Overview

ACTIVITY	ACTIVITY TITLE	TIME	ONLINE/OFFLINE
GET READY	Introduction to Volume and Problem Solving (B)	**2** minutes	🖥️
	Multiplying and Dividing by 50 Math Facts	**8** minutes	🖥️
LEARN AND **TRY IT**	Finding Volumes of Composite Solids	**15** minutes	🖥️
	Find Volumes of Composite Solids	**10** minutes	🖥️
	Practice Finding Volumes of Composite Solids	**20** minutes	🖥️ and 📄
WRAP-UP	Finding Volumes of Composite Solids	**5** minutes	🖥️

Content Background

In this lesson, students will apply their knowledge about volume of prisms to find volumes of composite solids. Each solid can be decomposed into two or three rectangular prisms. The volumes of the decomposed prisms must not overlap. Once students find the volume of each prism, the volumes should be added to find the total volume. They will encounter problems with and without a real-world contexts.

Lesson Goals

- Find the volume of composite solids that can be separated into rectangular prisms.

MATERIALS

Supplied
- *Summit Math 5 Activity Book:* Practice Finding Volumes of Composite Solids

KEYWORDS

composite solid – a solid composed, or made up, of more than one solid

---

GET READY

Introduction to Volume and Problem Solving (B)

Students will get a glimpse of what they will learn about in the lesson. They will also read the lesson goals and keywords. Have students select each keyword and preview its definition.

Multiplying and Dividing by 50 Math Facts

Students will practice multiplying and dividing by 50.

LEARN Finding Volumes of Composite Solids

Students will find the volume of composite solids made of rectangular prisms. They will encounter problems with and without real-world contexts.

TRY IT Find Volumes of Composite Solids

Students will practice finding the volumes of composite solids. Support will be provided to help students overcome misconceptions.

SUPPORT   For students having difficulty recognizing how to separate a composite figure, encourage them to draw a line where they would "cut" a solid into two parts. Ask them if each part is a rectangular prism. If the parts aren't prisms, students can erase their line and try again. If they do get two prisms, they can list the dimensions of each prism before finding the volume.

TRY IT Practice Finding Volumes of Composite Solids

Students will complete online practice problems. Then they will complete Practice Finding Volumes of Composite Solids from *Summit Math 5 Activity Book*.

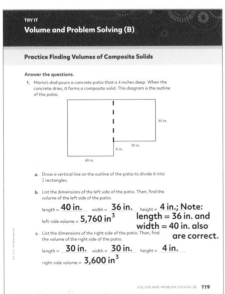

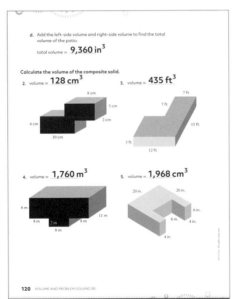

Finding Volumes of Composite Solids

Students will solve a problem to show that they understand how to find the volume of a composite solid.

Volume and Problem Solving (C)

Lesson Overview

ACTIVITY	ACTIVITY TITLE	TIME	ONLINE/OFFLINE
GET READY	Introduction to Volume and Problem Solving (C)	**2** minutes	🖥️
TRY IT	Review Volume and Problem Solving	**18** minutes	🖥️
QUIZ	Volume and Problem Solving	**25** minutes	🖥️
WRAP-UP	More Math Practice	**15** minutes	🖥️

Lesson Goals

- Review solving real-world problems involving the volume of a rectangular prism and finding the volume of a composite solid.

- Take a quiz.

MATERIALS

There are no materials to gather for this lesson.

GET READY

Introduction to Volume and Problem Solving (C)

Students will read the lesson goals.

TRY IT

Review Volume and Problem Solving

Students will answer questions to review what they have learned about volume and problem solving.

QUIZ

Volume and Problem Solving

Students will complete the Volume and Problem Solving quiz.

More Math Practice

Students will practice skills according to their individual needs.

Big Ideas: Extended Problems

Lesson Overview

Big Ideas lessons provide students the opportunity to further apply the knowledge and skills acquired throughout previous units. Each Big Ideas lesson consists of three parts:

1. **Cumulative Review:** Students keep their skills fresh by reviewing prior content.

2. **Preview:** Students practice answering the types of questions they will commonly find on standardized tests.

3. **Synthesis:** Students complete an assignment that allows them to interweave and apply what they've learned. These synthesis assignments will vary throughout the course.

   In the Synthesis portion of this Big Ideas lesson, students will complete multistep problems that go beyond the short answer and multiple choice problems they encounter in their regular lessons. These problems give students an opportunity to demonstrate problem solving, reasoning, communication, and modeling skills. Students will need to use pencil and paper and/or technology to show their work.

   LEARNING COACH CHECK-IN   This is a graded assessment. Make sure students complete, review, and submit the assignment to their teacher.

All materials needed for this lesson are linked online. The materials are not provided in this Lesson Guide or in the Activity Book.

Decimals

Exploring Decimals (A)

Lesson Overview

ACTIVITY	ACTIVITY TITLE	TIME	ONLINE/OFFLINE
GET READY	Introduction to Exploring Decimals (A)	**2** minutes	🖥️
	Decimals in 60 Seconds	**3** minutes	🖥️
	Look Back at Different Forms of Whole Numbers	**5** minutes	🖥️
LEARN AND **TRY IT**	Converting Between Forms of Numbers	**15** minutes	🖥️
	Convert Between Forms of Numbers	**10** minutes	🖥️
	Practice Converting Between Forms of Numbers	**20** minutes	🖥️ and 📄
WRAP-UP	Converting Between Forms of Numbers	**5** minutes	🖥️

Content Background

In this lesson, students will learn how to convert between standard and expanded forms of numbers with decimals up through thousandths. Decimal numbers name wholes and parts of a whole, as do fractions and mixed numbers. But unlike fractions—which can be expressed with denominators of any size—decimals are expressed as tenths, hundredths, thousandths, ten thousandths, and so on. Decimal numbers are simply different names for their equivalent fractions and mixed numbers. Thinking about decimal numbers correctly promotes a strong and needed understanding of place value.

In previous grades, expanded form was simply a sum such as $27.83 = 20 + 7 + 0.8 + 0.03$. In this lesson, expanded form includes products of powers of 10. So, the correct expanded form at this level is

$$27.83 = (2 \times 10) + (7 \times 1) + \left(8 \times \frac{1}{10}\right) + \left(3 \times \frac{1}{100}\right).$$

Note that the parentheses around each product are not necessary because multiplication is always performed before addition by the order of operations. However, parentheses help keep the expression organized.

OPTIONAL   As students study this unit, encourage them to look for examples of decimal numbers in their everyday lives (for example, consider sports events, gas prices, money, science books and articles, and news stories) and to recognize that in many situations, it is easier to use a decimal number than the equivalent fraction or mixed number.

MATERIALS

Supplied
- *Summit Math 5 Activity Book:* Practice Converting Between Forms of Numbers

Lesson Goals

- Convert a number in standard form to expanded form.

- Convert a number in expanded form to standard form.

GET READY

Introduction to Exploring Decimals (A)

Students will get a glimpse of what they will learn about in the lesson. They will also read the lesson goals and keywords. Have students select each keyword and preview its definition.

Decimals in 60 Seconds

Students will watch a short video designed to spark their interest in upcoming topics.

Look Back at Different Forms of Whole Numbers

Students will practice the prerequisite skill of converting between the standard and expanded form of whole numbers.

LEARN AND TRY IT

LEARN   Converting Between Forms of Numbers

Students will learn how to convert decimals from standard form to expanded form and expanded form to standard form.

TIP   Encourage students to make their own place value chart to refer to throughout the lesson. The chart only needs to go through the thousandths place after the decimal for this course. However, decimals do continue on as needed through the ten thousandths, hundred thousandths, millionths, and beyond.

TRY IT   Convert Between Forms of Numbers

Students will practice converting between standard form and expanded form of decimal numbers. Support will be provided to help students overcome misconceptions.

KEYWORDS

expanded form – a way to write a number that shows the place value of each of its digits; for example, 543 = 500 + 40 + 3 or 5 hundreds + 4 tens + 3 ones

hundredths – the place value immediately to the right of the tenths place; 10 thousandths = 1 hundredth and 10 hundredths = 1 tenth

place value – the value of a digit depending on its position, or place, in a number

place value chart – a chart that shows the value of each digit in a number

power of 10 – a number that can be written as a power with a base of 10

standard form – the usual way of writing a number using digits

tenths – the place value immediately to the right of the ones place after the decimal; 10 hundredths = 1 tenth and 10 tenths = 1

thousandths – the place value immediately to the right of the hundredths place after the decimal; 10 thousandths = 1 hundredth

---

TRY IT Practice Converting Between Forms of Numbers

Students will complete online practice problems. Then they will complete Practice Converting Between Forms of Numbers from *Summit Math 5 Activity Book.*

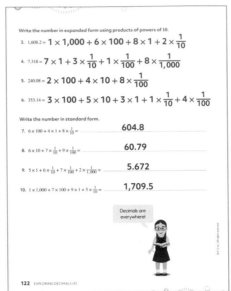

Problems where students must write a number in expanded form can have more than one correct answer. An answer is correct whether parentheses are included around each product.

WRAP-UP

Converting Between Forms of Numbers

Students will solve problems to show that they understand how to convert a decimal from standard form to expanded form and how to convert a decimal from expanded form to standard form.

Exploring Decimals (B)

Lesson Overview

ACTIVITY	ACTIVITY TITLE	TIME	ONLINE/OFFLINE
GET READY	Introduction to Exploring Decimals (B)	**2** minutes	📶
	Multiplying and Dividing by 50 with Instant Recall	**8** minutes	📶
LEARN AND **TRY IT**	Reading and Writing Decimal Numbers	**15** minutes	🖥️
	Read and Write Decimal Numbers	**10** minutes	🖥️
	Practice Reading and Writing Decimal Numbers	**20** minutes	🖥️ and 📄
WRAP-UP	Reading and Writing Decimal Numbers	**5** minutes	📶

Content Background

In this lesson, students will learn how to read decimal numbers. They will convert between number names and decimals written in standard form.

Thinking about decimal numbers correctly promotes a strong and needed understanding of place value. Use the word *and* to indicate the location of the decimal as you read a number. For example, encourage students to think and say, "thirty-five and nineteen hundredths" when they see 35.19, rather than thinking or saying, "thirty-five point nineteen."

The word *and* should only be used to indicate a decimal point and should not be used when reading a whole number aloud. For example, the number 305 is not read "three hundred and five." The correct number name for 305 is "three hundred five." Precise language must be emphasized to avoid confusion when reading decimals. Students could misinterpret "three hundred and five thousandths" to mean 0.305 instead of the correct number 300.005.

How to Read a Decimal Number

1. Read the whole number part of the number from left to right. This is the part to the left of the decimal point.

2. Read the decimal point as *and*. Do not use *point* or *decimal* for the decimal point. Saying *and* separates the whole number portion from the decimal portion of the number. This is the only time *and* is used when reading or writing a number in words.

3. Read the decimal part of the number as if it were a whole number, but end with the place value farthest to the right in that number. Check to make sure the place value name ends in *–ths*.

OPTIONAL   The rule for using the word *and* to indicate a decimal point is applied when a mixed number is read or written in words. A mixed number is read by saying the whole number, the word *and*, and then the fraction part of the number. For example, $1\frac{1}{2}$ is read "one and one-half." You can teach students that the word *and* separates the whole number part of a number from the decimal *or* fraction part of a number.

Lesson Goals

- Write a number in words when given the number in standard form.
- Write a number in standard form when given the number in words.

GET READY

Introduction to Exploring Decimals (B)

Students will get a glimpse of what they will learn about in the lesson. They will also read the lesson goals.

Multiplying and Dividing by 50 with Instant Recall

Students will practice multiplying and dividing by **50** with instant recall.

LEARN AND TRY IT

LEARN   Reading and Writing Decimal Numbers

Students will learn how to read and write number names for decimal numbers. They will also write decimals in standard form for given number names.

SUPPORT   For students who have difficulty reading or writing number names, encourage them to make and use a place value chart. Once a number is entered into a place value chart, the number can be read or written in words using the digits and place value names.

TRY IT   Read and Write Decimal Numbers

Students will practice converting between number names and decimal numbers in standard form. Support will be provided to help students overcome misconceptions.

NOTE   Although it is not mathematically necessary to write a zero digit before the decimal point if there is no whole number part of a number, it is helpful to avoid confusion.

TRY IT   Practice Reading and Writing Decimal Numbers

Students will complete online practice problems. Then they will complete Practice Reading and Writing Decimal Numbers from *Summit Math 5 Activity Book*.

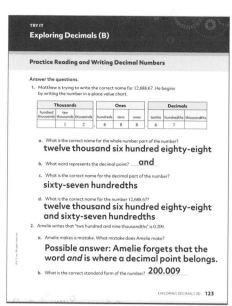

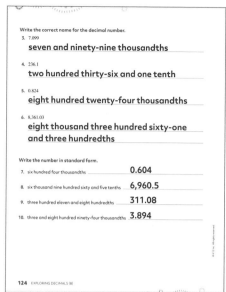

Reading and Writing Decimal Numbers

Students will solve problems to show that they understand how to write a decimal number using number names and how to write a number name as a decimal in standard form.

Exploring Decimals (C)

Lesson Overview

ACTIVITY	ACTIVITY TITLE	TIME	ONLINE/OFFLINE
GET READY	Introduction to Exploring Decimals (C)	**2** minutes	🖥️
	Multiplying and Dividing by 50 Math Facts Game	**8** minutes	🖥️
LEARN AND **TRY IT**	Plotting Decimals on a Number Line	**15** minutes	🖥️
	Plot Decimals on a Number Line	**10** minutes	🖥️
	Practice Plotting Decimals on a Number Line	**20** minutes	🖥️ and 📄
WRAP-UP	Plotting Decimals on a Number Line	**5** minutes	🖥️

Content Background

In this lesson, students will apply their understanding of decimals and place value to plot decimals on a number line. They should have experience representing whole numbers and fractions on a number line. Students will learn that any two numbers on a number line can be divided into tenths as many times as needed to plot a number correctly.

MATERIALS

Supplied
- *Summit Math 5 Activity Book:* Practice Plotting Decimals on a Number Line

Lesson Goals

- Plot decimals on a number line.

GET READY

Introduction to Exploring Decimals (C)
Students will get a glimpse of what they will learn about in the lesson. They will also read the lesson goals.

Multiplying and Dividing by 50 Math Facts Game
Students will practice multiplying and dividing by 50.

LEARN Plotting Decimals on a Number Line

Students will learn how to plot decimals on a number line. They will encounter decimals to the tenths, hundredths, and thousandths places.

TIP Depending on the number line that is given, a point may be plotted on a tick mark or between two tick marks. Encourage students to examine a number line closely before plotting a point.

TRY IT Plot Decimals on a Number Line

Students will practice plotting numbers on a number line. Support will be provided to help students overcome misconceptions.

TRY IT Practice Plotting Decimals on a Number Line

Students will complete online practice problems. Then they will complete Practice Plotting Decimals on a Number Line from *Summit Math 5 Activity Book*.

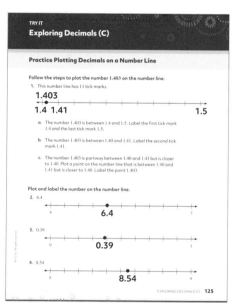

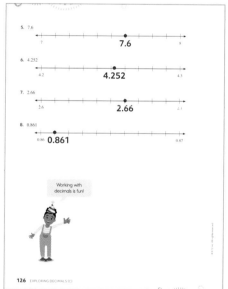

Plotting Decimals on a Number Line

Students will solve a problem to show that they understand how to plot numbers on a number line.

Exploring Decimals (D)

Lesson Overview

ACTIVITY	ACTIVITY TITLE	TIME	ONLINE/OFFLINE
GET READY	Introduction to Exploring Decimals (D)	**2** minutes	📶
TRY IT	Review Exploring Decimals	**18** minutes	📶
QUIZ	Exploring Decimals	**25** minutes	📶
WRAP-UP	More Math Practice	**15** minutes	📶

Lesson Goals

- Review converting between the standard and expanded forms of decimals, reading and writing decimals, and plotting decimals on a number line.

- Take a quiz.

GET READY

Introduction to Exploring Decimals (D)

Students will read the lesson goals.

TRY IT

Review Exploring Decimals

Students will answer questions to review what they have learned about exploring decimals.

QUIZ

Exploring Decimals

Students will complete the Exploring Decimals quiz.

More Math Practice

Students will practice skills according to their individual needs.

Comparing Decimals (A)

Lesson Overview

ACTIVITY	ACTIVITY TITLE	TIME	ONLINE/OFFLINE
GET READY	Introduction to Comparing Decimals (A)	**2** minutes	📶
	Look Back at Comparing Whole Numbers	**8** minutes	📶
LEARN AND TRY IT	Comparing Decimals Ending in the Same Place	**15** minutes	📶
	Compare Decimals Ending in the Same Place	**10** minutes	📶
	Practice Comparing Decimals Ending in the Same Place	**20** minutes	📶 and 📄
WRAP-UP	Comparing Decimals Ending in the Same Place	**5** minutes	📶

Content Background

In this lesson, students will learn how to use place value to compare decimal numbers that end in the same place value. They will compare numbers that are less than 1 as well as numbers that are greater than 1. They will use the less-than symbol (<) and the greater-than symbol (>) to compare decimal numbers.

It is important to help students recognize that there is more than one correct comparison statement. For example, if $3.5 < 3.8$, then $3.8 > 3.5$.

Precise language is important when reading number comparisons. For example, a student might read $3 < 7$ as "3 less than 7." But, "3 less than 7" is really $7 - 3$. The correct way to read $3 < 7$ is "3 **is** less than 7."

Lesson Goals

- Use symbols to compare decimals that are to the same place.

MATERIALS

Supplied
- *Summit Math 5 Activity Book:* Practice Comparing Decimals Ending in the Same Place

KEYWORDS

greater-than symbol (>) – a symbol that shows that one amount is greater than another

less-than symbol (<) – a symbol that shows that one amount is less than another

GET READY

Introduction to Comparing Decimals (A)

Students will get a glimpse of what they will learn about in the lesson. They will also read the lesson goals and keywords. Have students select each keyword and preview its definition.

Look Back at Comparing Whole Numbers

Students will practice the prerequisite skill of comparing whole numbers.

LEARN Comparing Decimals Ending in the Same Place

Students will learn how to compare decimal numbers that are to the same place value. They will use various strategies to determine the relationship between two numbers, including a number line and a place value chart.

NOTE   When comparing two numbers, examine the digits in each number from left to right to determine the first place value where the digits are different. This skill is similar to determining the alphabetical order of two words. When determining alphabetical order, examine the letters in two words in order from left to right to determine the first letter where the words are different.

TRY IT Compare Decimals Ending in the Same Place

Students will practice comparing decimals that are to the same place value. Support will be provided to help students overcome misconceptions.

TRY IT Practice Comparing Decimals Ending in the Same Place

Students will complete online practice problems. Then they will complete Practice Comparing Decimals Ending in the Same Place from *Summit Math 5 Activity Book.*

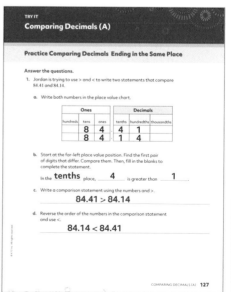

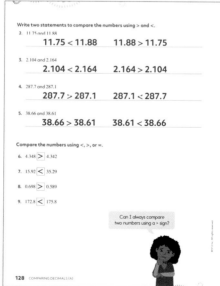

Comparing Decimals Ending in the Same Place

Students will solve problems to show that they understand how to compare decimals that are to the same place value.

Comparing Decimals (B)

Lesson Overview

ACTIVITY	ACTIVITY TITLE	TIME	ONLINE/OFFLINE
GET READY	Introduction to Comparing Decimals (B)	**2** minutes	📶
	Multiplying and Dividing by 60 Math Facts	**8** minutes	📶
LEARN AND **TRY IT**	Comparing Decimals Ending in Different Places	**15** minutes	📶
	Compare Decimals Ending in Different Places	**10** minutes	📶
	Practice Comparing Decimals Ending in Different Places	**20** minutes	📶 and 📄
WRAP-UP	Comparing Decimals Ending in Different Places	**5** minutes	📶

Content Background

In this lesson, students will learn how to use place value to compare decimal numbers that end in different place values. A common misconception with this skill is that a number with more digits is always greater than a number with fewer digits. That rule is true with whole numbers. A five-digit *whole* number is always greater than a number with one, two, three, or four digits. The same is not true with decimals. For example, 0.5 is greater than 0.105 even though 0.105 has more digits than 0.5. One method for comparing decimals is to make all numbers have the same number digits to the right of the decimal point by adding zeros to the number, such as $0.5 = 0.500$. Adding zeros helps students understand that $0.500 > 0.105$, so $0.5 > 0.105$. Using a place value chart is another method to compare two numbers with different decimal place values.

Lesson Goals

- Use symbols to compare decimals that are to different places.

GET READY

Introduction to Comparing Decimals (B)

Students will get a glimpse of what they will learn about in the lesson. They will also read the lesson goals.

Multiplying and Dividing by 60 Math Facts

Students will practice multiplying and dividing by 60.

LEARN AND TRY IT

LEARN   Comparing Decimals Ending in Different Places

Students will learn how to compare decimal numbers that are to different place values.

TIP   Help students recognize that the first step is to add zeros to the end of the number with fewer decimal place values. Then compare the numbers using a place value chart or by writing the numbers vertically with all place values aligned.

TRY IT   Compare Decimals Ending in Different Places

Students will practice comparing decimals that are to different place values. Support will be provided to help students overcome misconceptions.

TRY IT   Practice Comparing Decimals Ending in Different Places

Students will complete online practice problems. Then they will complete Practice Comparing Decimals Ending in Different Places from *Summit Math 5 Activity Book*.

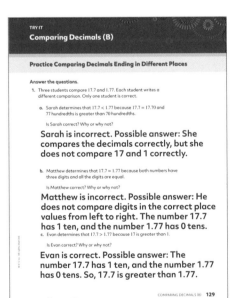

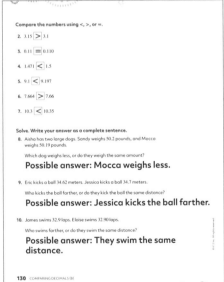

WRAP-UP

Comparing Decimals Ending in Different Places

Students will solve problems to show that they understand how to compare decimals that are to different place values.

Comparing Decimals (C)

Lesson Overview

ACTIVITY	ACTIVITY TITLE	TIME	ONLINE/OFFLINE
GET READY	Introduction to Comparing Decimals (C)	**2** minutes	🖥️
TRY IT	Review Comparing Decimals	**18** minutes	🖥️
QUIZ	Comparing Decimals	**25** minutes	🖥️
WRAP-UP	More Math Practice	**15** minutes	🖥️

Lesson Goals

- Review comparing decimals that are to the same place and to different places.

- Take a quiz.

MATERIALS

There are no materials to gather for this lesson.

GET READY

Introduction to Comparing Decimals (C)

Students will read the lesson goals.

TRY IT

Review Comparing Decimals

Students will answer questions to review what they have learned about comparing decimals.

QUIZ

Comparing Decimals

Students will complete the Comparing Decimals quiz.

More Math Practice

Students will practice skills according to their individual needs.

Rounding Decimals (A)

Lesson Overview

ACTIVITY	ACTIVITY TITLE	TIME	ONLINE/OFFLINE
GET READY	Introduction to Rounding Decimals (A)	**2** minutes	📶
	Look Back at Rounding Whole Numbers	**8** minutes	📶
LEARN AND **TRY IT**	Rounding to the Nearest Whole or Tenth	**15** minutes	📶
	Round to the Nearest Whole or Tenth	**10** minutes	📶
	Practice Rounding to the Nearest Whole or Tenth	**20** minutes	📶 and 📄
WRAP-UP	Rounding to the Nearest Whole or Tenth	**5** minutes	📶

Content Background

In this lesson, students will round decimals to the tenths place and whole numbers. Decimal numbers name wholes and parts of a whole. The names of the parts of a whole are tenths, hundredths, thousandths, and so on.

Rounding numbers in a problem can make finding an estimate easier. Decimals can be rounded to friendly numbers such as 0.5, 1, 1.5, and so on. They can also be rounded to a specific place, such as the nearest whole number or the nearest tenth.

When students round a number ending in a 5, they cannot round to the nearer number since 5 is halfway between two boundary numbers. For instance, 1.25 is halfway between 1.2 and 1.3. The general rule is that numbers ending in 5 (or greater) are rounded to the greater number. So, 1.25 rounded to nearest tenth is 1.3. However, it is important to note that some situations call for rounding down regardless of the final digit. For example, suppose a baker divides the amount of flour he has by the number of cups of flour needed for a batch of muffins and gets 4.7 batches. The baker could not make 5 batches of muffins. Even though 4.7 rounded to the nearest whole number is 5, the baker doesn't have enough flour to make 5 batches of muffins. In this scenario, the number 4.7 must be rounded down to 4.

MATERIALS

Supplied
- *Summit Math 5 Activity Book:* Practice Rounding to the Nearest Whole or Tenth

KEYWORDS

round (v.) – to change a number to the nearest place value asked in a problem; for example, rounding 532 to the nearest ten would be 530

tenths – the place value immediately to the right after the decimal; 10 hundredths = 1 tenth and 10 tenths = 1

whole numbers – zero and the counting numbers (0, 1, 2, 3, 4, 5, 6, and so on)

Lesson Goals

- Round decimals to the nearest whole number.

- Round decimals to the nearest tenth.

GET READY

Introduction to Rounding Decimals (A)

Students will get a glimpse of what they will learn about in the lesson. They will also read the lesson goals and keywords. Have students select each keyword and preview its definition.

Look Back at Rounding Whole Numbers

Students will practice the prerequisite skill of rounding multidigit whole numbers to any place.

LEARN AND TRY IT

LEARN   Rounding to the Nearest Whole or Tenth

Students will learn how to round decimal numbers to the nearest whole number or tenth.

TRY IT   Round to the Nearest Whole or Tenth

Students will practice rounding decimal numbers to the nearest whole number or tenth. Support will be provided to help students overcome misconceptions.

SUPPORT   Since rounding up means increasing a number, students could mistakenly decrease a number to round down. For example, students might claim that 5.3 rounds down to 4. Showing a number on a number line may help resolve this misconception. Show students that the number 5.3 is between 5 and 6, so the *nearest* whole number is 5, not 4.

TRY IT   Practice Rounding to the Nearest Whole or Tenth

Students will complete online practice problems. Then they will complete Practice Rounding to the Nearest Whole or Tenth from *Summit Math 5 Activity Book*.

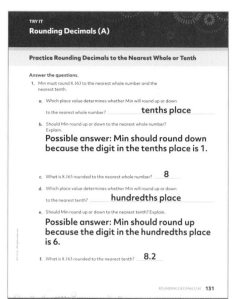

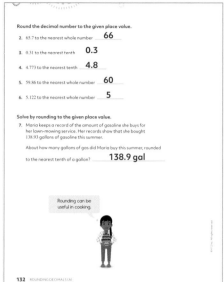

TIP   A rounded answer should not include additional digits beyond the indicated place value. For example, if 61.7 is rounded to the nearest whole number, the correct answer is 62, not 62.0, even though $62 = 62.0$.

WRAP-UP

Rounding to the Nearest Whole or Tenth

Students will solve problems to show that they understand how to round decimal numbers to the nearest whole number or tenth.

Rounding Decimals (B)

Lesson Overview

ACTIVITY	ACTIVITY TITLE	TIME	ONLINE/OFFLINE
GET READY	Introduction to Rounding Decimals (B)	**2** minutes	📶
	Multiplying and Dividing by 60 with Instant Recall	**8** minutes	📶
LEARN AND **TRY IT**	Rounding to the Hundredths and Thousandths Places	**15** minutes	📶
	Round to the Hundredths and Thousandths Places	**10** minutes	📶
	Practice Rounding to the Hundredths and Thousandths Places	**20** minutes	📶 and 📄
WRAP-UP	Rounding to the Hundredths and Thousandths Place	**5** minutes	📶

Content Background

In this lesson, students will round decimals to the hundredths and thousandths places. Rounding numbers in a problem can make finding an estimate easier. Decimals can be rounded to friendly numbers such as 0.05, 0.10, 0.25, and so on. They can also be rounded to a specific place, such as the hundredths place or thousandths place.

NOTE   Although students have only named decimal places up through the thousandths place, they will see decimals with more place values in this lesson. A number that ends in the thousandths place cannot be rounded to the thousandths place. Whether to round up or down depends on the digit to the right of the place value to which you are rounding. Rounding to the thousandths place depends on the digit in the ten-thousandths place. You could also refer to this number as "the digit to the right of the thousandths place."

Lesson Goals

- Round decimals to the nearest hundredth.

- Round decimals to the nearest thousandth.

Introduction to Rounding Decimals (B)

Students will get a glimpse of what they will learn about in the lesson. They will also read the lesson goals and keywords. Have students select each keyword and preview its definition.

Multiplying and Dividing by 60 with Instant Recall

Students will practice multiplying and dividing by 60 with instant recall.

LEARN AND TRY IT

LEARN   Rounding to the Hundredths and Thousandths Place

Students will learn how to round decimal numbers to the nearest hundredth or thousandth.

TRY IT   Round to the Hundredths and Thousandths Place

Students will practice rounding a decimal number to the nearest hundredth or thousandth. Support will be provided to help students overcome misconceptions.

TRY IT   Practice Rounding to the Hundredths and Thousandths Place

Students will complete online practice problems. Then they will complete Practice Rounding to the Hundredths and Thousandths Place from *Summit Math 5 Activity Book*.

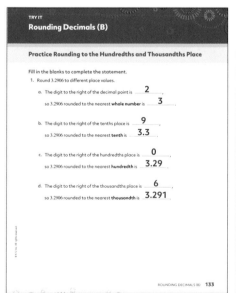

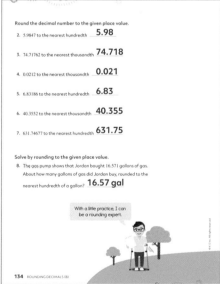

A rounded answer should not include additional digits beyond the indicated place value. For example, if 0.6512 is rounded to the nearest hundredth, the correct answer is 0.65, not 0.650, even though $0.65 = 0.650$

WRAP-UP

Rounding to the Hundredths and Thousandths Place

Students will solve problems to show that they understand how to round a decimal number to the nearest hundredths or thousandths place value.

Rounding Decimals (C)

Lesson Overview

ACTIVITY	ACTIVITY TITLE	TIME	ONLINE/OFFLINE
GET READY	Introduction to Rounding Decimals (C)	**2** minutes	📶
TRY IT	Review Rounding Decimals	**18** minutes	📶
QUIZ	Rounding Decimals	**25** minutes	📶
WRAP-UP	More Math Practice	**15** minutes	📶

Lesson Goals

- Review rounding decimals to the nearest whole, tenth, hundredth, and thousandth.
- Take a quiz.

MATERIALS

There are no materials to gather for this lesson.

GET READY

Introduction to Rounding Decimals (C)

Students will read the lesson goals.

TRY IT

Review Rounding Decimals

Students will answer questions to review what they have learned about rounding decimals.

QUIZ

Rounding Decimals

Students will complete the Rounding Decimals quiz.

More Math Practice

Students will practice skills according to their individual needs.

Place Value Relationships to Thousandths (A)

Lesson Overview

ACTIVITY	ACTIVITY TITLE	TIME	ONLINE/OFFLINE
GET READY	Introduction to Place Value Relationships to Thousandths (A)	**2** minutes	🖥️
	Look Back at Numbers in Expanded Form	**8** minutes	🖥️
LEARN AND **TRY IT**	Comparing a Digit to a Like Digit to Its Right	**15** minutes	🖥️
	Compare a Digit to a Like Digit to Its Right	**10** minutes	🖥️
	Practice Comparing a Digit to a Like Digit to Its Right	**20** minutes	🖥️ and 📄
WRAP-UP	Comparing a Digit to a Like Digit to Its Right	**5** minutes	🖥️

Content Background

In this lesson, students will investigate and describe the relationship between a digit in a number and a like digit to its right. They will only compare like digits. In other words, they will not compare a 3 to a 4. They will compare two 3s or two 4s. Students will also compare digits within one number as well as digits in two different numbers. They will be led to recognize the following pattern:

- The value of a digit is 10 times the value of a like digit one place to its right.

- The value of a digit is 10 times 10, or 100, times the value of a like digit two places to its right.

- The value of a digit is 10 times 10 times 10, or 1,000, times the value of a like digit three places to its right.

Lesson Goals

- Describe the relationship between a digit and a like digit to the right of it in the same number.

- Describe the relationship between a digit and a like digit to the right of it in a different number.

Introduction to Place Value Relationship to Thousandths (A)

Students will get a glimpse of what they will learn about in the lesson. They will also read the lesson goals.

Look Back at Numbers in Expanded Form

Students will practice the prerequisite skill of representing a number in expanded form.

LEARN AND TRY IT

LEARN   Comparing a Digit to a Like Digit to Its Right

Students will compare a digit in a number to a like digit to its right in the same number or a different number. They will only compare like digits, such as a 2 in the tens place to a 2 in the hundredths place.

NOTE   Students are expected to complete or write their own statement comparing two digits. The statement should always describe a digit in relation to a digit to its right. The digit on the left will be 10, 100, or 1,000 times greater than the digit on its right.

TRY IT   Compare a Digit to a Like Digit to Its Right

Students will practice comparing a digit in a number to a like digit to its right in the same number or a different number. Support will be provided to help students overcome misconceptions.

TRY IT   Practice Comparing a Digit to a Like Digit to Its Right

Students will complete online practice problems. Then they will complete Practice Comparing a Digit to a Like Digit to Its Right from *Summit Math 5 Activity Book*.

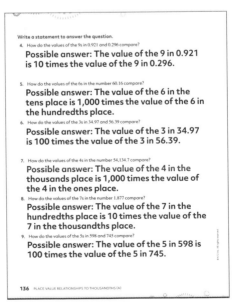

Comparing a Digit to a Like Digit to Its Right

Students will solve problems to show that they understand how to compare a digit in a number to a like digit to its right in the same number and in a different number.

Place Value Relationships to Thousandths (B)

Lesson Overview

ACTIVITY	ACTIVITY TITLE	TIME	ONLINE/OFFLINE
GET READY	Introduction to Place Value Relationships to Thousandths (B)	**2** minutes	🖥️
	Multiplying and Dividing by 60 Math Facts Game	**8** minutes	🖥️
LEARN AND **TRY IT**	Comparing a Digit to a Like Digit to Its Left	**7** minutes	🖥️
	Compare a Digit to a Like Digit to Its Left	**7** minutes	🖥️
	Comparing Values of Like Digits	**7** minutes	🖥️
	Compare Values of Like Digits	**7** minutes	🖥️
	Practice Comparing Values of Like Digits	**20** minutes	🖥️ and 📄
WRAP-UP	Comparing Values of Like Digits	**2** minutes	🖥️

Content Background

In this lesson, students will describe the relationship between like digits. They will begin by comparing a digit to a like digit to its left. When two digits are compared, one digit is on the right and one is on the left. The direction of the comparison determines whether the relationship is a whole number, like 10, or a fraction, like $\frac{1}{10}$. Students will work with these relationships:

- The value of a digit is 10 times the value of a like digit one place to its right and $\frac{1}{10}$ the value of a like digit one place to its left.

- The value of a digit is 100 times the value of a like digit two places to its right and $\frac{1}{100}$ the value of a like digit two places to its left.

- The value of a digit is 1,000 times the value of a like digit three places to its right and $\frac{1}{1,000}$ the value of a like digit three places to its left.

Students will continue to compare only like digits. They will also compare digits in one number as well as digits in two different numbers.

MATERIALS

Supplied
- *Summit Math 5 Activity Book:* Practice Comparing Values of Like Digits

Lesson Goals

- Describe the relationship between a digit and a like digit in the same number.
- Describe the relationship between a digit and a like digit in a different number.

GET READY

Introduction to Place Value Relationships to Thousandths (B)

Students will get a glimpse of what they will learn about in the lesson. They will also read the lesson goals.

Multiplying and Dividing by 60 Math Facts Game

Students will practice multiplying and dividing by 60.

LEARN AND TRY IT

LEARN   Comparing a Digit to a Like Digit to Its Left

Students will compare a digit in a number to a like digit to its left in the same number or a different number. They will only compare like digits, such as a 2 in the tenths place to a 2 in the hundreds place.

TRY IT   Compare a Digit to a Like Digit to Its Left

Students will practice comparing a digit in a number to a like digit to its left in the same number or a different number. Support will be provided to help students overcome misconceptions.

LEARN   Comparing Values of Like Digits

Students will compare two like digits in the same number or in two different numbers. They will make two comparison statements, one to compare from right to left and another to compare from left to right. The two values are always related. For example, if one digit is 100 times the value of the digit to its right, the digit on the right is $\frac{1}{100}$ the value of the digit on the left.

SUPPORT   For students having difficulty remembering whether the value is a whole number or a fraction, encourage them to expand a simple number and compare the digits. For example, 88 is $80 + 8$ and 80 is 10×8. Comparing left to right will always be a whole number, and comparing right to left will always be a fraction.

TRY IT   Compare Values of Like Digits

Students will practice comparing values of like digits in the same number or in two different numbers. Support will be provided to help students overcome misconceptions.

TRY IT   Practice Comparing Values of Like Digits

Students will complete online practice problems. Then they will complete Practice Comparing Values of Like Digits from *Summit Math 5 Activity Book*.

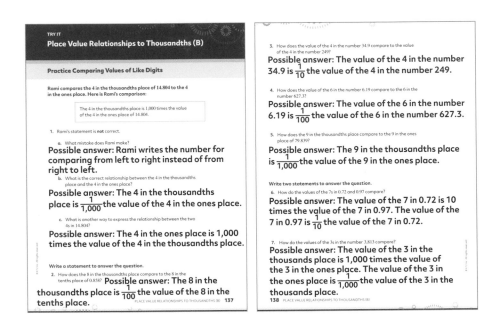

Comparing Values of Like Digits

Students will solve problems to show that they understand how to compare like digits in the same number and in two different numbers.

Place Value Relationships to Thousandths (C)

Lesson Overview

ACTIVITY	ACTIVITY TITLE	TIME	ONLINE/OFFLINE
GET READY	Introduction to Place Value Relationships to Thousandths (C)	**2** minutes	📶
TRY IT	Review Place Value Relationships to Thousandths	**18** minutes	📶
QUIZ	Place Value Relationships to Thousandths	**25** minutes	📶
WRAP-UP	More Math Practice	**15** minutes	📶

Lesson Goals

- Review comparing place values of like digits in numbers.
- Take a quiz.

MATERIALS

There are no materials to gather for this lesson.

GET READY

Introduction to Place Value Relationships to Thousandths (C)

Students will read the lesson goals.

TRY IT

Review Place Value Relationships to Thousandths

Students will answer questions to review what they have learned about place value relationships to thousandths.

QUIZ

Place Value Relationships to Thousandths

Students will complete the Place Value Relationships to Thousandths quiz.

More Math Practice

Students will practice skills according to their individual needs.

Big Ideas: Challenge Problems

Lesson Overview

Big Ideas lessons provide students the opportunity to apply the knowledge and skills acquired throughout previous units. Each Big Ideas lesson consists of three parts:

1. **Cumulative Review:** Students keep their skills fresh by reviewing prior content.

2. **Preview:** Students practice answering the types of questions they will commonly find on standardized tests.

3. **Synthesis:** Students complete an assignment that allows them to interweave and apply what they've learned. These synthesis assignments will vary throughout the course.

   In the Synthesis portion of this Big Ideas lesson, students will complete one or more challenge problems that will guide them to discover new concepts. Through hard work and perseverance, students will learn that they can use the math they already know combined with logical thinking to solve problems about new concepts. Students will need to use pencil and paper and/or technology to show their work.

   LEARNING COACH CHECK-IN   Make sure students complete, review, and submit the assignment to their teacher

All materials needed for this lesson are linked online. The materials are not provided in this Lesson Guide or in the Activity Book.

MATERIALS

Supplied
- Challenge Problems Instructions (printout)

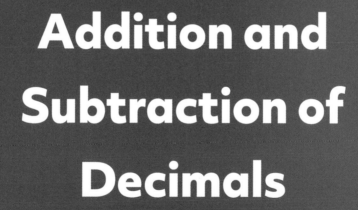

Addition and Subtraction of Decimals

Decimal Addition (A)

Lesson Overview

ACTIVITY	ACTIVITY TITLE	TIME	ONLINE/OFFLINE
GET READY	Introduction to Decimal Addition (A)	**2** minutes	🖥️
	Addition and Subtraction of Decimals in 60 Seconds	**3** minutes	🖥️
	Look Back at Adding Whole Numbers Using the Algorithm	**5** minutes	🖥️
LEARN AND **TRY IT**	Adding Decimals to Tenths by Modeling	**7** minutes	🖥️
	Add Decimals to Tenths by Modeling	**7** minutes	🖥️
	Adding Decimals to Tenths Without Models	**7** minutes	🖥️
	Add Decimals to Tenths Without Models	**7** minutes	🖥️
	Practice Adding Decimals to Tenths	**20** minutes	🖥️ and 📄
WRAP-UP	Adding Decimals to Tenths	**2** minutes	🖥️

Content Background

In this lesson, students will use models to gain greater understanding of place value and the role of place value in addition of decimal numbers to the tenths place. Then they will learn the standard algorithm for adding decimals to the tenths place. When learning addition of decimal numbers, many adults and children have been told to "line up the decimals," but that direction does not promote a true understanding of decimal addition. Encourage students to work through the examples with models before applying the standard algorithm for addition.

MATERIALS

Supplied
- *Summit Math 5 Activity Book:* Practice Adding Decimals to Tenths

Lesson Goals
- Add decimals that are to the tenths place by modeling.
- Add decimals that are to the tenths place without modeling.

Introduction to Decimal Addition (A)

Students will get a glimpse of what they will learn about in the lesson. They will also read the lesson goals.

Addition and Subtraction of Decimals in 60 Seconds

Students will watch a short video designed to spark their interest in upcoming topics.

Look Back at Adding Whole Numbers Using the Algorithm

Students will practice the prerequisite skill of adding whole numbers using the algorithm.

LEARN AND TRY IT

LEARN Adding Decimals to Tenths by Modeling

Students will add decimals to tenths by modeling. They will encounter problems with and without regrouping.

NOTE Addition problems are modeled using base-10 blocks, shading base-10 grids, and making jumps on a number line. Students do not need to become experts in each strategy. One strategy may make more sense than another to different students. It is helpful for students to be comfortable with at least one modeling strategy to use when they encounter difficulties.

TRY IT Add Decimals to Tenths by Modeling

Students will practice adding decimals to tenths by modeling. Support will be provided to help students overcome misconceptions.

LEARN Adding Decimals to Tenths Without Models

Students will add decimals to tenths without models using the standard algorithm. They will encounter problems with and without regrouping. Students are encouraged to use estimation to determine whether their answer is reasonable.

TIP Remind students that they can create a model if a problem or its answer doesn't make sense.

TRY IT Add Decimals to Tenths Without Models

Students will practice adding decimals to tenths without models. Support will be provided to help students overcome misconceptions.

TRY IT Practice Adding Decimals to Tenths

Students will complete online practice problems. Then they will complete Practice Adding Decimals to Tenths from *Summit Math 5 Activity Book*.

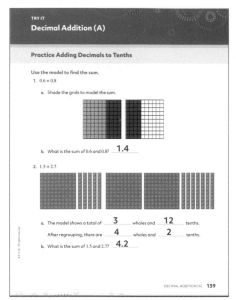

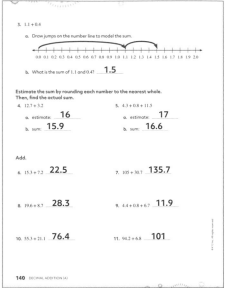

WRAP-UP

Adding Decimals to Tenths

Students will solve a problem to show that they understand how to add decimals to tenths.

Decimal Addition (B)

Lesson Overview

ACTIVITY	ACTIVITY TITLE	TIME	ONLINE/OFFLINE
GET READY	Introduction to Decimal Addition (B)	**2** minutes	🖥️
	Multiplying and Dividing by 70 Math Facts	**8** minutes	🖥️
LEARN AND **TRY IT**	Adding Decimals to Hundredths by Modeling	**7** minutes	🖥️
	Add Decimals to Hundredths by Modeling	**7** minutes	🖥️
	Adding Decimals to Hundredths Without Models	**7** minutes	🖥️
	Add Decimals to Hundredths Without Models	**7** minutes	🖥️
	Practice Adding Decimals to Hundredths	**20** minutes	🖥️ and 📄
WRAP-UP	Adding Decimals to Hundredths	**2** minutes	🖥️

Content Background

In this lesson, students will use models to gain greater understanding of place value and the role of place value in addition of decimal numbers to the hundredths place. Then they will learn the standard algorithm for adding decimals to the hundredths place.

Students can use centimeter grid paper to align numbers and the decimal point when adding two decimals using the standard algorithm.

	2	.	7	4	
+	5	.	2	1	
	7	.	9	5	

> ### MATERIALS
>
> **Supplied**
> - *Summit Math 5 Activity Book:* Practice Adding Decimals to Hundredths

Lesson Goals

- Add decimals that are to the hundredths place, or to the tenths and hundredths places, by modeling.

- Add decimals that are to the hundredths place, or to the tenths and hundredths places, without modeling.

Introduction to Decimal Addition (B)

Students will get a glimpse of what they will learn about in the lesson. They will also read the lesson goals.

Multiplying and Dividing by 70 Math Facts

Students will practice multiplying and dividing by 70.

LEARN AND TRY IT

LEARN   Adding Decimals to Hundredths by Modeling

Students will add decimals to hundredths by modeling. They will encounter problems with and without regrouping.

NOTE   Addition problems are modeled using base-10 blocks and shading base-10 grids. Students do not need to become experts in both strategies. One strategy may make more sense than another to different students. It is helpful for students to be comfortable with at least one modeling strategy to use when they encounter difficulties.

TRY IT   Add Decimals to Hundredths by Modeling

Students will practice adding decimals to hundredths by modeling. Support will be provided to help students overcome misconceptions.

LEARN   Adding Decimals to Hundredths Without Models

Students will add decimals to hundredths without models using the standard algorithm. They will encounter problems with and without regrouping. Students are encouraged to use estimation to determine whether their answer is reasonable.

TRY IT   Add Decimals to Hundredths Without Models

Students will practice adding decimals to hundredths without models. Support will be provided to help students overcome misconceptions.

TRY IT   Practice Adding Decimals to Hundredths

Students will complete online practice problems. Then they will complete Practice Adding Decimals to Hundredths from *Summit Math 5 Activity Book*.

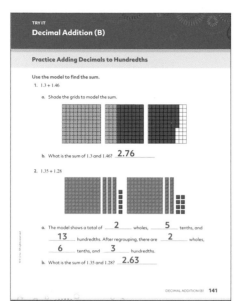

Adding Decimals to Hundredths

Students will solve a problem to show that they understand how to add decimals to hundredths.

Decimal Addition (C)

Lesson Overview

ACTIVITY	ACTIVITY TITLE	TIME	ONLINE/OFFLINE
GET READY	Introduction to Decimal Addition (C)	**2** minutes	
TRY IT	Review Decimal Addition	**18** minutes	
QUIZ	Decimal Addition	**25** minutes	
WRAP-UP	More Math Practice	**15** minutes	

Lesson Goals

- Review adding decimals to tenths and hundredths with and without models.

- Take a quiz.

GET READY

Introduction to Decimal Addition (C)

Students will read the lesson goals.

TRY IT

Review Decimal Addition

Students will answer questions to review what they have learned about decimal addition.

QUIZ

Decimal Addition

Students will complete the Decimal Addition quiz.

More Math Practice

Students will practice skills according to their individual needs.

Decimal Subtraction (A)

Lesson Overview

ACTIVITY	ACTIVITY TITLE	TIME	ONLINE/OFFLINE
GET READY	Introduction to Decimal Subtraction (A)	**2** minutes	📶
	Look Back at Subtracting Whole Numbers Using the Algorithm	**8** minutes	📶
LEARN AND **TRY IT**	Subtracting Decimals to Tenths by Modeling	**7** minutes	📶
	Subtract Decimals to Tenths by Modeling	**7** minutes	📶
	Subtracting Decimals to Tenths Without Models	**7** minutes	📶
	Subtract Decimals to Tenths Without Models	**7** minutes	📶
	Practice Subtracting Decimals to Tenths	**20** minutes	📶 and 📄
WRAP-UP	Subtracting Decimals to Tenths	**2** minutes	📶

Content Background

In this lesson, students will use models to gain greater understanding of place value and the role of place value in subtraction of decimal numbers to the tenths place. When learning subtraction of decimal numbers, many adults and children have been told to "line up the decimals," but that direction does not promote a true understanding of decimal subtraction. Encourage students to work through the examples with models before applying the standard algorithm for subtraction.

Students will also gain a greater understanding of the inverse relationship between addition and subtraction as related to decimal numbers.

> ### Lesson Goals
> - Subtract decimals that are to the tenths place by modeling.
> - Subtract decimals that are to the tenths place without modeling.

MATERIALS

Supplied
- *Summit Math 5 Activity Book:* Practice Subtracting Decimals to Tenths

Introduction to Decimal Subtraction (A)

Students will get a glimpse of what they will learn about in the lesson. They will also read the lesson goals.

Look Back at Subtracting Whole Numbers Using the Algorithm

Students will practice the prerequisite skill of subtracting whole numbers using the standard algorithm.

LEARN AND TRY IT

LEARN   Subtracting Decimals to Tenths by Modeling

Students will subtract decimals to the hundredths place by modeling. They will encounter problems with and without regrouping. Subtraction problems are modeled using base-10 blocks, shading and crossing out base-10 grids, and making jumps on number lines.

TIP   Remind students that they can check their answers using addition.

TRY IT   Subtract Decimals to Tenths by Modeling

Students will practice subtracting decimals to tenths by modeling. Support will be provided to help students overcome misconceptions.

LEARN   Subtracting Decimals to Tenths Without Models

Students will subtract decimals to tenths without models using the standard algorithm. They will encounter problems with and without regrouping. Students are encouraged to use estimation to determine whether their answer is reasonable.

TIP   Remind students that they can create a model if a problem or its answer doesn't make sense.

TRY IT   Subtract Decimals to Tenths Without Models

Students will practice subtracting decimals to tenths without models. Support will be provided to help students overcome misconceptions.

TRY IT   Practice Subtracting Decimals to Tenths

Students will complete online practice problems. Then they will complete Practice Subtracting Decimals to Tenths from *Summit Math 5 Activity Book*.

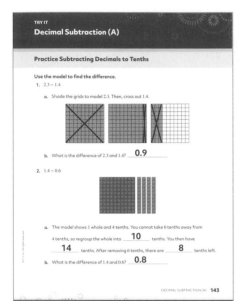

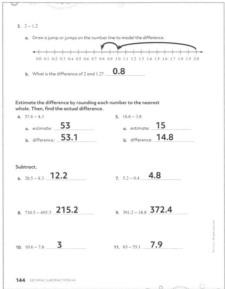

WRAP-UP

Subtracting Decimals to Tenths

Students will solve a problem to show that they understand how to subtract decimals to the tenths place.

Decimal Subtraction (B)

Lesson Overview

ACTIVITY	ACTIVITY TITLE	TIME	ONLINE/OFFLINE
GET READY	Introduction to Decimal Subtraction (B)	**2** minutes	🖥️
	Multiplying and Dividing by 70 with Instant Recall	**8** minutes	🖥️
LEARN AND **TRY IT**	Subtracting Decimals to Hundredths by Modeling	**7** minutes	🖥️
	Subtract Decimals to Hundredths by Modeling	**7** minutes	🖥️
	Subtracting Decimals to Hundredths Without Models	**7** minutes	🖥️
	Subtract Decimals to Hundredths Without Models	**7** minutes	🖥️
	Practice Subtracting Decimals to Hundredths	**20** minutes	🖥️ and 📄
WRAP-UP	Subtracting Decimals to Hundredths	**2** minutes	🖥️

Content Background

In this lesson, students will use models to gain greater understanding of place value and the role of place value in subtraction of decimal numbers to the hundredths place. Encourage students to work through the examples with models before applying the standard algorithm for subtraction.

When using the standard algorithm, students can use centimeter grid paper to align numbers and the decimal point when subtracting two decimals.

	3	5	.	7	3	
−	2	1	.	5	0	
	1	4	.	2	3	

Students will continue to use the inverse relationship between addition and subtraction to check their answers.

Lesson Goals

- Subtract decimals that are to the hundredths place, or to the tenths and hundredths places, by modeling.
- Subtract decimals that are to the hundredths place, or to the tenths and hundredths places, without modeling.

GET READY

Introduction to Decimal Subtraction (B)
Students will get a glimpse of what they will learn about in the lesson. They will also read the lesson goals.

Multiplying and Dividing by 70 with Instant Recall
Students will practice multiplying and dividing by 70 with instant recall.

LEARN AND TRY IT

LEARN   Subtracting Decimals to Hundredths by Modeling
Students will subtract decimals to hundredths by modeling. Students will encounter problems with and without regrouping.

NOTE   Subtraction problems are modeled using base-10 blocks and shading base-10 grids. Students do not need to become experts in both strategies. One strategy may make more sense than another to different students. It is helpful for students to be comfortable with at least one modeling strategy to use when they encounter difficulties.

TRY IT   Subtract Decimals to Hundredths by Modeling
Students will practice subtracting decimals to hundredths by modeling. Support will be provided to help students overcome misconceptions.

LEARN   Subtracting Decimals to Hundredths Without Models
Students will subtract decimals to hundredths without models using the standard algorithm. They will encounter problems with and without regrouping. Students are encouraged to use estimation to determine whether their answer is reasonable.

TRY IT   Subtract Decimals to Hundredths Without Models
Students will practice subtracting decimals to hundredths without models. Support will be provided to help students overcome misconceptions.

TRY IT   Practice Subtracting Decimals to Hundredths

Students will complete online practice problems. Then they will complete Practice Subtracting Decimals to Hundredths from *Summit Math 5 Activity Book*.

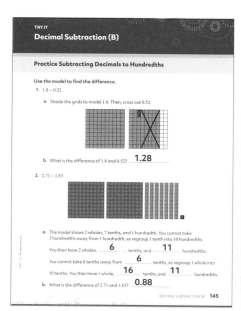

Subtracting Decimals to Hundredths

Students will solve a problem to show that they understand how to subtract decimals to the hundredths place.

Decimal Subtraction (C)

Lesson Overview

ACTIVITY	ACTIVITY TITLE	TIME	ONLINE/OFFLINE
GET READY	Introduction to Decimal Subtraction (C)	**2** minutes	🖥️
TRY IT	Review Decimal Subtraction	**18** minutes	🖥️
QUIZ	Decimal Subtraction	**25** minutes	🖥️
WRAP-UP	More Math Practice	**15** minutes	🖥️

Lesson Goals

- Review subtracting decimals to tenths and hundredths with and without models.

- Take a quiz.

MATERIALS

There are no materials to gather for this lesson.

GET READY

Introduction to Decimal Subtraction (C)

Students will read the lesson goals.

TRY IT

Review Decimal Subtraction

Students will answer questions to review what they have learned about decimal subtraction.

QUIZ

Decimal Subtraction

Students will complete the Decimal Subtraction quiz.

More Math Practice

Students will practice skills according to their individual needs.

Add and Subtract Decimals in the Real World (A)

Lesson Overview

ACTIVITY	ACTIVITY TITLE	TIME	ONLINE/OFFLINE
GET READY	Introduction to Add, Subtract Decimals in the Real World (A)	**2** minutes	🖥️
	Look Back at Adding and Subtracting Decimals	**8** minutes	🖥️
LEARN AND **TRY IT**	Solving Real-World Money Problems	**15** minutes	🖥️
	Solve Real-World Money Problems	**10** minutes	🖥️
	Practice Solving Real-World Money Problems	**20** minutes	🖥️ and 📄
WRAP-UP	Solving Real-World Money Problems	**5** minutes	🖥️

Content Background

In this lesson, students will apply what they have learned about adding and subtracting decimals to the hundredths place to solve real-world problems involving money. Money amounts will include both dollars and cents. Remind students that a dollar amount such as $5 can be written as $5.00. Also, an answer such as $3.70 will be marked incorrect if it is not given to the hundredths place. For example, the answers $3.700 or $3.7 would be marked incorrect.

Lesson Goals

- Solve real-world problems by adding or subtracting amounts of money.

GET READY

Introduction to Add, Subtract Decimals in the Real World (A)
Students will get a glimpse of what they will learn about in the lesson. They will also read the lesson goals.

Look Back at Adding and Subtracting Decimals
Students will practice the prerequisite skill of adding and subtracting decimals.

LEARN   Solving Real-World Money Problems

Students will solve real-world money problems involving adding or subtracting decimals to the hundredths place.

OPTIONAL   Discuss the following scenario with students: Suppose they purchase some items from a store and the total comes to $10.02. Discuss the difference between the change from a $20 bill versus $20 and 2 pennies. The change from a $20 bill would be $20 − $10.02 = $9.98. With the fewest number of bills and coins, the change is a $5 bill, four $1 bills, 3 quarters, 2 dimes, and 3 pennies—that's a lot of change! On the other hand, if they pay with a $20 bill and 2 pennies, the change is $20.02 − $10.02 = $10, or one $10 bill, which is much less change to keep track of.

TRY IT   Solve Real-World Money Problems

Students will practice solving real-world money problems. Support will be provided to help students overcome misconceptions.

TRY IT   Practice Solving Real-World Money Problems

Students will complete online practice problems. Then they will complete Practice Solving Real-World Money Problems from *Summit Math 5 Activity Book*.

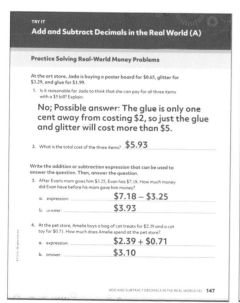

Solving Real-World Money Problems

Students will solve a problem to show that they understand how to add or subtract decimals to solve real-world problem involving money.

Add and Subtract Decimals in the Real World (B)

Lesson Overview

ACTIVITY	ACTIVITY TITLE	TIME	ONLINE/OFFLINE
GET READY	Introduction to Add, Subtract Decimals in the Real World (B)	**2** minutes	🖥️
	Multiplying and Dividing by 70 Math Facts Game	**8** minutes	🖥️
LEARN AND **TRY IT**	Adding and Subtracting Decimals in the Real World	**15** minutes	🖥️
	Add and Subtract Decimals in the Real World	**10** minutes	🖥️
	Practice Adding and Subtracting Decimals in the Real World	**20** minutes	🖥️ and 📄
WRAP-UP	Adding and Subtracting Decimals in the Real World	**5** minutes	🖥️

Content Background

In this lesson, students will apply their knowledge of decimal addition and subtraction to solve real-world problems.

Lesson Goals

- Solve real-world problems by adding or subtracting decimals.

GET READY

Introduction to Add, Subtract Decimals in the Real World (B)

Students will get a glimpse of what they will learn about in the lesson. They will also read the lesson goals.

Multiplying and Dividing by 70 Math Facts Game

Students will practice multiplying and dividing by 70.

LEARN Adding and Subtracting Decimals in the Real World

Students will solve real-world problems by adding or subtracting decimals to the tenths or hundredths place.

SUPPORT   Some problems require students to add to or subtract from a whole number. Remind students that they can add zero digits after the decimal point to the tenths or hundredths place as needed.

TRY IT Add and Subtract Decimals in the Real World

Students will practice adding and subtracting decimals to solve real-world problems. Support will be provided to help students overcome misconceptions.

TRY IT Practice Adding and Subtracting Decimals in the Real World

Students will complete online practice problems. Then they will complete Practice Adding and Subtracting Decimals in the Real World from *Summit Math 5 Activity Book*.

Adding and Subtracting Decimals in the Real World

Students will solve a problem to show that they understand how to add and subtract decimals to solve real-world problems.

Add and Subtract Decimals in the Real World (C)

Lesson Overview

ACTIVITY	ACTIVITY TITLE	TIME	ONLINE/OFFLINE
GET READY	Introduction to Add, Subtract Decimals in the Real World (C)	**2** minutes	🖥️
	Multiplying and Dividing by 80 Math Facts	**8** minutes	🖥️
LEARN AND TRY IT	Solving Multistep, Real-World Problems with Decimals	**15** minutes	🖥️
	Solve Multistep, Real-World Problems with Decimals	**10** minutes	🖥️
	Practice Solving Multistep, Real-World Problems with Decimals	**20** minutes	🖥️ and 📄
WRAP-UP	Solving Multistep, Real-World Problems with Decimals	**5** minutes	🖥️

Content Background

In this lesson, students will apply their knowledge of decimal addition and subtraction to solve real-world problems with multiple steps.

Lesson Goals

- Solve real-world multistep problems with decimals.

GET READY

Introduction to Add, Subtract Decimals in the Real World (C)

Students will get a glimpse of what they will learn about in the lesson. They will also read the lesson goals.

Multiplying and Dividing by 80 Math Facts

Students will practice multiplying and dividing by 80.

LEARN   Solving Multistep, Real-World Problems with Decimals

Students will solve multistep, real-world problems by adding and/or subtracting decimals to the hundredths place.

NOTE   Remind students that answers representing amounts of money must always be given to the hundredths place or they will be incorrect.

TRY IT   Solving Multistep, Real-World Problems with Decimals

Students will practice solving multistep, real-world problems involving adding and/or subtracting decimals. Support will be provided to help students overcome misconceptions.

TRY IT   Practice Solving Multistep, Real-World Problems with Decimals

Students will complete online practice problems. Then they will complete Practice Solving Multistep, Real-World Problems with Decimals from *Summit Math 5 Activity Book*.

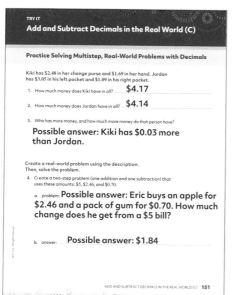

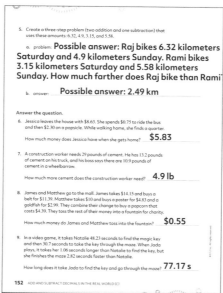

Solving Multistep, Real-World Problems with Decimals

Students will solve a problem to show that they understand how to add and subtract decimals to solve multistep, real-world problems.

Add and Subtract Decimals in the Real World (D)

Lesson Overview

ACTIVITY	ACTIVITY TITLE	TIME	ONLINE/OFFLINE
GET READY	Introduction to Add, Subtract Decimals in the Real World (D)	**2** minutes	🖥️
TRY IT	Review Add and Subtract Decimals in the Real World	**18** minutes	🖥️
QUIZ	Add and Subtract Decimals in the Real World	**25** minutes	🖥️
WRAP-UP	More Math Practice	**15** minutes	🖥️

Lesson Goals

- Review solving real-world problems by adding and subtracting decimals.

- Take a quiz.

MATERIALS

There are no materials to gather for this lesson.

GET READY

Introduction to Add, Subtract Decimals in the Real World (D)

Students will read the lesson goals.

TRY IT

Review Add and Subtract Decimals in the Real World

Students will answer questions to review what they have learned about addition and subtraction of decimal numbers in the real world.

QUIZ

Add and Subtract Decimals in the Real World

Students will complete the Addition and Subtraction of Decimal Numbers in the Real World quiz.

More Math Practice

Students will practice skills according to their individual needs.

Big Ideas: Extended Problems

Lesson Overview

Big Ideas lessons provide students the opportunity to further apply the knowledge and skills acquired throughout previous units. Each Big Ideas lesson consists of three parts:

1. **Cumulative Review:** Students keep their skills fresh by reviewing prior content.

2. **Preview:** Students practice answering the types of questions they will commonly find on standardized tests.

3. **Synthesis:** Students complete an assignment that allows them to interweave and apply what they've learned. These synthesis assignments will vary throughout the course.

   In the Synthesis portion of this Big Ideas lesson, students will complete multistep problems that go beyond the short answer and multiple choice problems they encounter in their regular lessons. These problems give students an opportunity to demonstrate problem solving, reasoning, communication, and modeling skills. Students will need to use pencil and paper and/or technology to show their work.

   LEARNING COACH CHECK-IN   This is a graded assessment. Make sure students complete, review, and submit the assignment to their teacher.

All materials needed for this lesson are linked online. The materials are not provided in this Lesson Guide or in the Activity Book.

Multiplication
with Decimals

Multiplying Whole Numbers by Decimals (A)

Lesson Overview

ACTIVITY	ACTIVITY TITLE	TIME	ONLINE/OFFLINE
GET READY	Introduction to Multiplying Whole Numbers by Decimals (A)	**2** minutes	🖥️
	Multiplying with Decimals in 60 Seconds	**3** minutes	🖥️
	Look Back at Representing Decimals on a Number Line	**5** minutes	🖥️
LEARN AND **TRY IT**	Using Number Lines to Multiply Wholes by Decimals	**7** minutes	🖥️
	Use Number Lines to Multiply Wholes by Decimals	**7** minutes	🖥️
	Using Models to Multiply Wholes by Decimals	**7** minutes	🖥️
	Use Models to Multiply Wholes by Decimals	**7** minutes	🖥️
	Practice Using Models to Multiply Wholes by Decimals	**20** minutes	🖥️ and 📄
WRAP-UP	Using Models to Multiply Wholes by Decimals	**2** minutes	🖥️

Content Background

In this lesson, students will use models to "see" how decimal multiplication works. They will use numbers lines, base-10 blocks, and grids to model the multiplication of a decimal number by a whole number.

The traditional multiplication algorithm can give students answers that they often do not understand. They struggle to know whether the decimal point is in the correct place and whether their answer makes sense. Models help students see the regrouping that occurs so they begin acquiring an intuitive sense about the correctness of their answers before they begin using the algorithm.

TIP   When students write and compute with decimal numbers, they often use numbers that are between 0 and 1—for example, 0.1. While it is acceptable to write this number as .1, mathematicians usually write the leading zero, 0.1, to show that the whole number value for the decimal number is zero and to avoid confusion about the value of the number.

> ### MATERIALS
>
> **Supplied**
> - *Summit Math 5 Activity Book:* Practice Using Models to Multiply Wholes by Decimals

Lesson Goals

- Determine the product of a whole number and a decimal using number lines, grids, and base-10 blocks.

Introduction to Multiplying Whole Numbers by Decimals (A)

Students will get a glimpse of what they will learn about in the lesson. They will also read the lesson goals.

Multiplying with Decimals in 60 Seconds

Students will watch a short video designed to spark their interest in upcoming topics.

Look Back at Representing Decimals on a Number Line

Students will practice the prerequisite skill of using a number line to represent decimals.

LEARN AND TRY IT

LEARN   Using Number Lines to Multiply Wholes by Decimals

Students will use a number line to model the product of a whole number and a decimal to the hundredths place.

TIP   When you multiply a whole number by a decimal using a number line, let the whole number be the number of jumps along the number line. Then let the decimal be the length of each jump.

TRY IT   Use Number Lines to Multiply Wholes by Decimals

Students will practice multiplying a whole number by a decimal using a number line. Support will be provided to help students overcome misconceptions.

LEARN   Using Models to Multiply Wholes by Decimals

Students will multiply a whole number by a decimal using various models. They will explore examples with 10×10 grids and base-10 blocks.

SUPPORT   Students sometimes have difficulty when they must regroup tenths or hundredths. Remind them that there are 10 hundredths in 1 tenth and 10 tenths in 1 whole. Students can count by tenths or hundredths to regroup and find the correct product.

TRY IT   Use Models to Multiply Wholes by Decimals

Students will practice multiplying a whole number by a decimal using other models. Support will be provided to help students overcome misconceptions.

TRY IT   Practice Using Models to Multiply Wholes by Decimals

Students will complete online practice problems. Then they will complete Practice Using Models to Multiply Wholes by Decimals from *Summit Math 5 Activity Book*.

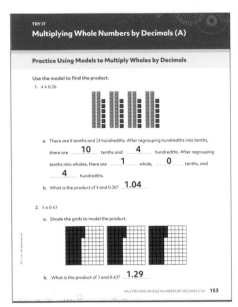

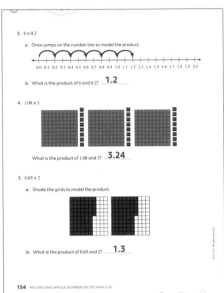

TIP   If you have a physical set of base-10 blocks, students can use it as a tool to help solve the online and Activity Book practice problems.

WRAP-UP

Using Models to Multiply Wholes by Decimals

Students will solve problems to show that they understand how to multiply a whole number by a decimal using different models.

Multiplying Whole Numbers by Decimals (B)

Lesson Overview

ACTIVITY	ACTIVITY TITLE	TIME	ONLINE/OFFLINE
GET READY	Introduction to Multiplying Whole Numbers by Decimals (B)	**2** minutes	
	Multiplying and Dividing by 80 with Instant Recall	**8** minutes	
LEARN AND **TRY IT**	Using the Algorithm to Multiply Wholes by Decimals	**15** minutes	
	Use the Algorithm to Multiply Wholes by Decimals	**10** minutes	
	Practice Using the Algorithm to Multiply Wholes by Decimals	**20** minutes	and
WRAP-UP	Using the Algorithm to Multiply Wholes by Decimals	**5** minutes	

Content Background

In this lesson, students will learn a step-by-step algorithm for multiplying a whole number by a decimal. To multiply a whole number by a decimal, follow these steps:

1. Multiply as you would multiply two whole numbers.
2. Count the number of digits after the decimal point in the decimal factor.
3. Move the decimal point in the product the same number places to the left.

> ### Lesson Goals
> • Multiply a whole number by a decimal using the algorithm.

MATERIALS

Supplied
• *Summit Math 5 Activity Book:* Practice Using the Algorithm to Multiply Wholes by Decimals

KEYWORDS

algorithm – step-by-step way to solve a problem

factor – one of two or more numbers that are multiplied

product – the answer to a multiplication problem

GET READY

Introduction to Multiplying Whole Numbers by Decimals (B)
Students will get a glimpse of what they will learn about in the lesson. They will also read the lesson goals and keywords. Have students select each keyword and preview its definition.

Multiplying and Dividing by 80 with Instant Recall
Students will practice multiplying and dividing by 80.

LEARN   Using the Algorithm to Multiply Wholes by Decimals

Students will learn how to multiply a decimal by a whole number using the algorithm.

SUPPORT   For students having difficulty determining whether their answer is correct, encourage them to begin by estimating the product. Have students check that the product has the same number of decimal places as the decimal factor.

TRY IT   Use the Algorithm to Multiply Wholes by Decimals

Students will practice multiplying a whole number by a decimal using the algorithm. Support will be provided to help students overcome misconceptions.

TRY IT   Practice Using the Algorithm to Multiply Wholes by Decimals

Students will complete online practice problems. Then they will complete Practice Using the Algorithm to Multiply Wholes by Decimals from *Summit Math 5 Activity Book.*

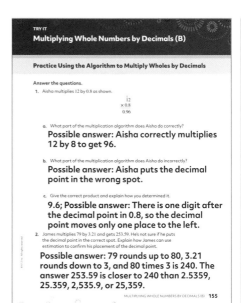

Using the Algorithm to Multiply Wholes by Decimals

Students will solve a problem to show that they understand how to multiply a decimal and a whole number using the algorithm.

Multiplying Whole Numbers by Decimals (C)

Lesson Overview

ACTIVITY	ACTIVITY TITLE	TIME	ONLINE/OFFLINE
GET READY	Introduction to Multiplying Whole Numbers by Decimals (C)	**2** minutes	🖥️
	Multiplying and Dividing by 80 Math Facts Game	**8** minutes	📶
LEARN AND **TRY IT**	Multiplying Wholes by Decimals in the Real World	**15** minutes	📶
	Multiply Wholes by Decimals in the Real World	**10** minutes	🖥️
	Practice Multiplying Wholes by Decimals in the Real World	**20** minutes	📶 and 📄
WRAP-UP	Multiplying Wholes by Decimals in the Real World	**5** minutes	📶

Content Background

In this lesson, students will apply their knowledge of multiplying a whole number by a decimal using the algorithm to solve real-world problems. They will solve problems involving a variety of situations.

Sometimes, a product will end with a zero after the decimal point. Sometimes, the zero can be dropped depending on the situation. For example, if the answer is 14.20 kilograms, the answer 14.2 kilograms would also be correct. However, if the answer relates to money such as $14.20, the answer $14.2 would be incorrect. Instruct students to read problems carefully to make sure that they are fully answering the question asked.

> ### MATERIALS
>
> **Supplied**
> - *Summit Math 5 Activity Book:* Practice Multiplying Wholes by Decimals in the Real World

Lesson Goals

- Solve real-world problems by multiplying a whole number by a decimal.

GET READY

Introduction to Multiplying Whole Numbers by Decimals (C)

Students will get a glimpse of what they will learn about in the lesson. They will also read the lesson goals.

Multiplying and Dividing by 80 Math Facts Game

Students will practice multiplying and dividing by 80.

LEARN Multiplying Wholes by Decimals in the Real World

Students will learn how to solve real-world problems by multiplying a whole number and a decimal.

NOTE The most efficient way to solve each problem is to use the algorithm. However, students can use models if they get stuck on a problem.

TRY IT Multiply Wholes by Decimals in the Real World

Students will practice solving real-world problems involving the product of a whole number and a decimal. Support will be provided to help students overcome misconceptions.

TRY IT Practice Multiplying Wholes by Decimals in the Real World

Students will complete online practice problems. Then they will complete Practice Multiplying Wholes by Decimals in the Real World from *Summit Math 5 Activity Book*.

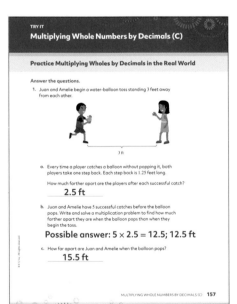

WRAP-UP

Multiplying Wholes by Decimals in the Real World

Students will solve a problem to show that they understand how to solve a real-world problem by multiplying a whole number by a decimal.

Multiplying Whole Numbers by Decimals (D)

Lesson Overview

ACTIVITY	ACTIVITY TITLE	TIME	ONLINE/OFFLINE
GET READY	Introduction to Multiplying Whole Numbers by Decimals (D)	**2** minutes	🖥️
TRY IT	Review Multiplying Whole Numbers by Decimals	**18** minutes	🖥️
QUIZ	Multiplying Whole Numbers by Decimals	**25** minutes	🖥️
WRAP-UP	More Math Practice	**15** minutes	🖥️

Lesson Goals

- Review multiplying whole numbers by decimals using models, using the algorithm, and solving real-world problems.

- Take a quiz.

MATERIALS

There are no materials to gather for this lesson.

GET READY

Introduction to Multiplying Whole Numbers by Decimals (D)

Students will read the lesson goals.

TRY IT

Review Multiplying Whole Numbers by Decimals

Students will answer questions to review what they have learned about multiplying whole numbers by decimals.

QUIZ

Multiplying Whole Numbers by Decimals

Students will complete the Multiplying Whole Numbers by Decimals quiz.

More Math Practice

Students will practice skills according to their individual needs.

Multiplying Decimals by Powers of 10 (A)

Lesson Overview

ACTIVITY	ACTIVITY TITLE	TIME	ONLINE/OFFLINE
GET READY	Introduction to Multiplying Decimals by Powers of 10 (A)	**2** minutes	🖥️
	Look Back at Representing Powers of 10 Using Exponents	**8** minutes	🖥️
LEARN AND **TRY IT**	Explaining How to Multiply a Decimal by Powers of 10	**15** minutes	🖥️
	Explain How to Multiply a Decimal by Powers of 10	**10** minutes	🖥️
	Practice Explaining How to Multiply a Decimal by Powers of 10	**20** minutes	🖥️ and 📄
WRAP-UP	Explaining How to Multiply a Decimal by Powers of 10	**5** minutes	🖥️

Content Background

In this lesson, students will explain how to multiply a decimal by a power of 10. They may already understand to multiply a whole number by a power of 10, the number of zeros in the power of 10 is added to the whole number. Because a whole number has an *understood* decimal point at the end, adding zeros to a whole number is the same as moving the decimal point to the right. The pattern for multiplying decimals by a power of 10 is the same. When multiplying a decimal by a power of 10, the number of zeros in the power of 10 is the number of places the decimal point moves to the right.

The focus of this lesson is to explain how to multiply rather than to actually multiply. Powers of 10 are given as whole numbers, such as 100 or 10,000, and using exponents, like 10^3.

Lesson Goals

- Describe how to multiply a decimal by a power of 10.

MATERIALS

Supplied
- *Summit Math 5 Activity Book:* Practice Explaining How to Multiply a Decimal by Powers of 10

KEYWORDS

power of 10 – a number that can be written as a power with a base of 10

GET READY

Introduction to Multiplying Decimals by Powers of 10
Students will get a glimpse of what they will learn about in the lesson. They will also read the lesson goals and keywords. Have students select each keyword and preview its definition.

Look Back at Representing Powers of 10 Using Exponents

Students will practice representing powers of 10 using exponents.

LEARN AND TRY IT

LEARN Explaining How to Multiply a Decimal by Powers of 10

Students will learn how to explain the process for multiplying a decimal by a power of 10.

TRY IT Explain How to Multiply a Decimal by Powers of 10

Students will practice explaining how to multiply a decimal by a power of 10. Support will be provided to help students overcome misconceptions.

TRY IT Practice Explaining How to Multiply a Decimal by Powers of 10

Students will complete online practice problems. Then they will complete Practice Explaining How to Multiply a Decimal by Powers of 10 from *Summit Math 5 Activity Book*.

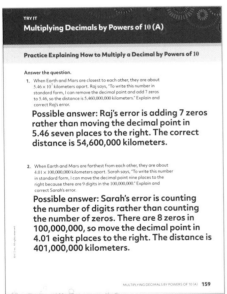

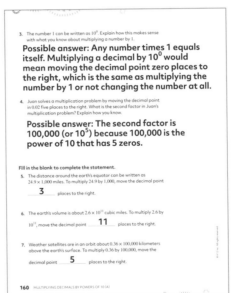

WRAP-UP

Explaining How to Multiply a Decimal by Powers of 10

Students will solve problems to show that they understand how to explain how to multiply a decimal by a power of 10.

Multiplying Decimals by Powers of 10 (B)

Lesson Overview

ACTIVITY	ACTIVITY TITLE	TIME	ONLINE/OFFLINE
GET READY	Introduction to Multiplying Decimals by Powers of 10 (B)	**2** minutes	🖥️
	Multiplying and Dividing by 90 Math Facts	**8** minutes	🖥️
LEARN AND **TRY IT**	Multiplying Decimals by Powers of 10	**15** minutes	🖥️
	Multiply Decimals by Powers of 10	**10** minutes	🖥️
	Practice Multiplying Decimals by Powers of 10	**20** minutes	🖥️ and 📄
WRAP-UP	Multiplying Decimals by Powers of 10	**5** minutes	🖥️

Content Background

In this lesson, students will multiply a decimal by a power of 10. The shortcut to multiply a decimal by a power of 10 is to determine the number of zeros in the power of 10, and then move the decimal point that many places to the right, adding commas as needed.

The focus of this lesson is to actually multiply rather than to explain how to multiply. Powers of 10 are given as whole numbers, such as 100 or 10,000, and using exponents, like 10^3.

MATERIALS

Supplied
- *Summit Math 5 Activity Book:* Practice Multiplying Decimals by Powers of 10

Lesson Goals

- Multiply a decimal by a power of 10.

GET READY

Introduction to Multiplying Decimals by Powers of 10 (B)

Students will get a glimpse of what they will learn about in the lesson. They will also read the lesson goals.

Multiplying and Dividing by 90 Math Facts

Students will practice multiplying and dividing by 90.

LEARN   Multiplying Decimals by Powers of 10

Students will learn how to multiply a decimal by a power of 10.

TRY IT   Multiply Decimals by Powers of 10

Students will practice multiplying decimals by powers of 10. Support will be provided to help students overcome misconceptions.

TRY IT   Practice Multiplying Decimals by Powers of 10

Students will complete online practice problems. Then they will complete Practice Multiplying Decimals by Powers of 10 from *Summit Math 5 Activity Book*.

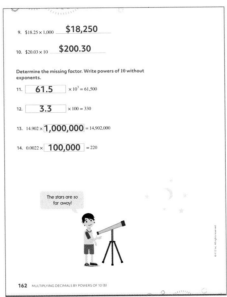

Multiplying Decimals by Powers of 10

Students will solve a problem to show that they understand how to multiply a decimal by a power of 10.

Multiplying Decimals by Powers of 10 (C)

Lesson Overview

ACTIVITY	ACTIVITY TITLE	TIME	ONLINE/OFFLINE
GET READY	Introduction to Multiplying Decimals by Powers of 10 (C)	**2** minutes	🖥
TRY IT	Review Multiplying Decimals by Powers of 10	**18** minutes	🖥
QUIZ	Multiplying Decimals by Powers of 10	**25** minutes	🖥
WRAP-UP	More Math Practice	**15** minutes	🖥

Lesson Goals

- Review describing how to multiply a decimal by a power of 10 and multiplying a decimal by a power of 10.

- Take a quiz.

GET READY

Introduction to Multiplying Decimals by Powers of 10 (C)

Students will read the lesson goals.

TRY IT

Review Multiplying Decimals by Powers of 10

Students will answer questions to review what they have learned about multiplying decimals by powers of 10.

QUIZ

Multiplying Decimals by Powers of 10

Students will complete the Multiplying Decimals by Powers of 10 quiz.

More Math Practice

Students will practice skills according to their individual needs.

Multiplying Two Decimals (A)

Lesson Overview

ACTIVITY	ACTIVITY TITLE	TIME	ONLINE/OFFLINE
GET READY	Introduction to Multiplying Two Decimals (A)	**2** minutes	📶
	Look Back at Multiplying a Whole by a Decimal to the Tenths	**8** minutes	📶
LEARN AND TRY IT	Using Models to Multiply Decimals to Tenths	**7** minutes	📶
	Use Models to Multiply Decimals to Tenths	**7** minutes	📶
	Using the Algorithm to Multiply Decimals to Tenths	**7** minutes	📶
	Use the Algorithm to Multiply Decimals to Tenths	**7** minutes	📶
	Practice Multiplying Decimals to Tenths	**20** minutes	📶 and 📄
WRAP-UP	Multiplying Decimals to Tenths	**2** minutes	📶

Content Background

In this lesson, students will multiply decimals to the tenths place using models and the algorithm. They will begin by modeling products using 10×10 grids. Each row and column of the 10×10 grid represents one-tenth. Each square of the 10×10 grid represents one-hundredth, so the product of two decimals to the tenths place is a decimal to the hundredths place.

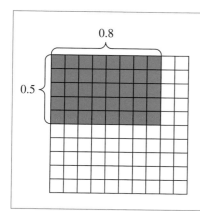

This model represents the product of 0.8 and 0.5. There are 40 shaded squares. Therefore, the product is 40 hundredths, which is written as 0.40 or 0.4.

Students will then learn how to multiply using the algorithm. To multiply two decimals, first multiply as you would multiply two whole numbers. Then count the number of digits after the decimal point in *both* factors. Finally, place the decimal point in the product so that it has that number of digits to the right of the decimal point.

> ### MATERIALS
>
> **Supplied**
> - *Summit Math 5 Activity Book:* Practice Multiplying Decimals to Tenths

$$\begin{array}{r} \overset{4}{0.8} \\ \times\ 0.5 \\ \hline 0.40 \end{array}$$

Consider the product of 0.8 and 0.5 again. Multiply 8 and 5 as whole numbers: $8 \times 5 = 40$. Each factor has one digit to the right of the decimal point, so the product will have two digits to the right of the decimal point. Expressing the answer as .40 is acceptable, but mathematicians usually write the leading zero and often leave off the final zero. Therefore, $0.8 \times 0.5 = 0.40$ or 0.4.

Lesson Goals

- Use models to multiply decimals to the tenths place.
- Use the algorithm to multiply decimals to the tenths place.

GET READY

Introduction to Multiplying Two Decimals (A)

Students will get a glimpse of what they will learn about in the lesson. They will also read the lesson goals.

Look Back at Multiplying a Whole by a Decimal to the Tenths

Students will practice multiplying a whole number by a decimal to the tenths place.

LEARN AND TRY IT

LEARN   Using Models to Multiply Decimals to Tenths

Students will learn how to use grids to model the product of two decimals to the tenths place.

TRY IT   Use Models to Multiply Decimals to Tenths

Students will practice using models to find the product of two decimal numbers to the tenths place. Support will be provided to help students overcome misconceptions.

LEARN   Using the Algorithm to Multiply Decimals to Tenths

Students will learn how to multiply two decimal numbers to the tenths place using the algorithm.

TIP   Remind students that they can use estimation to check that their answers are reasonable. For example, 32.8×5.7 is 18696 before placing the decimal point. Students may not know whether the answer is 1.8696, 18.696, or 186.96. To estimate, round 32.8 to 30 and 5.7 to 6. The product $30 \times 6 = 180$ confirms that 186.96 is the reasonable answer.

TRY IT   Use the Algorithm to Multiply Decimals to Tenths

Students will practice using the algorithm to find the product of two decimal numbers to the tenths place. Support will be provided to help students overcome misconceptions.

TRY IT   Practice Multiplying Decimals to Tenths

Students will complete online practice problems. Then they will complete Practice Multiplying Decimals to Tenths from *Summit Math 5 Activity Book*.

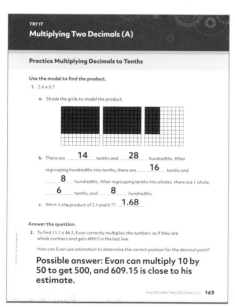
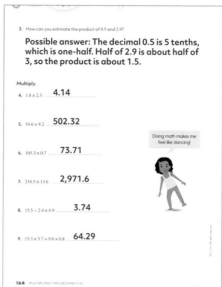

Multiplying Decimals to Tenths

Students will solve a problem to show that they understand how to multiply two decimal numbers to the tenths place.

Multiplying Two Decimals (B)

Lesson Overview

ACTIVITY	ACTIVITY TITLE	TIME	ONLINE/OFFLINE
GET READY	Introduction to Multiplying Two Decimals (B)	**2** minutes	🖥️
	Multiplying and Dividing by 90 with Instant Recall	**8** minutes	🖥️
LEARN AND **TRY IT**	Modeling Products of Decimals to Tenths and Hundredths	**7** minutes	🖥️
	Model Products of Decimals to Tenths and Hundredths	**7** minutes	🖥️
	Multiplying Decimals to Tenths and Hundredths	**7** minutes	🖥️
	Multiply Decimals to Tenths and Hundredths	**7** minutes	🖥️
	Practice Multiplying Decimals to Tenths and Hundredths	**20** minutes	🖥️ and 📄
WRAP-UP	Multiplying Decimals to Tenths and Hundredths	**2** minutes	🖥️

Content Background

In this lesson, students will multiply two decimal numbers using models and the algorithm. Each problem will be the product of one decimal number to the tenths place and one decimal number to the hundredths place.

Students can use a 10×10 grid to model the product of two decimal numbers. Each square in a 10×10 grid represents one-hundredth. Each hundredth can be divided into 10 equal parts, each of which represents one-thousandth. So, each hundredth square is equal to ten-thousandth.

Students will also apply the algorithm for decimal multiplication to products of decimals with tenths and hundredths. The process is the same as multiplying two decimals to the tenths place. First, multiply as you would multiply two whole numbers. Then, count the number of digits after the decimal point in *both* factors. The decimal number to the tenths place has one digit to the right of the decimal point, and the decimal number to the hundredths place has two digits to the right of the decimal point. Therefore, the product should have three digits to the right of the decimal point. The only exception will be when the product ends in one or more zeros. For example, the product 0.300 could also be written as 0.30 or 0.3.

Using the model or the algorithm, the rule of thumb is that the product of a decimal number to the tenths place and a decimal number to the hundredths place is a decimal number to the thousandths place.

MATERIALS

Supplied

- *Summit Math 5 Activity Book:* Practice Multiplying Decimals to Tenths and Hundredths

Lesson Goals

- Multiply decimals to tenths and hundredths using models.
- Multiply decimals to tenths and hundredths using the algorithm.

GET READY

Introduction to Multiplying Two Decimals (B)

Students will get a glimpse of what they will learn about in the lesson. They will also read the lesson goals.

Multiplying and Dividing by 90 with Instant Recall

Students will practice multiplying and dividing by 90.

LEARN AND TRY IT

LEARN Modeling Products of Decimals to Tenths and Hundredths

Students will learn how to use grids to model the product of a decimal number to the tenths place and a decimal number to the hundredths place.

SUPPORT   Sometimes, students struggle to remember the names of each place value to the right of the decimal point. The first digit to the right of a decimal point is in the tenths place, such as 0.5 or 5 tenths. The second digit to the right of a decimal point is in the hundredths place, such as 0.05 or 5 hundredths. The third digit to the right of a decimal point is in the thousandths place, such as 0.005 or 5 thousandths.

TRY IT Model Products of Decimals to Tenths and Hundredths

Students will practice using models to find the product of decimal numbers to the tenths and hundredths places. Support will be provided to help students overcome misconceptions.

LEARN Multiplying Decimals to Tenths and Hundredths

Students will learn how to multiply decimal numbers to the tenths and hundredths places using the algorithm.

TRY IT Multiplying Decimals to Tenths and Hundredths

Students will practice using the algorithm to find the product of decimal numbers to the tenths and hundredths places. Support will be provided to help students overcome misconceptions.

TRY IT Practice Multiplying Decimals to Tenths and Hundredths

Students will complete online practice problems. Then they will complete Practice Multiplying Decimals to Tenths and Hundredths from *Summit Math 5 Activity Book*.

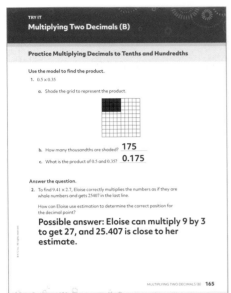

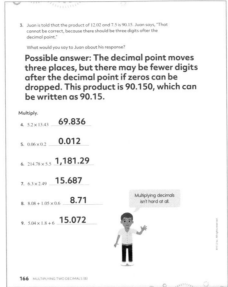

Multiplying Decimals to Tenths and Hundredths

Students will solve a problem to show that they understand how to multiply decimal numbers to the tenths and hundred places.

Multiplying Two Decimals (C)

Lesson Overview

ACTIVITY	ACTIVITY TITLE	TIME	ONLINE/OFFLINE
GET READY	Introduction to Multiplying Two Decimals (C)	**2** minutes	🖥️
	Multiplying and Dividing by 90 Math Facts Game	**8** minutes	📶
LEARN AND **TRY IT**	Using Models to Multiply Decimals to Hundredths	**7** minutes	🖥️
	Use Models to Multiply Decimals to Hundredths	**7** minutes	📶
	Using the Algorithm to Multiply Decimals to Hundredths	**7** minutes	🖥️
	Use the Algorithm to Multiply Decimals to Hundredths	**7** minutes	📶
	Practice Multiplying Decimals to Hundredths	**20** minutes	📶 and 📄
WRAP-UP	Multiplying Decimals to Hundredths	**2** minutes	📶

Content Background

In this lesson, students will multiply two decimal numbers to the hundredths place using models and the algorithm. A 100×100 grid can be used to model the product of two decimal numbers to the hundredths place. Each square in a 100×100 grid represents one ten-thousandth. It is likely the first time students will encounter the ten-thousandths place. The ten-thousandths place is immediately to the right of the thousandths place.

Consider the decimal number 0.3148 shown in a place value chart. This number is read "three thousand, one hundred forty-eight ten-thousandths."

> **MATERIALS**
>
> **Supplied**
> - *Summit Math 5 Activity Book:* Practice Multiplying Decimals to Hundredths

Ones			Decimals			
hundreds	tens	ones	tenths	hundredths	thousandths	ten tousandths
		0	3	1	4	8

Students will also apply the algorithm for decimal multiplication to products of decimals to the hundredths place. The process is the same as multiplying two decimals to the tenths place. First, multiply as you would multiply two whole numbers. Then, count the number of digits after the decimal point in *both* factors. Both decimal numbers have two digits to the right of the decimal point. Therefore, the product should have four digits to the right of the decimal point. The only exception will be when the product ends in one or more zeros. For example, the product 0.7300 could also be written as 0.730 or 0.73.

Using the model or the algorithm, the rule of thumb is that the product of two decimal numbers to the hundredths place is a decimal number to the ten-thousandths place.

Lesson Goals

- Multiply decimals to hundredths using models.
- Multiply decimals to hundredths using the algorithm.

GET READY

Introduction to Multiplying Two Decimals (C)

Students will get a glimpse of what they will learn about in the lesson. They will also read the lesson goals.

Multiplying and Dividing by 90 Math Facts Game

Students will practice multiplying and dividing by 90.

LEARN AND TRY IT

LEARN   Using Models to Multiply Decimals to Hundredths

Students will learn how to use grids to model the product of two decimal numbers to the hundredths place.

TRY IT   Use Models to Multiply Decimals to Hundredths

Students will practice using models to find the product of two decimal numbers to the hundredths place. Support will be provided to help students overcome misconceptions.

LEARN   Using the Algorithm to Multiply Decimals to Hundredths

Students will learn how to multiply decimal numbers to the hundredths place using the algorithm.

OPTIONAL   An example problem in this activity involves converting a price from Euros to U.S. dollars. Students may find it interesting to check the exchange rates online for different currencies over the course of a few days to see if they change.

TRY IT   Use the Algorithm to Multiply Decimals to Hundredths

Students will practice using the algorithm to find the product of two decimal numbers to the hundredths place. Support will be provided to help students overcome misconceptions.

TRY IT Practice Multiplying Decimals to Hundredths

Students will complete online practice problems. Then they will complete Practice Multiplying Decimals to Hundredths from *Summit Math 5 Activity Book*.

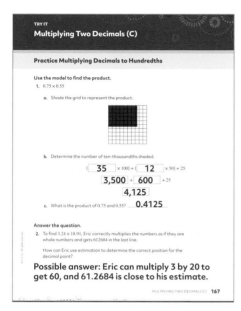

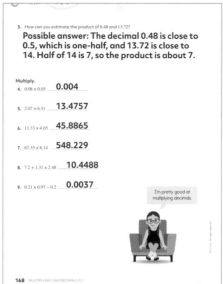

Multiplying Decimals to Hundredths

Students will solve a problem to show that they understand how to multiply two decimal numbers to the hundredths place.

Multiplying Two Decimals (D)

Lesson Overview

ACTIVITY	ACTIVITY TITLE	TIME	ONLINE/OFFLINE
GET READY	Introduction to Multiplying Two Decimals (D)	**2** minutes	📡
	Multiplying Whole Numbers by Powers of 10 Math Facts	**8** minutes	📡
LEARN AND **TRY IT**	Multiplying Decimals in the Real World	**15** minutes	📡
	Multiply Decimals in the Real World	**10** minutes	📡
	Practice Multiplying Decimals in the Real World	**20** minutes	📡 and 📄
WRAP-UP	Multiplying Decimals in the Real World	**5** minutes	📡

Content Background

In this lesson, students will apply their knowledge of decimal multiplication to solve real-world problems.

When students write and compute with decimal numbers, they often use numbers that are between 0 and 1—for example, 0.1. While it is acceptable to write this number as .1, mathematicians usually write the leading zero. Also, it is usually acceptable to drop a zero after the decimal point unless the solution is an amount of money. Dollar amounts that include cents should always be given to the hundredths place.

Lesson Goals

- Solve real-world problems by multiplying decimals.

GET READY

Introduction to Multiplying Two Decimals (D)
Students will get a glimpse of what they will learn about in the lesson. They will also read the lesson goals.

Multiplying Whole Numbers by Powers of 10 Math Facts
Students will practice multiplying whole numbers by powers of 10.

LEARN   Multiplying Decimals in the Real World

Students will learn how to solve real-world problems by multiplying decimal numbers.

NOTE   Students are not instructed to use a specific method when solving. Encourage students to use the standard algorithm to multiply. However, if an answer doesn't make sense, students can check their answer by rounding or using a model.

TRY IT   Multiply Decimals in the Real World

Students will practice multiplying decimals to solve real-world problems. Support will be provided to help students overcome misconceptions.

TRY IT   Practice Multiplying Decimals in the Real World

Students will complete online practice problems. Then they will complete Practice Multiplying Decimals in the Real World from *Summit Math 5 Activity Book.*

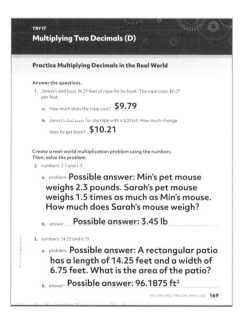

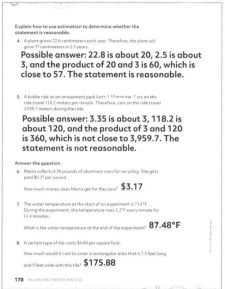

Multiplying Decimals in the Real World

Students will solve a problem to show that they understand how to multiply decimals to solve real-world problems.

Multiplying Two Decimals (E)

Lesson Overview

ACTIVITY	ACTIVITY TITLE	TIME	ONLINE/OFFLINE
GET READY	Introduction to Multiplying Two Decimals (E)	**2** minutes	
TRY IT	Review Multiplying Two Decimals	**18** minutes	
QUIZ	Multiplying Two Decimals	**25** minutes	
WRAP-UP	More Math Practice	**15** minutes	

Lesson Goals

- Review multiplying two decimals using models and the algorithm.

- Take a quiz.

MATERIALS

There are no materials to gather for this lesson.

GET READY

Introduction to Multiplying Two Decimals (E)

Students will read the lesson goals.

TRY IT

Review Multiplying Two Decimals

Students will answer questions to review what they have learned about multiplying two decimals.

QUIZ

Multiplying Two Decimals

Students will complete the Multiplying Two Decimals quiz.

More Math Practice

Students will practice skills according to their individual needs.

Big Ideas: Challenge Problems

Lesson Overview

Big Ideas lessons provide students the opportunity to apply the knowledge and skills acquired throughout previous units. Each Big Ideas lesson consists of three parts:

1. **Cumulative Review:** Students keep their skills fresh by reviewing prior content.

2. **Preview:** Students practice answering the types of questions they will commonly find on standardized tests.

3. **Synthesis:** Students complete an assignment that allows them to interweave and apply what they've learned. These synthesis assignments will vary throughout the course.

   In the Synthesis portion of this Big Ideas lesson, students will complete one or more challenge problems that will guide them to discover new concepts. Through hard work and perseverance, students will learn that they can use the math they already know combined with logical thinking to solve problems about new concepts. Students will need to use pencil and paper and/or technology to show their work.

   LEARNING COACH CHECK-IN   Make sure students complete, review, and submit the assignment to their teacher

All materials needed for this lesson are linked online. The materials are not provided in this Lesson Guide or in the Activity Book.

Division
with Decimals

Dividing Whole Numbers and Decimals (A)

Lesson Overview

ACTIVITY	ACTIVITY TITLE	TIME	ONLINE/OFFLINE
GET READY	Introduction to Dividing Whole Numbers and Decimals (A)	**2** minutes	🖥️
	Division with Decimals in 60 Seconds	**3** minutes	🖥️
	Look Back at Dividing 2 Digits by 1 Digit	**5** minutes	🖥️
LEARN AND **TRY IT**	Dividing Wholes by Decimals with Models	**7** minutes	🖥️
	Divide Wholes by Decimals with Models	**7** minutes	🖥️
	Dividing Wholes by Decimals with the Algorithm	**7** minutes	🖥️
	Divide Wholes by Decimals with the Algorithm	**7** minutes	🖥️
	Practice Dividing Wholes by Decimals	**20** minutes	🖥️ and 📄
WRAP-UP	Dividing Wholes by Decimals	**2** minutes	🖥️

Content Background

Decimal numbers and whole numbers can be dividends or divisors when students are finding quotients. In this lesson, students will divide whole numbers by decimal numbers. First, students will use number lines and base-10 blocks to model division problems. Then they will use the standard algorithm to solve problems dividing whole numbers by decimal numbers. Here are the steps of the standard division algorithm for dividing by a decimal number:

1. Use the long division symbol to write the problem.

2. Move the decimal point in both the dividend and divisor the same number of places to the right so that the divisor is a whole number. Add zeros to the end of the dividend as needed.

3. Divide as usual.

MATERIALS

Supplied
- *Summit Math 5 Activity Book:* Practice Dividing Wholes by Decimals

KEYWORDS

dividend – the number to be divided; the dividend divided by the divisor equals the quotient

divisor – the number that divides the dividend; the dividend divided by the divisor equals the quotient

quotient – the answer to a division problem; the dividend divided by the divisor equals the quotient

This example shows how to apply the algorithm to divide 5 by 0.2:

Use the long division symbol to write the problem $5 \div 0.2$.

$0.2\overline{)5.0}$

Move the decimal one place to the right to change 0.2 to 2. Move the decimal one place to the right in the dividend and add a zero to change 5 to 50.

$$
\begin{array}{r}
25 \\
2\overline{)50} \\
-40 \\
\hline
10 \\
-10 \\
\hline
0
\end{array}
$$

Divide as usual: $5 \div 0.2 = 25$.

Students will also solve real-world problems involving the division of a whole number by a decimal number.

Lesson Goals

- Divide a whole number by a decimal using a model.
- Divide a whole number by a decimal using the algorithm.

GET READY

Introduction to Dividing Whole Numbers and Decimals (A)

Students will get a glimpse of what they will learn about in the lesson. They will also read the lesson goals and keywords. Have students select each keyword and preview its definition.

Division with Decimals in 60 Seconds

Students will watch a short video designed to spark their interest in upcoming topics.

Look Back at Dividing 2 Digits by 1 Digit

Students will practice the prerequisite skill of dividing a two-digit number by a one-digit number.

LEARN   Dividing Wholes by Decimals with Models

Students will learn how to use number lines and base-10 blocks to divide a whole number by a decimal number.

> **TIP**   Remind students that they can use multiplication to check their answers.

TRY IT   Divide Wholes by Decimals with Models

Students will practice dividing whole numbers by decimal numbers using models. Support will be provided to help students overcome misconceptions.

LEARN   Dividing Wholes by Decimals with the Algorithm

Students will learn how to use the standard division algorithm to divide a whole number by a decimal number.

> **TIP**   Remind students that they can use a model to represent the problem when they get an answer that doesn't make sense.

TRY IT   Divide Wholes by Decimals with the Algorithm

Students will practice dividing whole numbers by decimal numbers using the algorithm. Support will be provided to help students overcome misconceptions.

TRY IT   Practice Dividing Wholes by Decimals

Students will complete online practice problems. Then they will complete Practice Dividing Wholes by Decimals from *Summit Math 5 Activity Book*.

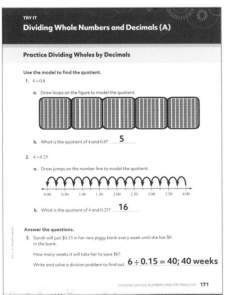

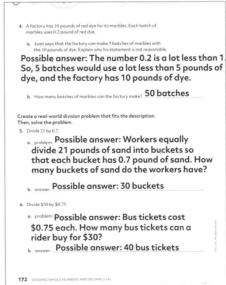

Dividing Wholes by Decimals

Students will solve a problem to show that they understand how to apply the standard algorithm for dividing a whole number by a decimal number to solve a real-world problem.

Dividing Whole Numbers and Decimals (B)

Lesson Overview

ACTIVITY	ACTIVITY TITLE	TIME	ONLINE/OFFLINE
GET READY	Introduction to Dividing Whole Numbers and Decimals (B)	**2** minutes	🖥️
	Multiplying Whole Numbers by Powers of 10 with Instant Recall	**8** minutes	🖥️
LEARN AND **TRY IT**	Dividing Decimals by Wholes with Models	**7** minutes	🖥️
	Divide Decimals by Wholes with Models	**7** minutes	🖥️
	Dividing Decimals by Wholes with the Algorithm	**7** minutes	🖥️
	Divide Decimals by Wholes with the Algorithm	**7** minutes	🖥️
	Practice Dividing Decimals by Wholes	**20** minutes	🖥️ and 📄
WRAP-UP	Dividing Decimals by Wholes	**2** minutes	🖥️

Content Background

In this lesson, students will divide decimal numbers by whole numbers. First, they will use number lines and base-10 blocks to model division problems. Then they will use the standard division algorithm.

When students learned how to divide multidigit numbers, they were taught to use place value.

$$\begin{array}{r} 1 \\ 4\overline{)640} \\ -400 \\ \hline \end{array}$$

For example, in the first step of dividing 640 by 4, the first digit of the quotient is 1. Since 1 is in the hundreds place, it actually represents 100. You may have learned to multiply 4 by 1, subtract 4 from 6, and carry down the remaining digits. In this course, students are taught to multiply 4 by *100*. When students use this method to divide, it reinforces their understanding of place value. It also helps avoid errors and misunderstandings when carrying down digits from the dividend.

Students will continue to use place value when dividing a decimal by a whole number. Here are the steps of the standard division algorithm for dividing a decimal number by a whole number:

1. Use the long division symbol to write the problem.

2. Place the decimal point in the quotient directly above the decimal point in the dividend.

3. Divide as usual taking place value into account.

This example shows how to apply the algorithm to divide 6.25 by 5:

$$
\begin{array}{r}
1.25 \\
5\overline{)6.25} \\
-5.00 \\
\hline
1.25 \\
-1.00 \\
\hline
0.25 \\
-0.25 \\
\hline
0
\end{array}
$$

Use the long division symbol to write the problem $6.25 \div 5$.

Place the decimal point in the quotient directly above the decimal point in 6.25.

Divide as usual.

The first digit of the quotient is 1 because 5 divides into 6 one time. Then, $1 \times 5 = 5.00$. Subtract 5.00 from 6.25 to get 1.25.

The second digit of the quotient is 2. How many times does 5 divide into 12? Since 2 is in the tenths place, it represents 0.2. The product of 5 and 0.2 is 1.00. Subtract 1.00 from 1.25 to get 0.25.

The last digit of the quotient is 5 because 5 divides into 25 exactly 5 times. Since 5 is in the hundredths place, it represents 0.05. The product of 5 and 0.05 is 0.25. Subtract 0.25 from 0.25 to get 0.

Therefore, $6.25 \div 5 = 1.25$.

Students will also solve real-world problems involving the division of a decimal number by a whole number.

Lesson Goals

- Divide a decimal by a whole number using a model.

- Divide a decimal by a whole number using the algorithm.

GET READY

Introduction to Dividing Whole Numbers and Decimals (B)

Students will get a glimpse of what they will learn about in the lesson. They will also read the lesson goals.

Multiplying Whole Numbers by Powers of 10 with Instant Recall

Students will practice multiplying whole numbers by powers of 10.

LEARN AND TRY IT

LEARN Dividing Decimals by Wholes with Models

Students will learn how to use number lines and base-10 blocks to divide a decimal number by a whole number.

TIP   Remind students that they can use multiplication to check their answers.

TRY IT Divide Decimals by Wholes with Models

Students will practice dividing decimal numbers by whole numbers using models. Support will be provided to help students overcome misconceptions.

LEARN Dividing Decimals by Wholes with the Algorithm

Students will learn how to use the standard division algorithm to divide a decimal number by a whole number.

TIP   Remind students that they can use a model to represent the problem when they get an answer that doesn't make sense.

TRY IT Divide Decimals by Wholes with the Algorithm

Students will practice dividing a decimal number by a whole number using the algorithm. Support will be provided to help students overcome misconceptions.

TRY IT Practice Dividing Decimals by Wholes

Students will complete online practice problems. Then they will complete Practice Dividing Decimals by Wholes from *Summit Math 5 Activity Book*.

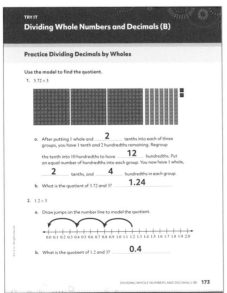

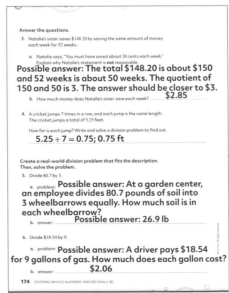

Dividing Decimals by Wholes

Students will solve a problem to show that they understand how to apply the standard algorithm for dividing a decimal number by a whole number to solve a real-world problem.

Dividing Whole Numbers and Decimals (C)

Lesson Overview

ACTIVITY	ACTIVITY TITLE	TIME	ONLINE/OFFLINE
GET READY	Introduction to Dividing Whole Numbers and Decimals (C)	**2** minutes	🖥️
	Multiplying Whole Numbers by Powers of 10 Math Facts Game	**8** minutes	🖥️
LEARN AND **TRY IT**	Dividing a Whole by a Greater Whole with Models	**7** minutes	🖥️
	Divide a Whole by a Greater Whole with Models	**7** minutes	🖥️
	Dividing a Whole by a Greater Whole with the Algorithm	**7** minutes	🖥️
	Divide a Whole by a Greater Whole with the Algorithm	**7** minutes	🖥️
	Practice Dividing a Whole by a Greater Whole	**20** minutes	🖥️ and 📄
WRAP-UP	Dividing a Whole by a Greater Whole	**2** minutes	🖥️

Content Background

In this lesson, students will learn how to divide a whole number by a greater whole number. When a whole number is divided by another whole number that is greater, the quotient is a decimal—for example, $5 \div 10 = 0.5$.

First, students will use number lines and base-10 blocks to model division problems. Then they will use the standard division algorithm. Here are the steps of the standard division algorithm for dividing a whole number by a greater whole number:

1. Use the long division symbol to write the problem. The greater number should be to the left of the division house.

2. The divisor will not divide into the dividend as it is written. Write a zero above the last digit of the dividend. Add a decimal point and a zero to the end of the dividend.

3. Place the decimal point in the quotient directly above the decimal point in the dividend.

4. Divide as usual using additional zeros as needed in the dividend.

This example shows how to apply the algorithm to divide 26 by 50:

Use the long division symbol to write the problem $26 \div 50$.

Since 50 doesn't divide into 26, write a 0 above the 6 in the dividend. Place a decimal point after the digit 6 and a 0 after the decimal point.

Place a decimal point after the 0 in the quotient and directly above the decimal point is 26.0.

$$\begin{array}{r} 0.52 \\ 50\overline{)26.00} \\ -25.0 \\ \hline 1.00 \\ -1.00 \\ \hline 0 \end{array}$$

Divide as usual.

The second digit of the quotient is 5. To get this digit, think about how many times 50 divides into 260. The digit 5 is in the tenths place, so it represents 0.5. The product of 50 and 0.5 is 25.0. Subtract 25.0 from 26.0 to get 1.0.

Since 50 does not divide into 10, add another zero to the dividend and 1.0.

The last digit of the quotient is 2 because 50 divides into 100 exactly two times. Since 2 is in the hundredths place, it represents 0.02. The product of 50 and 0.02 is 1.00. Subtract 1.00 from 1.00 to get 0.

Therefore, $26 \div 50 = 0.52$.

Students will also solve real-world problems involving the division of a whole number by a greater whole number.

Lesson Goals

- Divide a whole number by a greater whole number using a model.
- Divide a whole number by a greater whole number using the algorithm.

Introduction to Dividing Whole Numbers and Decimals (C)

Students will get a glimpse of what they will learn about in the lesson. They will also read the lesson goals.

Multiplying Whole Numbers by Powers of 10 Math Facts Game

Students will practice multiplying whole numbers by powers of 10.

LEARN   Dividing a Whole by a Greater Whole with Models

Students will learn how to use number lines and base-10 blocks to divide a whole number by a greater whole number.

NOTE   The answer to each problem should always be a decimal number between 0 and 1. For example, the number 0.81 could be a reasonable quotient. While it is acceptable to write this number as .81, mathematicians usually write the leading zero, to show that the whole number value for the decimal number is 0 and to avoid confusion about the value of the number.

TRY IT   Divide a Whole by a Greater Whole with Models

Students will practice using models to divide a whole number by a greater whole number. Support will be provided to help students overcome misconceptions.

LEARN   Dividing a Whole by a Greater Whole with the Algorithm

Students will learn how to use the standard division algorithm to divide a whole number by a greater whole number.

TRY IT   Divide a Whole by a Greater Whole with the Algorithm

Students will practice dividing a whole number by a greater whole number using the standard algorithm. Support will be provided to help students overcome misconceptions.

TRY IT   Practice Dividing a Whole by a Greater Whole

Students will complete online practice problems. Then they will complete Practice Dividing a Whole by a Greater Whole from *Summit Math 5 Activity Book*.

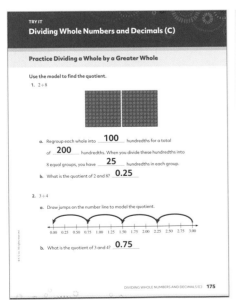

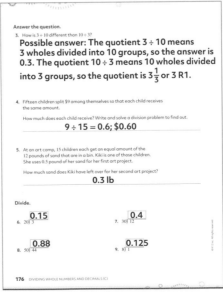

Dividing a Whole by a Greater Whole

Students will solve a problem to show that they understand how to apply the standard algorithm for dividing a whole number by a greater whole number to solve a real-world problem.

Dividing Whole Numbers and Decimals (D)

Lesson Overview

ACTIVITY	ACTIVITY TITLE	TIME	ONLINE/OFFLINE
GET READY	Introduction to Dividing Whole Numbers and Decimals (D)	**2** minutes	
TRY IT	Review Dividing Whole Numbers and Decimals	**18** minutes	
QUIZ	Dividing Whole Numbers and Decimals	**25** minutes	
WRAP-UP	More Math Practice	**15** minutes	

Lesson Goals

- Review dividing whole numbers and decimals.
- Take a quiz.

MATERIALS

There are no materials to gather for this lesson.

GET READY

Introduction to Dividing Whole Numbers and Decimals (D)

Students will read the lesson goals.

TRY IT

Review Dividing Whole Numbers and Decimals

Students will answer questions to review what they have learned about dividing whole numbers and decimals.

QUIZ

Dividing Whole Numbers and Decimals

Students will complete the Dividing Whole Numbers and Decimals quiz.

More Math Practice

Students will practice skills according to their individual needs.

Dividing Decimals by Powers of 10 (A)

Lesson Overview

ACTIVITY	ACTIVITY TITLE	TIME	ONLINE/OFFLINE
GET READY	Introduction to Dividing Decimals by Powers of 10 (A)	**2** minutes	📶
	Look Back at Representing Powers of 10	**8** minutes	📶
LEARN AND **TRY IT**	Explaining How to Divide a Decimal by Powers of 10	**15** minutes	📶
	Explain How to Divide a Decimal by Powers of 10	**10** minutes	📶
	Practice Explaining How to Divide a Decimal by Powers of 10	**20** minutes	📶 and 📄
WRAP-UP	Explaining How to Divide a Decimal by Powers of 10	**5** minutes	📶

Content Background

In this lesson, students will explain how to divide decimals by powers of 10. They may already understand division by powers of 10 with whole numbers. The pattern for decimals is the same as the pattern for whole numbers. When dividing a decimal by a power of 10, the number of zeros in the power of 10 is the number of places the decimal point moves to the left. The focus of this lesson is to explain how to divide rather than actually divide. Powers of 10 are given as whole numbers, such as 100 or 10,000, and using exponents, such as 10^3.

Lesson Goals

- Describe how to divide a decimal by a power of 10.

MATERIALS

Supplied
- *Summit Math 5 Activity Book:* Practice Explaining How to Divide a Decimal by Powers of 10

GET READY

Introduction to Dividing Decimals by Powers of 10 (A)

Students will get a glimpse of what they will learn about in the lesson. They will also read the lesson goals.

Look Back at Representing Powers of 10

Students will practice the prerequisite skill of representing powers of 10.

LEARN   Explaining How to Divide a Decimal by Powers of 10

Students will learn how to explain the process for dividing a decimal by a power of 10.

OPTIONAL   Once students learn the pattern for dividing by powers of 10, it is helpful to compare it to the pattern for multiplying by powers of 10. Help students understand that multiplying by a power of 10 moves the decimal point to the right and dividing by a power of 10 moves the decimal point to the left. Have students think about why this is true. Ask them how they can remember to move the decimal point to the right when multiplying and to the left when dividing.

TRY IT   Explain How to Divide a Decimal by Powers of 10

Students will practice explaining how to divide a decimal by a power of 10. Support will be provided to help students overcome misconceptions.

TRY IT   Practice Explaining How to Divide a Decimal by Powers of 10

Students will complete online practice problems. Then they will complete Practice Explaining How to Divide a Decimal by Powers of 10 from *Summit Math 5 Activity Book*.

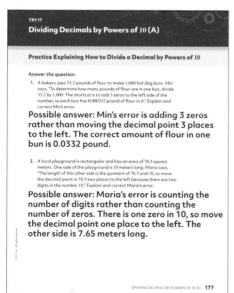

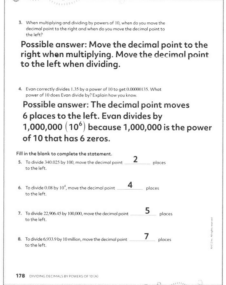

Explaining How to Divide a Decimal by Powers of 10

Students will solve a problem to show that they understand how to explain how to divide a decimal by a power of 10.

Dividing Decimals by Powers of 10 (B)

Lesson Overview

ACTIVITY	ACTIVITY TITLE	TIME	ONLINE/OFFLINE
GET READY	Introduction to Dividing Decimals by Powers of 10 (B)	**2** minutes	🖥️
	Multiplying Decimal Numbers by Powers of 10 Math Facts	**8** minutes	🖥️
LEARN AND **TRY IT**	Dividing Decimals by Powers of 10	**15** minutes	🖥️
	Divide Decimals by Powers of 10	**10** minutes	🖥️
	Practice Dividing Decimals by Powers of 10	**20** minutes	🖥️ and 📄
WRAP-UP	Dividing Decimals by Powers of 10	**5** minutes	🖥️

Content Background

In this lesson, students will divide a decimal by a power of 10. The focus of this lesson is to actually divide rather than explain how to divide. Powers of 10 will be given as whole numbers, such as 100 or 10,000, and using exponents, such as 10^3.

Lesson Goals

- Divide a decimal by a power of 10.

GET READY

Introduction to Dividing Decimals by Powers of 10 (B)

Students will get a glimpse of what they will learn about in the lesson. They will also read the lesson goals.

Multiplying Decimal Numbers by Powers of 10 Math Facts

Students will practice multiplying decimal numbers by powers of 10.

LEARN   Dividing Decimals by Powers of 10

Students will learn how to divide a decimal by a power of 10. In each problem, students will move the decimal place to the left. The number of places the decimal moves is the same as the number of zeros in the power of 10.

TRY IT   Divide Decimals by Powers of 10

Students will practice multiplying decimals by powers of 10. Support will be provided to help students overcome misconceptions.

TRY IT   Practice Dividing Decimals by Powers of 10

Students will complete online practice problems. Then they will complete Practice Dividing Decimals by Powers of 10 from *Summit Math 5 Activity Book*.

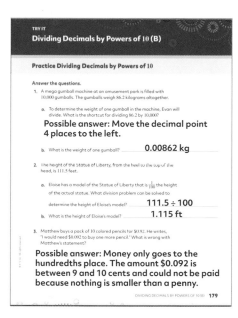

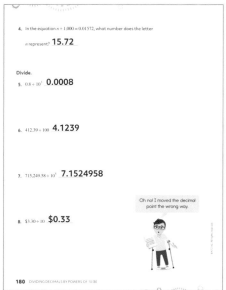

Dividing Decimals by Powers of 10

Students will solve a problem to show that they understand how to divide a decimal by a power of 10.

Dividing Decimals by Powers of 10 (C)

Lesson Overview

ACTIVITY	ACTIVITY TITLE	TIME	ONLINE/OFFLINE
GET READY	Introduction to Dividing Decimals by Powers of 10 (C)	**2** minutes	🖥️
TRY IT	Review Dividing Decimals by Powers of 10	**18** minutes	🖥️
QUIZ	Dividing Decimals by Powers of 10	**25** minutes	🖥️
WRAP-UP	More Math Practice	**15** minutes	🖥️

Lesson Goals

- Review explaining how to divide decimals by powers of 10 and dividing decimals by powers of 10.

- Take a quiz.

GET READY

Introduction to Dividing Decimals by Powers of 10 (C)

Students will read the lesson goals.

TRY IT

Review Dividing Decimals by Powers of 10

Students will answer questions to review what they have learned about dividing decimals by powers of 10.

QUIZ

Dividing Decimals by Powers of 10

Students will complete the Dividing Decimals by Powers of 10 quiz.

More Math Practice

Students will practice skills according to their individual needs.

Decimal Division (A)

Lesson Overview

ACTIVITY	ACTIVITY TITLE	TIME	ONLINE/OFFLINE
GET READY	Introduction to Decimal Division (A)	**2** minutes	🖥️
	Look Back at Dividing a Decimal by a Whole Number	**8** minutes	🖥️
LEARN AND **TRY IT**	Dividing Decimals to Tenths with Models	**7** minutes	🖥️
	Divide Decimals to Tenths with Models	**7** minutes	🖥️
	Dividing Decimals to Tenths with the Algorithm	**7** minutes	🖥️
	Divide Decimals to Tenths with the Algorithm	**7** minutes	🖥️
	Practice Dividing Decimals to Tenths	**20** minutes	🖥️ and 📄
WRAP-UP	Dividing Decimals to Tenths	**2** minutes	🖥️

Content Background

In this lesson, students will divide decimal numbers by decimal numbers. The dividend and divisor of each division problem in this lesson are decimal numbers to the tenths place. Students will also solve real-world problems involving the division of decimal numbers to the tenths place.

First, students will use base-10 blocks, number lines, and area models to solve division problems. In an area model, the dividend is the area of the rectangle, the divisor is one dimension of the rectangle (usually shown on the left side), and the quotient is the other dimension (usually shown on the top side).

For example, this area model represents $1.2 \div 0.8$. Each large square represents 1 whole, so each small square represents 1 hundredth.

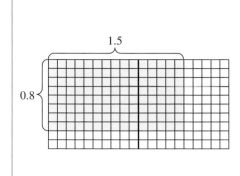

1.5

0.8

First, label the left dimension with 0.8, the divisor. Then, shade an area of 1.2 or 120 hundredths, the dividend.

When shading squares for the dividend, shade an equal number in each of the rows of the divisor. When the shading is complete, the top dimension of the shaded rectangle is the quotient: 1.5.

Therefore, $1.2 \div 0.8 = 1.5$.

Next, students will apply the steps of the standard division algorithm to divide decimal numbers to the tenths place. This example shows how to apply the algorithm to divide 1.2 by 0.8:

$0.8\overline{)1.2}$

Use the long division symbol to write the problem $1.2 \div 0.8$.

Move the decimal one place to the right to change 0.8 to 8 and 1.2 to 12.

Divide as usual.

The first digit of the quotient is 1 because 8 divides into 12 one time.

$$\begin{array}{r} 1.5 \\ 8\overline{)12.0} \\ -8 \\ \hline 4.0 \\ -4.0 \\ \hline 0 \end{array}$$

Then, $1 \times 8 = 8$. Subtract 8 from 12 to get 4.

Since 8 does not divide into 4, add a decimal point and a zero after 12 and 4. Add a decimal point after 1 in the quotient.

The last digit of the quotient is 5. To find this digit, think about how many times 8 divides into 40. The digit 5 is in the tenths place, so it represents 0.5. The product of 8 and 0.5 is 4.0. Subtract 4.0 from 4.0 to get 0.

Therefore, $1.2 \div 0.8 = 1.5$.

Notice that the result of using the algorithm and the area model to solve $1.2 \div 0.8$ is the same. Both methods give valid answers.

Lesson Goals

- Divide decimals to tenths using a model.
- Divide decimals to tenths using the algorithm.

GET READY

Introduction to Decimal Division (A)

Students will get a glimpse of what they will learn about in the lesson. They will also read the lesson goals.

Look Back at Dividing a Decimal by a Whole Number

Students will practice the prerequisite skill of dividing a decimal by a whole number.

LEARN AND TRY IT

LEARN Dividing Decimals to Tenths with Models

Students will learn how to use models to divide decimal numbers. Both decimal numbers are to the tenths place in each division problem.

> **TIP** Remind students that they can use multiplication to check their answers.

TRY IT Divide Decimals to Tenths with Models

Students will practice using models to divide decimal numbers to the tenths place. Support will be provided to help students overcome misconceptions.

LEARN Dividing Decimals to Tenths with the Algorithm

Students will learn to divide decimal numbers to the tenths place using the standard algorithm.

TRY IT Divide Decimals to Tenths with the Algorithm

Students will practice dividing decimal numbers to the tenths place using the standard algorithm. Support will be provided to help students overcome misconceptions.

TRY IT Practice Dividing Decimals to Tenths

Students will complete online practice problems. Then they will complete Practice Dividing Decimals to Tenths from *Summit Math 5 Activity Book*.

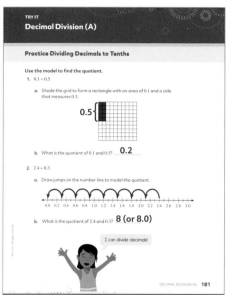

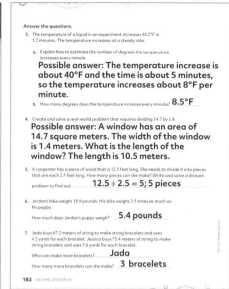

WRAP-UP

Dividing Decimals to Tenths

Students will solve a problem to show that they understand how to divide two decimal numbers to the tenths place using the standard algorithm.

Decimal Division (B)

Lesson Overview

ACTIVITY	ACTIVITY TITLE	TIME	ONLINE/OFFLINE
GET READY	Introduction to Decimal Division (B)	**2** minutes	🖥️
	Multiplying Decimal Numbers by Powers of 10 with Instant Recall	**8** minutes	🖥️
LEARN AND **TRY IT**	Dividing Hundredths by Tenths with Models	**7** minutes	🖥️
	Divide Hundredths by Tenths with Models	**7** minutes	🖥️
	Dividing Hundredths by Tenths with the Algorithm	**7** minutes	🖥️
	Divide Hundredths by Tenths with the Algorithm	**7** minutes	🖥️
	Practice Dividing Hundredths by Tenths	**20** minutes	🖥️ and 📄
WRAP-UP	Dividing Hundredths by Tenths	**2** minutes	🖥️

Content Background

In this lesson, students will divide decimal numbers to the hundredths place by decimal numbers to the tenths place. They will also solve real-world problems involving the division of decimal numbers to the tenths and hundredths places.

First, students will use area models to solve division problems. To divide using an area model, first label the left dimension with the divisor. Then, shade the number of hundredths in the dividend. When shading hundredths for the dividend, be sure to shade an equal number of squares in each of the rows of the divisor. When the shading is complete, the top dimension of the shaded rectangle is the quotient.

Next, students will apply the steps of the standard division algorithm to divide a decimal number to the hundredths place by a decimal to the tenths place. This example shows how to apply the algorithm to divide 0.45 by 0.9:

 Use the long division symbol to write the problem $0.45 \div 0.9$.

Move the decimal one place to the right to change 0.9 to 9 and 0.45 to 4.5.

Divide as usual.

$$\begin{array}{r} 0.5 \\ 9\overline{)04.5} \\ -4.5 \\ \hline 0 \end{array}$$

Place a decimal point in the quotient above the decimal point in 4.5.

The first digit of the quotient is 0 because 9 does not divide into 4.

The last digit of the quotient is 5. To find this digit, think about how many times 9 divides into 45. The digit 5 is in the tenths place, so it represents 0.5. The product of 9 and 0.5 is 4.5. Subtract 4.5 from 4.5 to get 0.

Therefore, $0.45 \div 0.9 = 0.5$.

Lesson Goals

- Divide decimals to hundredths by decimals to tenths using a model.

- Divide decimals to hundredths by decimals to tenths using the algorithm.

GET READY

Introduction to Decimal Division (B)

Students will get a glimpse of what they will learn about in the lesson. They will also read the lesson goals.

Multiplying Decimal Numbers by Powers of 10 with Instant Recall

Students will practice multiplying decimal numbers by powers of 10.

LEARN AND TRY IT

LEARN   Dividing Hundredths by Tenths with Models

Students will learn how to use area models to divide a decimal number to the hundredths place by a decimal number to the tenths place.

TIP   Remind students that they can use multiplication to check their answers.

TRY IT   Divide Hundredths by Tenths with Models

Students will practice dividing a decimal number to the hundredths place by a decimal number to the tenths place using area models. Support will be provided to help students overcome misconceptions.

LEARN   Dividing Hundredths by Tenths with the Algorithm

Students will learn how to divide a decimal number to the hundredths place by a decimal number to the tenths place using the standard algorithm.

TRY IT   Divide Hundredths by Tenths with the Algorithm

Students will practice dividing a decimal number to the hundredths place by a decimal number to the tenths place using the standard algorithm. Support will be provided to help students overcome misconceptions.

TRY IT   Practice Dividing Hundredths by Tenths

Students will complete online practice problems. Then they will complete Practice Dividing Hundredths by Tenths from *Summit Math 5 Activity Book*.

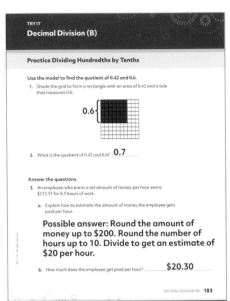

TRY IT
Decimal Division (B)

Practice Dividing Hundredths by Tenths

Use the model to find the quotient of 0.42 and 0.6.

1. Shade the grid to form a rectangle with an area of 0.42 and a side that measures 0.6.

2. What is the quotient of 0.42 and 0.6? **0.7**

Answer the questions.

3. An employee who earns a set amount of money per hour earns $172.55 for 8.5 hours of work.

   a. Explain how to estimate the amount of money the employee gets paid per hour.

   Possible answer: Round the amount of money up to $200. Round the number of hours up to 10. Divide to get an estimate of $20 per hour.

   b. How much does the employee get paid per hour? **$20.30**

DECIMAL DIVISION (B) **183**

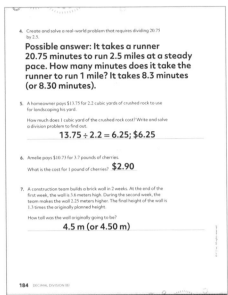

4. Create and solve a real-world problem that requires dividing 20.75 by 2.5.

   Possible answer: It takes a runner 20.75 minutes to run 2.5 miles at a steady pace. How many minutes does it take the runner to run 1 mile? It takes 8.3 minutes (or 8.30 minutes).

5. A homeowner pays $13.75 for 2.2 cubic yards of crushed rock to use for landscaping his yard.

   How much does 1 cubic yard of the crushed rock cost? Write and solve a division problem to find out.
   13.75 ÷ 2.2 = 6.25; $6.25

6. Amelie pays $10.73 for 3.7 pounds of cherries.

   What is the cost for 1 pound of cherries? **$2.90**

7. A construction team builds a brick wall in 2 weeks. At the end of the first week, the wall is 3.6 meters high. During the second week, the team makes the wall 2.25 meters higher. The final height of the wall is 1.3 times the originally planned height.

   How tall was the wall originally going to be?
   4.5 m (or 4.50 m)

184 DECIMAL DIVISION (B)

WRAP-UP

Dividing Hundredths by Tenths

Students will solve a problem to show that they understand how to divide a decimal number to the hundredths place by a decimal number to the tenths place.

Decimal Division (C)

Lesson Overview

ACTIVITY	ACTIVITY TITLE	TIME	ONLINE/OFFLINE
GET READY	Introduction to Decimal Division (C)	**2** minutes	🖥️
	Multiplying Decimal Numbers by Powers of 10 Math Facts Game	**8** minutes	🖥️
LEARN AND **TRY IT**	Dividing Hundredths by Hundredths with Models	**7** minutes	🖥️
	Divide Hundredths by Hundredths with Models	**7** minutes	🖥️
	Dividing Hundredths by Hundredths with the Algorithm	**7** minutes	🖥️
	Divide Hundredths by Hundredths with the Algorithm	**7** minutes	🖥️
	Practice Dividing Hundredths by Hundredths	**20** minutes	🖥️ and 📄
WRAP-UP	Dividing Hundredths by Hundredths	**2** minutes	🖥️

Content Background

In this lesson, students will divide decimal numbers by decimal numbers. The dividend and divisor of each division problem in this lesson are decimal numbers to the hundredths place. Students will also solve real-world problems involving the division of decimal numbers to the hundredths place.

First, students will use area models to solve division problems. Since the divisor is a decimal number to the hundredths place, students will be shading partial squares in the grid.

MATERIALS

Supplied
- *Summit Math 5 Activity Book:* Practice Dividing Hundredths by Hundredths

For example, this area model represents $0.18 \div 0.45$.

Each large square represents 1 whole, so each small square represents 1 hundredth. The width of each small square is 1 tenth.

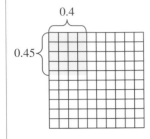

First, label the left dimension with 0.45, the divisor. This dimension is labeled with 4 tenths and 5 hundredths.

The shading in each column covers 4.5 or $4\frac{1}{2}$ squares, or hundredths. So, the shading in 2 columns covers 9 hundredths and the shading in 4 columns covers 18 hundredths, which is the dividend.

The top dimension of the shaded rectangle is the quotient: 0.4.

Therefore, $0.18 \div 0.45 = 0.4$.

Then students will apply the steps of the standard division algorithm to divide decimal numbers to the hundredths place. This example shows how to apply the algorithm to divide 0.18 by 0.45:

Use the long division symbol to write the problem $0.18 \div 0.45$.

Move the decimal two places to the right to change 0.45 to 45 and 0.18 to 18.

Divide as usual.

Place a decimal point in the quotient above the decimal point in 18.

The first digit of the quotient is 0 because 45 does not divide into 18.

Add a zero after the decimal point in 18.

The last digit of the quotient is 4. To find this digit, think about how many times 45 divides into 180. The digit 4 is in the tenths place, so it represents 0.4. The product of 45 and 0.4 is 18.0. Subtract 18.0 from 18.0 to get 0.

Therefore, $0.18 \div 0.45 = 0.4$.

Notice that the result of using the algorithm and the area model to solve $0.18 \div 0.45$ is the same. Both methods give valid answers.

Lesson Goals

- Divide decimals to hundredths using a model.
- Divide decimals to hundredths using the algorithm.

Introduction to Decimal Division (C)

Students will get a glimpse of what they will learn about in the lesson. They will also read the lesson goals.

Multiplying Decimal Numbers by Powers of 10 Math Facts Game

Students will practice multiplying decimal numbers by powers of 10.

LEARN AND TRY IT

LEARN   Dividing Hundredths by Hundredths with Models

Students will learn how to use models to divide decimal numbers. Both decimal numbers are to the hundredths place in each division problem.

TIP   Remind students that they can use multiplication to check their answers.

TRY IT   Divide Hundredths by Hundredths with Models

Students will practice using models to divide decimal numbers to the hundredths place. Support will be provided to help students overcome misconceptions.

LEARN   Dividing Hundredths by Hundredths with the Algorithm

Students will learn to divide decimal numbers to the hundredths place using the standard algorithm.

TRY IT   Divide Hundredths by Hundredths with the Algorithm

Students will practice dividing decimal numbers to the hundredths place using the standard algorithm. Support will be provided to help students overcome misconceptions.

TRY IT   Practice Dividing Hundredths by Hundredths

Students will complete online practice problems. Then they will complete Practice Dividing Hundredths by Hundredths from *Summit Math 5 Activity Book*.

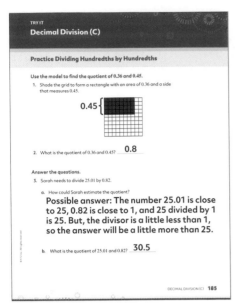

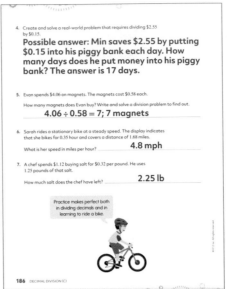

WRAP-UP

Dividing Hundredths by Hundredths

Students will solve a problem to show that they understand how to divide two decimal numbers to the hundredths place using the standard algorithm.

Decimal Division (D)

Lesson Overview

ACTIVITY	ACTIVITY TITLE	TIME	ONLINE/OFFLINE
GET READY	Introduction to Decimal Division (D)	**2** minutes	
	Working with Multiples of 2, 3, 4, and 5 Math Facts	**8** minutes	
LEARN AND **TRY IT**	Dividing Tenths by Hundredths with Models	**7** minutes	
	Divide Tenths by Hundredths with Models	**7** minutes	
	Dividing Tenths by Hundredths with the Algorithm	**7** minutes	
	Divide Tenths by Hundredths with the Algorithm	**7** minutes	
	Practice Dividing Tenths by Hundredths	**20** minutes	and
WRAP-UP	Dividing Tenths by Hundredths	**2** minutes	

Content Background

In this lesson, students will divide decimal numbers to the tenths place by decimal numbers to the hundredths place. They will also solve real-world problems involving the division of decimal numbers to the tenths and hundredths places.

First, students will use area models to solve division problems. Since the divisor is a decimal number to the hundredths place, they will shade partial squares in the grid.

Next, students will apply the steps of the standard division algorithm to divide a decimal number to the tenths place by a decimal number to the hundredths place. This example shows how to apply the algorithm to divide 2.4 by 0.32:

MATERIALS

Supplied
- *Summit Math 5 Activity Book:* Practice Dividing Tenths by Hundredths

Use the long division symbol to write the problem 2.4 ÷ 0.32.

Move the decimal two places to the right to change 0.32 to 32. Add a 0 after the last digit of 2.4 to move the decimal point two places to the right so that 2.4 is changed to 240.

Divide as usual.

Place a decimal point in the quotient above the decimal point in 240.

$$\begin{array}{r} 7.5 \\ 32\overline{)240.0} \\ -224 \\ \hline 16.0 \\ -16.0 \\ \hline 0 \end{array}$$

The first digit of the quotient is 7 because 32 divides into 240 seven times. The product of 32 and 7 is 224. Subtract 224 from 240 to get 16.

Since 32 does not divide into 16, add a zero after the decimal point in 240 and 16.

The last digit of the quotient is 5. To find this digit, think about how many times 32 divides into 160. The digit 5 is in the tenths place, so it represents 0.5. The product of 32 and 0.5 is 16.0. Subtract 16.0 from 16.0 to get 0.

Therefore, $2.4 \div 0.32 = 7.5$.

Lesson Goals

- Divide decimals to tenths by decimals to hundredths using a model.
- Divide decimals to tenths by decimals to hundredths using the algorithm.

GET READY

Introduction to Decimal Division (D)

Students will get a glimpse of what they will learn about in the lesson. They will also read the lesson goals.

Working with Multiples of 2, 3, 4, and 5 Math Facts

Students will practice working with multiples 2, 3, 4, and 5.

LEARN AND TRY IT

LEARN   Dividing Tenths by Hundredths with Models

Students will learn how to use area models to divide a decimal number to the tenths place by a decimal number to the hundredths place.

TIP   Remind students that they can use multiplication to check their answers.

TRY IT   Divide Tenths by Hundredths with Models

Students will practice dividing a decimal number to the tenths place by a decimal number to the hundredths place using area models. Support will be provided to help students overcome misconceptions.

LEARN   Dividing Tenths by Hundredths with the Algorithm

Students will learn how to divide a decimal number to the tenths place by a decimal number to the hundredths place using the standard algorithm.

TRY IT   Divide Tenths by Hundredths with the Algorithm

Students will practice dividing a decimal number to the tenths place by a decimal number to the hundredths place using the standard algorithm. Support will be provided to help students overcome misconceptions.

TRY IT   Practice Dividing Tenths by Hundredths

Students will complete online practice problems. Then they will complete Practice Dividing Tenths by Hundredths from *Summit Math 5 Activity Book*.

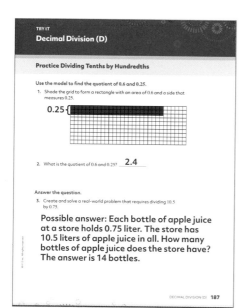

Dividing Tenths by Hundredths

Students will solve a problem to show that they understand how to divide a decimal number to the tenths place by a decimal number to the hundredths place.

Decimal Division (E)

Lesson Overview

ACTIVITY	ACTIVITY TITLE	TIME	ONLINE/OFFLINE
GET READY	Introduction to Decimal Division (E)	**2** minutes	📶
TRY IT	Review Decimal Division	**18** minutes	📶
QUIZ	Decimal Division	**25** minutes	📶
WRAP-UP	More Math Practice	**15** minutes	📶

Lesson Goals

- Review dividing decimal numbers to the tenths and hundredths places.

- Take a quiz.

MATERIALS

There are no materials to gather for this lesson.

GET READY

Introduction to Decimal Division (E)

Students will read the lesson goals.

TRY IT

Review Decimal Division

Students will answer questions to review what they have learned about decimal division.

QUIZ

Decimal Division

Students will complete the Decimal Division quiz.

More Math Practice

Students will practice skills according to their individual needs.

Big Ideas: Extended Problems

Lesson Overview

Big Ideas lessons provide students the opportunity to further apply the knowledge and skills acquired throughout previous units. Each Big Ideas lesson consists of three parts:

1. **Cumulative Review:** Students keep their skills fresh by reviewing prior content.

2. **Preview:** Students practice answering the types of questions they will commonly find on standardized tests.

3. **Synthesis:** Students complete an assignment that allows them to interweave and apply what they've learned. These synthesis assignments will vary throughout the course.

In the Synthesis portion of this Big Ideas lesson, students will complete multistep problems that go beyond the short answer and multiple choice problems they encounter in their regular lessons. These problems give students an opportunity to demonstrate problem solving, reasoning, communication, and modeling skills. Students will need to use pencil and paper and/or technology to show their work.

LEARNING COACH CHECK-IN   This is a graded assessment. Make sure students complete, review, and submit the assignment to their teacher.

All materials needed for this lesson are linked online. The materials are not provided in this Lesson Guide or in the Activity Book.

Points on a Coordinate Plane

Coordinate System (A)

Lesson Overview

ACTIVITY	ACTIVITY TITLE	TIME	ONLINE/OFFLINE
GET READY	Introduction to Coordinate System (A)	**2** minutes	
	The Coordinate System in 60 Seconds	**3** minutes	
	Look Back at Plotting Numbers on a Number Line	**5** minutes	
LEARN AND **TRY IT**	Describing the Coordinate System	**15** minutes	
	Describe the Coordinate System	**10** minutes	
	Practice Describing the Coordinate System	**20** minutes	and
WRAP-UP	Describing the Coordinate System	**5** minutes	

Content Background

In this lesson, students will learn to identify important components of the coordinate plane.

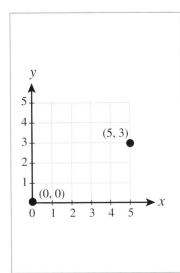

This is a *coordinate plane*. It is a grid formed by two perpendicular number lines called *axes*. The horizontal number line is the *x*-axis, and the vertical number line is the *y*-axis. The axes intersect at a point called the *origin*.

An *ordered pair* describes the location of a point. An ordered pair is always in the format (x, y). For example, this coordinate plane has a point at $(5, 3)$. The *x*-coordinate is 5 and the *y*-coordinate is 3. The *coordinates* of the origin are $(0, 0)$.

This coordinate plane shows the first quadrant. There are three other quadrants that appear when the axes are extended down and to the left to include negative numbers. If students have learned about negative numbers, they may be interested to investigate a coordinate plane showing all four quadrants. However, this unit will only include points in the first quadrant.

Lesson Goals

- Describe the coordinate plane and its parts.

GET READY

Introduction to Coordinate System (A)

Students will get a glimpse of what they will learn about in the lesson. They will also read the lesson goals and keywords. Have students select each keyword and preview its definition.

The Coordinate System in 60 Seconds

Students will watch a short video designed to spark their interest in upcoming topics.

Look Back at Plotting Numbers on a Number Line

Students will practice the prerequisite skill of plotting numbers on a number line.

LEARN AND TRY IT

LEARN Describing the Coordinate System

Students will be introduced to the coordinate system. They will identify key features of the coordinate plane and learn about ordered pairs.

TIP One way to remember the order of the coordinates in an ordered pair is to remember that the letter X comes before the letter Y in the alphabet just like x comes before y in an ordered pair: (x, y).

TRY IT Describe the Coordinate System

Students will practice describing the coordinate system and its parts. Support will be provided to help students overcome misconceptions.

TRY IT   Practice Describing the Coordinate System

Students will complete online practice problems. Then they will complete Practice Describing the Coordinate System from *Summit Math 5 Activity Book.*

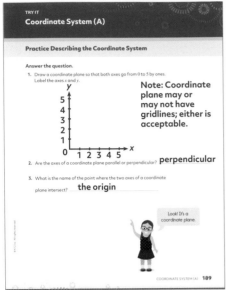

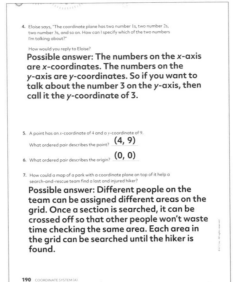

Describing the Coordinate System

Students will solve a problem to show that they understand how to describe the coordinate system.

Coordinate System (B)

Lesson Overview

ACTIVITY	ACTIVITY TITLE	TIME	ONLINE/OFFLINE
GET READY	Introduction to Coordinate System (B)	**2** minutes	🖥️
	Working with Multiples of 2, 3, 4, and 5 with Instant Recall	**8** minutes	🖥️
LEARN AND **TRY IT**	Writing Ordered Pairs	**15** minutes	🖥️
	Write Ordered Pairs	**10** minutes	🖥️
	Practice Writing Ordered Pairs	**20** minutes	🖥️ and 📄
WRAP-UP	Writing Ordered Pairs	**5** minutes	🖥️

Content Background

In this lesson, students will learn to write the coordinates of a point as an ordered pair. They will write ordered pairs for points in the first quadrant and on each axis. Starting at a point, students should go straight down to the x-axis to find the x-coordinate. Then they should go back the point and go directly left to the y-axis to find the y-coordinate. Both coordinates are combined in parentheses and separated by a comma in the form (x, y). A point on the x-axis has 0 as the y-coordinate, such as $(3, 0)$. A point on the y-axis has 0 as the x-coordinate, such as $(0, 6)$.

MATERIALS

Supplied
* *Summit Math 5 Activity Book:* Practice Writing Ordered Pairs

Lesson Goals
* Write the ordered pair for a given point on the coordinate plane.

GET READY

Introduction to Coordinate System (B)
Students will get a glimpse of what they will learn about in the lesson. They will also read the lesson goals.

Working with Multiples of 2, 3, 4, and 5 with Instant Recall
Students will practice working with multiples of 2, 3, 4, and 5.

LEARN   Writing Ordered Pairs

Students will learn how to write ordered pairs for points on the coordinate plane.

OPTIONAL   In this lesson, students will only write ordered pairs with coordinates that are whole numbers. However, some students might wonder if coordinates can have fraction or decimal parts. You can explain that every single point on the coordinate plane has an ordered pair, even points that are between grid lines. For example, the point $(3.2, 5.5)$ has coordinates that are not whole numbers.

TRY IT   Write Ordered Pairs

Students will practice writing ordered pairs for points on the coordinate plane. Support will be provided to help students overcome misconceptions.

TRY IT   Practice Writing Ordered Pairs

Students will complete online practice problems. Then they will complete Practice Writing Ordered Pairs from *Summit Math 5 Activity Book.*

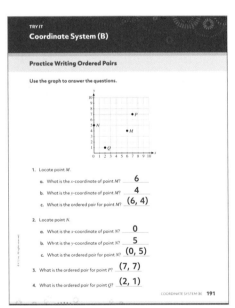

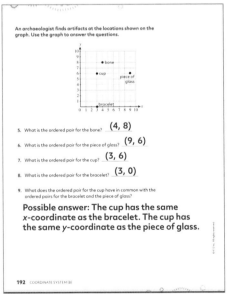

Writing Ordered Pairs

Students will solve a problem to show that they understand how to write an ordered pair.

Coordinate System (C)

Lesson Overview

ACTIVITY	ACTIVITY TITLE	TIME	ONLINE/OFFLINE
GET READY	Introduction to Coordinate System (C)	**2** minutes	🖥️
	Working with Multiples of 2, 3, 4, and 5 Math Facts Game	**8** minutes	📶
LEARN AND **TRY IT**	Graphing Points on an Axis	**7** minutes	📶
	Graph Points on an Axis	**7** minutes	📶
	Graphing Points Not on an Axis	**7** minutes	📶
	Graph Points Not on an Axis	**7** minutes	📶
	Practice Graphing Points	**20** minutes	📶 and 📄
WRAP-UP	Graphing Points	**2** minutes	📶

Content Background

In this lesson, students will graph points on each axis and in the first quadrant of the coordinate plane given their coordinates as ordered pairs. Every time students graph a point, they should begin at the origin, $(0, 0)$. The x-coordinate indicates how far to travel from the origin horizontally, along the x-axis. The y-coordinate indicates how far to travel from the origin vertically, along the y-axis.

A point with a y-coordinate of 0 is a point on the x-axis because the vertical distance is 0. A point with an x-coordinate of 0 is a point on the y-axis because the horizontal distance is 0.

To graph, or plot, a point with whole number coordinates, start at the origin then move right to the x-coordinate. Then move up from the x-axis the number of units given by the y-coordinate. For example, the point $(4, 2)$ is graphed by starting at the origin, moving 4 units right, and then moving 2 units up from the x-axis.

MATERIALS

Supplied
- *Summit Math 5 Activity Book:* Practice Graphing Points

Lesson Goals

- Graph a point on the coordinate plane given its ordered pair.

Introduction to Coordinate System (C)

Students will get a glimpse of what they will learn about in the lesson. They will also read the lesson goals.

Working with Multiples of 2, 3, 4, and 5 Math Facts Game

Students will practice working with multiples of 2, 3, 4, and 5.

LEARN AND TRY IT

LEARN   Graphing Points on an Axis

Students will learn how to graph points on the x-axis by moving horizontally and on the y-axes by moving vertically.

TRY IT   Graph Points on an Axis

Students will practice graphing points on an axis. Support will be provided to help students overcome misconceptions.

> **SUPPORT**   Students will graph points using an interactive coordinate plane. The coordinate plane has two tools: Point and Move. Students should select Point to graph a point. They can select Move to pick up and move a graphed point to a different location. Help students with their first few graphing problems to make sure they know how to use the tools appropriately.

LEARN   Graphing Points Not on an Axis

Students will learn how to graph points that are not on an axis by moving both horizontally and vertically.

TRY IT   Graph Points Not on an Axis

Students will practice graphing points that are not on an axis. Support will be provided to help students overcome misconceptions.

TRY IT   Practice Graphing Points

Students will complete online practice problems. Then they will complete Practice Graphing Points from *Summit Math 5 Activity Book*.

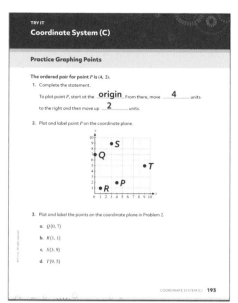

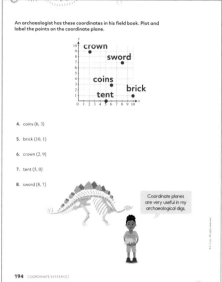

WRAP-UP

Graphing Points

Students will solve a problem to show that they understand how to plot a point in the coordinate plane.

Coordinate System (D)

Lesson Overview

ACTIVITY	ACTIVITY TITLE	TIME	ONLINE/OFFLINE
GET READY	Introduction to Coordinate System (D)	**2** minutes	🖥
TRY IT	Review Coordinate System	**18** minutes	🖥
QUIZ	Coordinate System	**25** minutes	🖥
WRAP-UP	More Math Practice	**15** minutes	🖥

Lesson Goals

- Review describing the coordinate system, writing ordered pairs, and graphing points.

- Take a quiz.

GET READY

Introduction to Coordinate System (D)

Students will read the lesson goals.

TRY IT

Review Coordinate System

Students will answer questions to review what they have learned about the coordinate system.

QUIZ

Coordinate System

Students will complete the Coordinate System quiz.

More Math Practice

Students will practice skills according to their individual needs.

Problem Solving on the Coordinate Plane (A)

Lesson Overview

ACTIVITY	ACTIVITY TITLE	TIME	ONLINE/OFFLINE
GET READY	Introduction to Problem Solving on the Coordinate Plane (A)	**2** minutes	🖥️
	Look Back at Graphing Points in the Coordinate Plane	**8** minutes	🖥️
LEARN AND **TRY IT**	Using the Coordinate Plane in the Real World	**7** minutes	🖥️
	Use the Coordinate Plane in the Real World	**7** minutes	🖥️
	Using the Coordinate Plane with Shapes	**7** minutes	🖥️
	Use the Coordinate Plane with Shapes	**7** minutes	🖥️
	Practice Using the Coordinate Plane	**20** minutes	🖥️ and 📄
WRAP-UP	Using the Coordinate Plane	**2** minutes	🖥️

Content Background

In this lesson, students will use a coordinate plane to solve real-world problems and represent shapes. In some examples, each unit along the *x*- or *y*-axis represents a distance in the real world. You can help students understand the meaning of the points and the significance of their locations on the coordinate plane by having them pretend to walk from one point to another point. Continue to emphasize that the *x*-coordinate represents horizontal distance and the *y*-coordinate represents vertical distance.

Points can also represent the vertices (or corners) of shapes on a coordinate plane. Students will graph points to create a shape. They will also use the graph of a shape to determine measurements such as distance, perimeter, and area.

Lesson Goals

- Graph and interpret points that represent a real-world situation in a coordinate plane.

- Graph points that are vertices of a polygon in a coordinate plane.

- Use points that are vertices of a polygon to determine a measurement.

MATERIALS

Supplied
- *Summit Math 5 Activity Book:* Practice Using the Coordinate Plane

KEYWORDS

polygon – a plane shape made of 3 or more straight sides that separate the inside of the shape from the outside

vertex (plural: vertices) – the common endpoint of two rays that form an angle

Introduction to Problem Solving on the Coordinate Plane (A)

Students will get a glimpse of what they will learn about in the lesson. They will also read the lesson goals and keywords. Have students select each keyword and preview its definition.

Look Back at Graphing Points in the Coordinate Plane

Students will practice the prerequisite skill of graphing points in the coordinate plane.

LEARN AND TRY IT

LEARN   Using the Coordinate Plane in the Real World

Students will learn how to graph and interpret points on the coordinate plane to solve real-world problems.

TIP   Remind students to think about the scale of each graph. For example, each 1 unit on the x-axis could represent a distance of 10 feet. So, an x-coordinate of 3 really represents 30 feet.

TRY IT   Use the Coordinate Plane in the Real World

Students will practice using the coordinate plane to solve real-world problems. Support will be provided to help students overcome misconceptions.

LEARN   Using the Coordinate Plane with Shapes

Students will learn how to work with shapes in the coordinate plane. First, students will graph points that represent the vertices of a polygon. Then students will use the vertices of a polygon to determine measurements.

TRY IT   Use the Coordinate Plane with Shapes

Students will practice working with shapes in the coordinate plane. Support will be provided to help students overcome misconceptions.

TRY IT   Practice Using the Coordinate Plane

Students will complete online practice problems. Then they will complete Practice Using the Coordinate Plane from *Summit Math 5 Activity Book*.

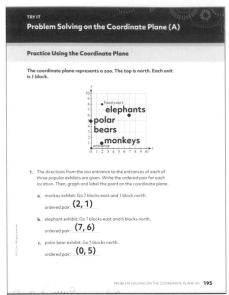

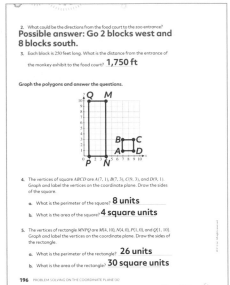

Using the Coordinate Plane

Students will solve problems to show that they understand how to use the coordinate plane to solve real-world problems.

Problem Solving on the Coordinate Plane (B)

Lesson Overview

ACTIVITY	ACTIVITY TITLE	TIME	ONLINE/OFFLINE
GET READY	Introduction to Problem Solving on the Coordinate Plane (B)	**2** minutes	🖥️
	Working with Multiples of 6, 7, 8, and 9 Math Facts	**8** minutes	📶
LEARN AND **TRY IT**	Plotting Data on the Coordinate Plane	**7** minutes	📶
	Plot Data on the Coordinate Plane	**7** minutes	🖥️
	Interpreting Data on the Coordinate Plane	**7** minutes	🖥️
	Interpret Data on the Coordinate Plane	**7** minutes	📶
	Practice Working with Data on the Coordinate Plane	**20** minutes	📶 and 📄
WRAP-UP	Working with Data on the Coordinate Plane	**2** minutes	📶

Content Background

In this lesson, students will graph and interpret data on the coordinate plane. First, students will graph data given in a table or as a list of ordered pairs. In a table, the x-coordinates are in the first column and the y-coordinates are in the second column.

Next, students will interpret data graphed on a coordinate plane. Sometimes, students struggle to understand the meaning of coordinates of points on a graph, which often happens when the scale on the y-axis is not 1. When students first learned to plot points, the x- and y-axes were each labeled every 1 unit: 0, 1, 2, 3, 4, and so on. However, when a graph represents real-world data, the scale on each axis might be different. For example, each tick mark or grid line on the y-axis could represent 5 minutes. So, the y-axis would be labeled 0, 5, 10, 15, 20, and so on. Remind students to think about what each axis represents for the data in the problem.

The data sets in this lesson do not necessarily represent a specific pattern. So, there may be two or more points with the same x-coordinate or the same y-coordinate.

> ### MATERIALS
>
> **Supplied**
> - *Summit Math 5 Activity Book:* Practice Working with Data on the Coordinate Plane

> ### KEYWORDS
>
> **data** – numerical information that has been gathered

Lesson Goals

- Graph points representing real-world situations on the coordinate plane.
- Interpret points on a coordinate plane that represent real-world situations.

Introduction to Problem Solving on the Coordinate Plane (B)

Students will get a glimpse of what they will learn about in the lesson. They will also read the lesson goals and keywords. Have students select each keyword and preview its definition.

Working with Multiples of 6, 7, 8, and 9 Math Facts

Students will practice working with multiples of 6, 7, 8, and 9.

LEARN AND TRY IT

LEARN   Plotting Data on the Coordinate Plane

Students will learn how to plot data points on the coordinate plane. Data will be given in a table or as a list of ordered pairs.

TIP   Remind students to label each axis and each tick mark on each axis. For example, suppose the columns of a table are labeled "Number of people" and "Time (min)." Students should label the x-axis "Number of people" and the y-axis "Time (min)." The scale of either axis does not need to be 1. Students can count by 2s, 5s, 10s, or any other number that is appropriate for the data.

TRY IT   Plot Data on the Coordinate Plane

Students will practice plotting data on the coordinate plane. Support will be provided to help students overcome misconceptions.

LEARN   Interpreting Data on the Coordinate Plane

Students will learn how to interpret data plotted on a coordinate plane.

TIP   Remind students to check the label and scale of each axis. For example, students may think a y-coordinate of a point is 5 because the point is 5 grid lines above the x-axis. However, if the y-axis represents "Distance (m)" and the tick marks are counted by 10s, then the fifth grid line, or tick mark, actually represents 50 meters.

TRY IT   Interpret Data on the Coordinate Plane

Students will practice interpreting data plotted on a coordinate plane. Support will be provided to help students overcome misconceptions.

TRY IT   Practice Working with Data on the Coordinate Plane

Students will complete online practice problems. Then they will complete Practice Working with Data on the Coordinate Plane from *Summit Math 5 Activity Book.*

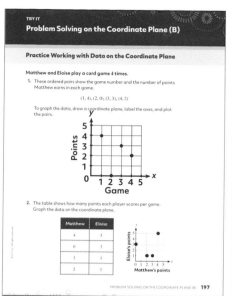

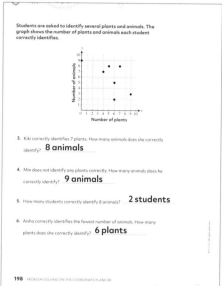

Working with Data on the Coordinate Plane

Students will solve problems to show that they understand how to plot and interpret data on a coordinate plane.

Problem Solving on the Coordinate Plane (C)

Lesson Overview

ACTIVITY	ACTIVITY TITLE	TIME	ONLINE/OFFLINE
GET READY	Introduction to Problem Solving on the Coordinate Plane (C)	**2** minutes	🖥️
	Working with Multiples of 6, 7, 8, and 9 with Instant Recall	**8** minutes	🖥️
LEARN AND **TRY IT**	Graphing a Steady Rate of Change	**7** minutes	🖥️
	Graph a Steady Rate of Change	**7** minutes	🖥️
	Interpreting a Graph with a Steady Rate of Change	**7** minutes	🖥️
	Interpret a Graph with a Steady Rate of Change	**7** minutes	🖥️
	Practice Working with Steady Rates of Change	**20** minutes	🖥️ and 📄
WRAP-UP	Working with Steady Rates of Change	**2** minutes	🖥️

Content Background

In this lesson, students will graph and interpret graphs of steady rates of change. They will encounter patterns that increase at a steady rate and others that decrease at a steady rate. A pattern has a steady rate if the y-coordinates increase or decrease by the same amount for each unit the x-coordinate increases. The points should form a straight line on the graph. The graphed points of an increasing pattern rise from left to right because the same amount is added to get from one y-coordinate to the next. The graphed points of a decreasing pattern fall from left to right because the same amount is subtracted to get from one y-coordinate to the next.

MATERIALS

Supplied
- *Summit Math 5 Activity Book:* Practice Working with Steady Rates of Change

Lesson Goals

- Graph points representing steady rates of change on the coordinate plane.
- Interpret points on a coordinate plane that represent steady rates of change.

Introduction to Problem Solving on the Coordinate Plane (C)

Students will get a glimpse of what they will learn about in the lesson. They will also read the lesson goals.

Working with Multiples of 6, 7, 8, and 9 with Instant Recall

Students will practice working with multiples of 6, 7, 8, and 9.

LEARN AND TRY IT

LEARN Graphing a Steady Rate of Change

Students will learn how to graph points that represent a steady rate of change.

TIP Students can do a quick check to make sure that their graph is correct by making sure their points lie in a straight line. There should be only one point for each x-coordinate. Students can also check the difference from each y-coordinate to the next. If the y-coordinates increase by the same amount, the points on the graph should rise from left to right. If the y-coordinates decrease by the same amount, the points on the graph should fall from left to right.

TRY IT Graph a Steady Rate of Change

Students will practice graphing points that represent a steady rate of change. Support will be provided to help students overcome misconceptions.

LEARN Interpreting a Graph with a Steady Rate of Change

Students will learn how to interpret a graph that has a steady rate of change.

TRY IT Interpret a Graph with a Steady Rate of Change

Students will practice interpreting a graph that has a steady rate of change. Support will be provided to help students overcome misconceptions.

TRY IT   Practice Working with Steady Rates of Change

Students will complete online practice problems. Then they will complete Practice Working with Steady Rates of Change from *Summit Math 5 Activity Book.*

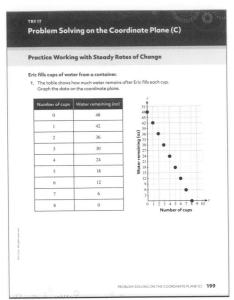

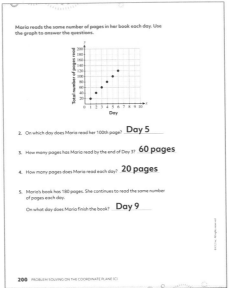

WRAP-UP

Working with Steady Rates of Change

Students will solve problems to show that they understand how to graph and interpret a graph with a steady rate of change.

Problem Solving on the Coordinate Plane (D)

Lesson Overview

ACTIVITY	ACTIVITY TITLE	TIME	ONLINE/OFFLINE
GET READY	Introduction to Problem Solving on the Coordinate Plane (D)	**2** minutes	🖥️
	Working with Multiples of 6, 7, 8, and 9 Math Facts Game	**8** minutes	🖥️
LEARN AND **TRY IT**	Generating and Comparing Number Patterns	**7** minutes	🖥️
	Generate and Compare Number Patterns	**7** minutes	🖥️
	Graphing Number Patterns	**7** minutes	🖥️
	Graph Number Patterns	**7** minutes	🖥️
	Practice Working with Number Patterns	**20** minutes	🖥️ and 📄
WRAP-UP	Working with Number Patterns	**2** minutes	🖥️

Content Background

In this lesson, students will generate, compare, and graph number patterns given rules. Each number in a pattern is called a *term*. Most rules will have students begin at 0 and add a specific amount. For example, the rule "add 6" generates the pattern 0, 6, 12, 18, 24, 30, and so on.

Students will use two different rules to create two patterns that they will compare in corresponding order. Here are the patterns for "add 8" and "add 4":

> add 8: 0, 8, 16, 24, 32
> add 4: 0, 4, 8, 12, 16

If you compare 0 to 0, 8 to 4, 16 to 8, 24 to 12, and 32 to 16, you notice that each term in the second pattern is half the corresponding term in the first pattern.

Students will graph patterns on a coordinate plane. Ordered pairs are created by treating the first pattern as the x-coordinates and the second pattern as the y-coordinates. For the patterns "add 8" and "add 4," the ordered pairs are $(0,0)$, $(8,4)$, $(16,8)$, $(24,12)$, and $(32,16)$. Students would then plot the list of points on a coordinate plane.

MATERIALS

Supplied
- *Summit Math 5 Activity Book:* Practice Working with Number Patterns

KEYWORDS

term in a pattern – each number or object in a pattern

Lesson Goals

- Create number patterns given the rules.
- Describe the relationship between corresponding terms in number patterns.
- Generate and graph ordered pairs form corresponding terms in number patterns.

GET READY

Introduction to Problem Solving on the Coordinate Plane (D)

Students will get a glimpse of what they will learn about in the lesson. They will also read the lesson goals and keywords. Have students select each keyword and preview its definition.

Working with Multiples of 6, 7, 8, and 9 Math Facts Game

Students will practice working with multiples of 6, 7, 8, and 9.

LEARN AND TRY IT

LEARN   Generating and Comparing Number Patterns

Students will learn how to generate number patterns. They will also learn how to compare corresponding terms in two number patterns to determine a relationship.

TRY IT   Generate and Compare Number Patterns

Students will practice generating and comparing number patterns. Support will be provided to help students overcome misconceptions.

LEARN   Graphing Number Patterns

Students will learn how to generate and graph number patterns on a coordinate plane.

TRY IT   Graph Number Patterns

Students will practice generating and graphing number patterns. Support will be provided to help students overcome misconceptions.

TRY IT   Practice Working with Number Patterns

Students will complete online practice problems. Then they will complete Practice Working with Number Patterns from *Summit Math 5 Activity Book*.

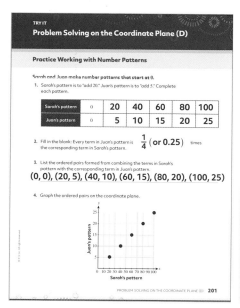

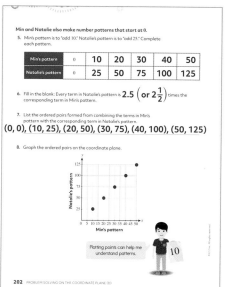

WRAP-UP

Working with Number Patterns

Students will solve problems to show that they understand how to generate and compare number patterns.

Problem Solving on the Coordinate Plane (E)

Lesson Overview

ACTIVITY	ACTIVITY TITLE	TIME	ONLINE/OFFLINE
GET READY	Introduction to Problem Solving on the Coordinate Plane (E)	**2** minutes	🖥️
TRY IT	Review Problem Solving on the Coordinate Plane	**18** minutes	🖥️
QUIZ	Problem Solving on the Coordinate Plane	**25** minutes	🖥️
WRAP-UP	More Math Practice	**15** minutes	🖥️

Lesson Goals

- Review using a coordinate plane to solve real-world and shape problems; graphing and interpreting data and steady rates of change; and generating, comparing, and graphing number patterns.

- Take a quiz.

GET READY

Introduction to Problem Solving on the Coordinate Plane (E)

Students will read the lesson goals.

TRY IT

Review Problem Solving on the Coordinate Plane

Students will answer questions to review what they have learned about problem solving on the coordinate plane.

QUIZ

Problem Solving on the Coordinate Plane

Students will complete the Problem Solving on the Coordinate Plane quiz.

More Math Practice

Students will practice skills according to their individual needs.

Big Ideas: Mini-Project

Lesson Overview

Big Ideas lessons provide students the opportunity to further apply the knowledge and skills acquired throughout previous units. Each Big Ideas lesson consists of three parts:

1. **Cumulative Review:** Students keep their skills fresh by reviewing prior content.

2. **Preview:** Students practice answering the types of questions they will commonly find on standardized tests.

3. **Synthesis:** Students complete an assignment that allows them to interweave and apply what they've learned. These synthesis assignments will vary throughout the course.

In the Synthesis portion of this Big Ideas lesson, students will complete a small, creative project designed to tie together concepts and skills that students have encountered across units. These small projects are designed to emphasize a real-world application that connects mathematics to other subjects, including science, technology, engineering, art, and history. Students will need to use pencil and paper and/or technology to show their work.

LEARNING COACH CHECK-IN Make sure students complete, review, and submit the assignment to their teacher.

All materials needed for this lesson are linked online. The materials are not provided in this Lesson Guide or in the Activity Book.

MATERIALS

Supplied
- Mini-Project Instructions (printout)

Measurement and Unit Conversion

Using Units of Length (A)

Lesson Overview

ACTIVITY	ACTIVITY TITLE	TIME	ONLINE/OFFLINE
GET READY	Introduction to Using Units of Length (A)	**2** minutes	🖥️
	Measurement and Unit Conversion in 60 Seconds	**3** minutes	🖥️
	Look Back at Measurements of Length	**5** minutes	🖥️
LEARN AND **TRY IT**	Converting Metric Units of Length	**7** minutes	🖥️
	Convert Metric Units of Length	**7** minutes	🖥️
	Converting Metric Units of Length to Solve Problems	**7** minutes	🖥️
	Convert Metric Units of Length to Solve Problems	**7** minutes	🖥️
	Practice Converting Metric Units of Length	**20** minutes	🖥️ and 📄
WRAP-UP	Converting Metric Units of Length	**2** minutes	🖥️

Content Background

In this lesson, students will convert a given length to an equivalent length within the metric system. They will also convert lengths to solve real-world problems.

The metric system is based on groups of 10. To gain a more complete understanding of the metric system, students will learn about decimeters (dm), decameters (dam), and hectometers (hm) and how they relate to millimeters (mm), centimeters (cm), meters (m), and kilometers (km).

$$10 \, mm = 1 \, cm$$
$$10 \, cm = 1 \, dm$$
$$10 \, dm = 1 \, m$$
$$10 \, m = 1 \, dam$$
$$10 \, dam = 1 \, hm$$
$$10 \, hm = 1 \, km$$

NOTE There are metric units of length smaller than the millimeter and larger than the kilometer. Interested students should be encouraged to investigate their names and sizes.

> **MATERIALS**
>
> **Supplied**
> - *Summit Math 5 Activity Book:* Practice Converting Metric Units of Length

Students will only convert with millimeters, centimeters, meters, and kilometers, so they should know these measurement facts: 1 km = 1,000 m; 1 m = 100 cm = 1,000 mm; and 1 cm = 10 mm.

Some problems require students to convert from larger to smaller units. To do this, *multiply* by a power of 10. For example, to find the number of centimeters in 3 meters, multiply 3 by 100 to get 300 centimeters. Other problems require students to convert from smaller to larger units. To do this, *divide* by a power of 10. For example, to find the number of kilometers in 1,300 meters, divide 1,300 by 1,000 to get 1.3 kilometers.

Lesson Goals

- Convert metric units of length.

- Solve real-world problems by converting metric units of length.

GET READY

Introduction to Using Units of Length (A)

Students will get a glimpse of what they will learn about in the lesson. They will also read the lesson goals.

Measurement and Unit Conversion in 60 Seconds

Students will watch a short video designed to spark their interest in upcoming topics.

Look Back at Measurements of Length

Students will practice the prerequisite skill of recalling measurement facts related to metric and U.S. customary units of distance or length.

LEARN AND TRY IT

LEARN   Converting Metric Units of Length

Students will learn how to convert metric units of length from larger to smaller units and smaller to larger units.

TIP   Since the metric system is based on powers of 10, students will be multiplying or dividing by powers of 10 to convert metric units. They may need to review how to multiply and divide by powers of 10.

TRY IT   Convert Metric Units of Length

Students will practice converting metric units of length. Support will be provided to help students overcome misconceptions.

LEARN Converting Metric Units of Length to Solve Problems

Students will learn how to convert metric units of length to solve real-world problems.

OPTIONAL Discuss with students about how there is sometimes more than one way to solve a problem. In the lesson, students solve a problem where Aisha walks a distance of 650 meters 8 times and the problem asks for the number of *kilometers* she walks. The example shows to multiply 650 by 8 to get 5,200 meters, and then convert that distance to 5.2 kilometers. Ask students how the problem could have been done differently to get a correct solution. (The conversion could have been done first instead: Convert 650 meters to 0.65 kilometers, and then $0.65 \times 8 = 5.2$.)

TRY IT Convert Metric Units of Length to Solve Problems

Students will practice converting metric units of length to solve real-world problems. Support will be provided to help students overcome misconceptions.

TRY IT Practice Converting Metric Units of Length

Students will complete online practice problems. Then they will complete Practice Converting Metric Units of Length from *Summit Math 5 Activity Book*.

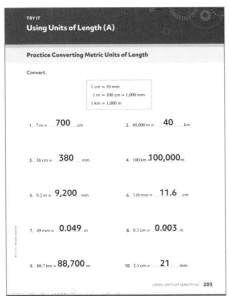

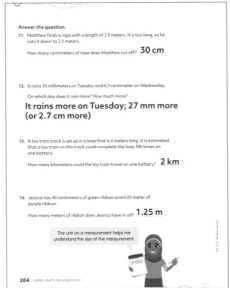

WRAP-UP

Converting Metric Units of Length

Students will solve problems to show that they understand how to convert metric units of length.

Using Units of Length (B)

Lesson Overview

ACTIVITY	ACTIVITY TITLE	TIME	ONLINE/OFFLINE
GET READY	Introduction to Using Units of Length (B)	**2** minutes	🖥️
	Multiples of 10, 25, 50, and 100 Math Facts	**8** minutes	🖥️
LEARN AND **TRY IT**	Converting Customary Units of Length	**7** minutes	🖥️
	Convert Customary Units of Length	**7** minutes	🖥️
	Converting Customary Units of Length to Solve Problems	**7** minutes	🖥️
	Convert Customary Units of Length to Solve Problems	**7** minutes	🖥️
	Practice Converting Customary Units of Length	**20** minutes	🖥️ and 📄
WRAP-UP	Converting Customary Units of Length	**2** minutes	🖥️

Content Background

In this lesson, students will convert a given length to an equivalent length within the U.S. customary system. They will also convert lengths to solve real-world problems.

The U.S. customary system is also known as the imperial system and the English system. Students will not be converting between the metric and U.S. customary systems, but they may be curious to know how the units compare. A meter is a little longer than a yard. A kilometer is a little more than half a mile. It takes most people about 20 minutes to walk 1 mile and about 12 minutes to walk 1 kilometer.

An inch is exactly 2.54 centimeters. Students can compare inches, centimeters, and millimeters on a ruler. They will convert between inches (in.), feet (ft), yards (yd), and miles (mi). Students should know these measurement facts:

1 mi = 1,760 yd = 5,280 ft
1 yd = 3 ft = 36 in.
1 ft = 12 in.

Some problems require students to convert from larger to smaller units. To do this, *multiply*. For example, to find the number of inches in 5 yards, multiply 5 by 36 inches to get 180 inches.

MATERIALS

Supplied
- *Summit Math 5 Activity Book:* Practice Converting Customary Units of Length

Other problems require students to convert from smaller to larger units. To do this, *divide*. For example, to find the number of feet in 30 inches, divide 30 by 12, and then simplify the fraction: $\frac{30}{12} = 2\frac{6}{12} = 2\frac{1}{2}$ ft.

Lesson Goals

- Convert customary units of length.

- Solve real-world problems by converting customary units of length.

GET READY

Introduction to Using Units of Length (B)

Students will get a glimpse of what they will learn about in the lesson. They will also read the lesson goals.

Multiples of 10, 25, 50, and 100 Math Facts

Students will practice working with multiples of 10, 25, 50, and 100.

LEARN AND TRY IT

LEARN   Converting Customary Units of Length

Students will learn how to convert customary units of length from larger to smaller units and from smaller to larger units.

TIP   Since the U.S. customary system is not based on powers of 10, students will need to use other procedures to multiply and divide. They may need to review converting improper fractions to mixed numbers, simplifying fractions, and the standard multiplication and division algorithms.

TRY IT   Convert Customary Units of Length

Students will practice converting customary units of length. Support will be provided to help students overcome misconceptions.

LEARN   Converting Customary Units of Length to Solve Problems

Students will learn how to convert customary units of length to solve real-world problems.

TRY IT   Convert Customary Units of Length to Solve Problems

Students will practice converting customary units of length to solve real-world problems. Support will be provided to help students overcome misconceptions.

TRY IT   Practice Converting Customary Units of Length

Students will complete online practice problems. Then they will complete Practice Converting Customary Units of Length from *Summit Math 5 Activity Book*.

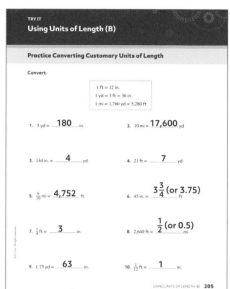

TRY IT
Using Units of Length (B)

Practice Converting Customary Units of Length

Convert.

| 1 ft = 12 in. |
| 1 yd = 3 ft = 36 in. |
| 1 mi = 1,760 yd = 5,280 ft |

1. 5 yd = __180__ in.

2. 10 mi = __17,600__ yd

3. 144 in. = __4__ yd

4. 21 ft = __7__ yd

5. $\frac{9}{10}$ mi = __4,752__ ft

6. 45 in. = __$3\frac{3}{4}$ (or 3.75)__ ft

7. $\frac{1}{4}$ ft = __3__ in.

8. 2,640 ft = __$\frac{1}{2}$ (or 0.5)__ mi

9. 1.75 yd = __63__ in.

10. $\frac{1}{12}$ ft = __1__ in.

USING UNITS OF LENGTH (B)   **205**

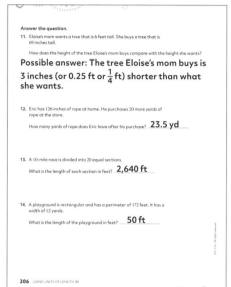

Answer the question.

11. Eloise's mom wants a tree that is 6 feet tall. She buys a tree that is 69 inches tall.

How does the height of the tree Eloise's mom buys compare with the height she wants?

Possible answer: The tree Eloise's mom buys is 3 inches (or 0.25 ft or $\frac{1}{4}$ ft) shorter than what she wants.

12. Eric has 126 inches of rope at home. He purchases 20 more yards of rope at the store.

How many yards of rope does Eric have after his purchase? __23.5 yd__

13. A 10-mile race is divided into 20 equal sections.

What is the length of each section in feet? __2,640 ft__

14. A playground is rectangular and has a perimeter of 172 feet. It has a width of 12 yards.

What is the length of the playground in feet? __50 ft__

206   USING UNITS OF LENGTH (B)

WRAP-UP

Converting Customary Units of Length

Students will solve a problem to show that they understand how to convert customary units of length.

Using Units of Length (C)

Lesson Overview

ACTIVITY	ACTIVITY TITLE	TIME	ONLINE/OFFLINE
GET READY	Introduction to Using Units of Length (C)	**2** minutes	🖥️
TRY IT	Review Using Units of Length	**18** minutes	🖥️
QUIZ	Using Units of Length	**25** minutes	🖥️
WRAP-UP	More Math Practice	**15** minutes	🖥️

Lesson Goals

- Review converting within metric units of length and within U.S. customary units of length and converting units to solve real-world problems.

- Take a quiz.

GET READY

Introduction to Using Units of Length (C)

Students will read the lesson goals.

TRY IT

Review Using Units of Length

Students will answer questions to review what they have learned about using units of length.

QUIZ

Using Units of Length

Students will complete the Using Units of Length quiz.

More Math Practice

Students will practice skills according to their individual needs.

Using Units of Liquid Volume (A)

Lesson Overview

ACTIVITY	ACTIVITY TITLE	TIME	ONLINE/OFFLINE
GET READY	Introduction to Using Units of Liquid Volume (A)	**2** minutes	🖥️
	Look Back at Measurements of Liquid Volume	**8** minutes	🖥️
LEARN AND **TRY IT**	Converting Metric Units of Liquid Volume	**7** minutes	🖥️
	Convert Metric Units of Liquid Volume	**7** minutes	🖥️
	Converting Metric Units of Liquid Volume to Solve Problems	**7** minutes	🖥️
	Convert Metric Units of Liquid Volume to Solve Problems	**7** minutes	🖥️
	Practice Converting Metric Units of Liquid Volume	**20** minutes	🖥️ and 📄
WRAP-UP	Converting Metric Units of Liquid Volume	**2** minutes	🖥️

Content Background

In this lesson, students will convert a given liquid volume to an equivalent liquid volume within the metric system. Students will also convert liquid volumes to solve real-world problems.

The metric system is based on groups of 10. To gain a more complete understanding of the metric system, students will learn about centiliters (cL) and deciliters (dL) and how they relate to milliliters (mL) and liters (L).

$$1 \text{ L} = 10 \text{ dL}$$
$$1 \text{ dL} = 10 \text{ cL}$$
$$1 \text{ cL} = 10 \text{ mL}$$

Students will only convert with milliliters and liters, so they should know that 1 L = 1,000 mL. Some problems require students to convert from larger to smaller units. To do this, *multiply* by 1,000. Other problems require students to convert from smaller to larger units. To do this, *divide* by 1,000.

OPTIONAL   You can use household objects to get a feel for the size of a liter and milliliter. If you have a 1-liter container available, let students see it and fill it to get a sense of 1 liter. Let them fill it to different levels to experience a half liter (500 mL) and a quarter liter (250 mL). Twenty drops of liquid make 1 milliliter, which is about the amount in an eye dropper.

MATERIALS

Supplied
- *Summit Math 5 Activity Book:* Practice Converting Metric Units of Liquid Volume

Lesson Goals

- Convert metric units of liquid volume.
- Solve real-world problems by converting metric units of liquid volume.

Introduction to Using Units of Liquid Volume (A)

Students will get a glimpse of what they will learn about in the lesson. They will also read the lesson goals.

Look Back at Measurements of Liquid Volume

Students will practice the prerequisite skill of recalling measurement facts related to metric or U.S. customary units of liquid volume.

LEARN AND TRY IT

LEARN   Converting Metric Units of Liquid Volume

Students will learn how to convert metric units of liquid volume from larger to smaller units and smaller to larger units.

TRY IT   Convert Metric Units of Liquid Volume

Students will practice converting metric units of liquid volume. Support will be provided to help students overcome misconceptions.

LEARN   Converting Metric Units of Liquid Volume to Solve Problems

Students will learn how to convert metric units of liquid volume to solve real-world problems.

TRY IT   Convert Metric Units of Liquid Volume to Solve Problems

Students will practice converting metric units of liquid volume to solve real-world problems. Support will be provided to help students overcome misconceptions.

TRY IT   Practice Converting Metric Units of Liquid Volume

Students will complete online practice problems. Then they will complete Practice Converting Metric Units of Liquid Volume from *Summit Math 5 Activity Book*.

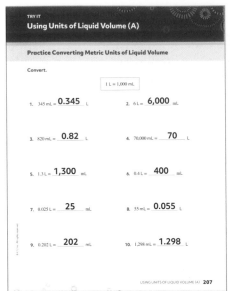

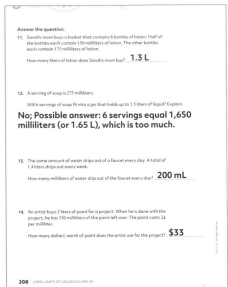

WRAP-UP

Converting Metric Units of Liquid Volume

Students will solve problems to show that they understand how to convert metric units of liquid volume.

Using Units of Liquid Volume (B)

Lesson Overview

ACTIVITY	ACTIVITY TITLE	TIME	ONLINE/OFFLINE
GET READY	Introduction to Using Units of Liquid Volume (B)	**2** minutes	🖥️
	Multiples of 10, 25, 50, and 100 with Instant Recall	**8** minutes	📶
LEARN AND **TRY IT**	Converting Customary Units of Liquid Volume	**7** minutes	🖥️
	Convert Customary Units of Liquid Volume	**7** minutes	📶
	Converting Customary Units of Liquid Volume to Solve Problems	**7** minutes	🖥️
	Convert Customary Units of Liquid Volume to Solve Problems	**7** minutes	🖥️
	Practice Converting Customary Units of Liquid Volume	**20** minutes	🖥️ and 📄
WRAP-UP	Converting Customary Units of Liquid Volume	**2** minutes	📶

Content Background

In this lesson, students will convert a given liquid volume to an equivalent liquid volume within the U.S. customary system. They will also convert liquid volumes to solve real-world problems.

The U.S. customary system is also known as the imperial system and the English system. Students will not be converting between the metric and U.S. customary systems, but they may be curious to know how the units compare. A quart and a liter are about the same size.

Students will convert between fluid ounces (fl oz), cups (c), pints (pt), quarts (qt), and gallons (gal). They should know these measurement facts:

$$1 \text{ c} = 8 \text{ fl oz}$$
$$1 \text{ pt} = 2 \text{ c} = 16 \text{ fl oz}$$
$$1 \text{ qt} = 2 \text{ pt} = 4 \text{ c} = 32 \text{ fl oz}$$
$$1 \text{ gal} = 4 \text{ qt} = 8 \text{ pt} = 16 \text{ c} = 128 \text{ fl oz}$$

TIP A quart is a quarter, or one-fourth, of a gallon.

Some problems require students to convert from larger to smaller units. To do this, *multiply*. For example, to find the number of fluid ounces in 7 pints, multiply 7 by 16 fluid ounces to get 112 fluid ounces. Other problems require students to convert from smaller to larger units. To do this, *divide*. For example, to find the number of gallons in 20 cups, divide 20 by 16, and then simplify the fraction: $\frac{20}{16} = 1\frac{4}{16} = 1\frac{1}{4}$ gal.

MATERIALS

Supplied
- *Summit Math 5 Activity Book:* Practice Converting Customary Units of Liquid Volume

Lesson Goals

- Convert customary units of liquid volume.

- Solve real-world problems by converting customary units of liquid volume.

Introduction to Using Units of Liquid Volume (B)

Students will get a glimpse of what they will learn about in the lesson. They will also read the lesson goals.

Multiples of 10, 25, 50, and 100 with Instant Recall

Students will practice working with multiples of 10, 25, 50, and 100.

LEARN AND TRY IT

LEARN   Converting Customary Units of Liquid Volume

Students will learn how to convert customary units of liquid volume from larger to smaller units and smaller to larger units.

TRY IT   Convert Customary Units of Liquid Volume

Students will practice converting customary units of liquid volume. Support will be provided to help students overcome misconceptions.

LEARN   Converting Customary Units of Liquid Volume to Solve Problems

Students will learn how to convert customary units of liquid volume to solve real-world problems.

TRY IT   Convert Customary Units of Liquid Volume to Solve Problems

Students will practice converting customary units of liquid volume to solve real-world problems. Support will be provided to help students overcome misconceptions.

TRY IT   Practice Converting Customary Units of Liquid Volume

Students will complete online practice problems. Then they will complete Practice Converting Customary Units of Liquid Volume from *Summit Math 5 Activity Book*.

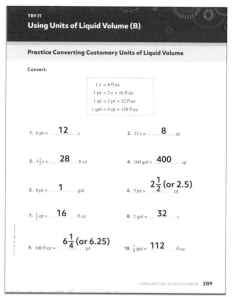

TRY IT

Using Units of Liquid Volume (B)

Practice Converting Customary Units of Liquid Volume

Convert.

> 1 c = 8 fl oz
> 1 pt = 2 c = 16 fl oz
> 1 qt = 2 pt = 32 fl oz
> 1 gal = 4 qt = 128 fl oz

1. 6 pt = **12** c

2. 32 c = **8** qt

3. $3\frac{1}{2}$ c = **28** fl oz

4. 100 gal = **400** qt

5. 8 pt = **1** gal

6. 5 pt = **$2\frac{1}{2}$ (or 2.5)** qt

7. $\frac{1}{2}$ qt = **16** fl oz

8. 2 gal = **32** c

9. 100 fl oz = **$6\frac{1}{4}$ (or 6.25)** pt

10. $\frac{7}{8}$ gal = **112** fl oz

USING UNITS OF LIQUID VOLUME (B)   **209**

Answer the question.

11. Juan's mom drinks 1 cup of tea with breakfast, 4 fluid ounces of tea with lunch, and 6 fluid ounces of tea with dinner.
How many cups of tea does Juan's mom drink? **$2\frac{1}{4}$ c (or 2.25 c)**

12. A bag holds 100 fluid ounces of water. Evan drains $1\frac{1}{2}$ quarts of water from the bag. Then, Matthew drains another 3 pints of water from the bag.
How many fluid ounces of water remain in the bag? **4 fl oz**

13. A hotel uses 300 quarts of bleach each month. It pays $1.78 for each gallon of bleach.
How much does the hotel spend on bleach each month? **$133.50**

14. A daycare center starts the day with 5 quarts of milk. At the end of the day, 4 cups of milk remain.
How many cups of milk do the children drink? **16 c**

210   USING UNITS OF LIQUID VOLUME (B)

WRAP-UP

Converting Customary Units of Liquid Volume

Students will solve a problem to show that they understand how to convert customary units of liquid volume.

Using Units of Liquid Volume (C)

Lesson Overview

ACTIVITY	ACTIVITY TITLE	TIME	ONLINE/OFFLINE
GET READY	Introduction to Using Units of Liquid Volume (C)	**2** minutes	📶
TRY IT	Review Using Units of Liquid Volume	**18** minutes	📶
QUIZ	Using Units of Liquid Volume	**25** minutes	📶
WRAP-UP	More Math Practice	**15** minutes	📶

Lesson Goals

- Review converting within metric units of liquid volume and within U.S. customary units of liquid volume and converting units to solve real-world problems.

- Take a quiz.

> **MATERIALS**
>
> There are no materials to gather for this lesson.

GET READY

Introduction to Using Units of Liquid Volume (C)

Students will read the lesson goals.

TRY IT

Review Using Units of Liquid Volume

Students will answer questions to review what they have learned about using units of liquid volume.

QUIZ

Using Units of Liquid Volume

Students will complete the Using Units of Liquid Volume quiz.

More Math Practice

Students will practice skills according to their individual needs.

Using Units of Mass and Weight (A)

Lesson Overview

ACTIVITY	ACTIVITY TITLE	TIME	ONLINE/OFFLINE
GET READY	Introduction to Using Units of Mass and Weight (A)	**2** minutes	🖥
	Look Back at Measurements of Mass and Weight	**8** minutes	🖥
LEARN AND **TRY IT**	Converting Units of Mass	**7** minutes	🖥
	Convert Units of Mass	**7** minutes	🖥
	Converting Units of Mass to Solve Problems	**7** minutes	🖥
	Convert Units of Mass to Solve Problems	**7** minutes	🖥
	Practice Converting Units of Mass	**20** minutes	🖥 and 📄
WRAP-UP	Converting Units of Mass	**2** minutes	🖥

Content Background

In this lesson, students will convert a given mass to an equivalent mass within the metric system. They will also convert mass to solve real-world problems.

The metric system is based on groups of 10. To gain a more complete understanding of the metric system, students will learn about centigrams (cg), decigrams (dg), decagrams (dag), and hectograms (hg) and how they relate to milligrams (mg), grams (g), and kilograms (kg).

$$10 \, mg = 1 \, cg$$
$$10 \, cg = 1 \, dg$$
$$10 \, dg = 1 \, g$$
$$10 \, g = 1 \, dag$$
$$10 \, dag = 1 \, hg$$
$$10 \, hg = 1 \, kg$$

Students will only convert with milligrams, grams, and kilograms, so they should know that $1 \, g = 1{,}000 \, mg$ and $1 \, kg = 1{,}000 \, g$.

NOTE   It is important for students to understand that mass is different from weight. Mass measures the amount of matter in an object, while weight measures the object's heaviness. Weight can change depending on the pull of gravity. For example, objects weigh less on the moon than they do on earth because the pull of gravity is less on the moon.

MATERIALS

Supplied
- *Summit Math 5 Activity Book:* Practice Converting Units of Mass

KEYWORDS

mass – the amount of matter in an object; the amount of mass remains the same no matter where the object is, but the weight of an object can change depending on the pull of gravity on the object

weight – the measure of how heavy an object is, such as 10 lb

Some problems require students to convert from larger to smaller units. To do this, *multiply* by 1,000. For example, to find the number of grams in 3 kilograms, multiply 3 by 1,000 to get 3,000 grams. Other problems require students to convert from smaller to larger units. To do this, *divide* by 1,000. For example, to find the number of grams in 3,750 milligrams, divide 3,750 by 1,000 to get 3.75 grams.

Lesson Goals

- Convert metric units of mass.

- Solve real-world problems by converting metric units of mass.

GET READY

Introduction to Using Units of Mass and Weight (A)

Students will get a glimpse of what they will learn about in the lesson. They will also read the lesson goals and keywords. Have students select each keyword and preview its definition.

Look Back at Measurements of Mass and Weight

Students will practice the prerequisite skill of recalling measurement facts related to metric units of mass and U.S. customary units of weight.

LEARN AND TRY IT

LEARN Converting Units of Mass

Students will learn how to convert metric units of mass from larger to smaller units and smaller to larger units.

TIP To convert between milligrams, grams, and kilograms, students will multiply or divide by 1,000. Move the decimal point 3 places to the right to multiply by 1,000. Move the decimal point 3 places to the left to divide by 1,000.

TRY IT Convert Units of Mass

Students will practice converting metric units of mass. Support will be provided to help students overcome misconceptions.

LEARN Converting Units of Mass to Solve Problems

Students will learn how to convert metric units of mass to solve real-world problems.

TRY IT   Convert Units of Mass to Solve Problems

Students will practice converting metric units of mass to solve real-world problems. Support will be provided to help students overcome misconceptions.

TRY IT   Practice Converting Units of Mass

Students will complete online practice problems. Then they will complete Practice Converting Units of Mass from *Summit Math 5 Activity Book*.

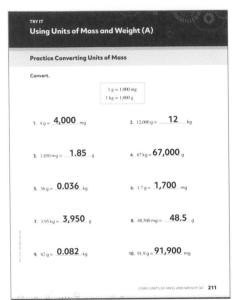

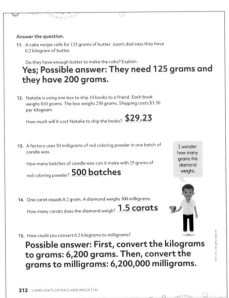

Using Units of Mass and Weight (B)

Lesson Overview

ACTIVITY	ACTIVITY TITLE	TIME	ONLINE/OFFLINE
GET READY	Introduction to Using Units of Mass and Weight (B)	**2** minutes	🖥️
	Multiples of 10, 25, 50, and 100 Math Facts Game	**8** minutes	🖥️
LEARN AND **TRY IT**	Converting Customary Units of Weight	**7** minutes	🖥️
	Convert Customary Units of Weight	**7** minutes	🖥️
	Converting Customary Units of Weight to Solve Problems	**7** minutes	🖥️
	Convert Customary Units of Weight to Solve Problems	**7** minutes	🖥️
	Practice Converting Customary Units of Weight	**20** minutes	🖥️ and 📄
WRAP-UP	Converting Customary Units of Weight	**2** minutes	🖥️

Content Background

In this lesson, students will convert a given weight to an equivalent weight within the U.S. customary system. They will also convert weights to solve real-world problems.

The U.S. customary system is also known as the imperial system and the English system. Students will not be converting between the metric and U.S. customary systems, but they may be curious to know how the units compare. One kilogram weighs about 2.2 pounds.

Students will convert between ounces (oz), pounds (lb), and tons. Students should know that 1 ton = 2,000 lb and 1 lb = 16 oz.

NOTE   It is important for students to understand that mass is different from weight. Mass measures the amount of matter in an object, while weight measures the object's heaviness. Weight can change depending on the pull of gravity. For example, objects weigh less on the moon than they do on earth because the pull of gravity is less on the moon. At this level, students should assume that all objects are on the earth.

Some problems require students to convert from larger to smaller units. To do this, *multiply*. Other problems require students to convert from smaller to larger units. To do this, *divide*.

MATERIALS

Supplied
- *Summit Math 5 Activity Book:* Practice Converting Customary Units of Weight

KEYWORDS

ton – the English, or customary, unit for measuring weight that equals 2,000 lb

Lesson Goals

- Convert customary units of weight.
- Solve real-world problems by converting customary units of weight.

GET READY

Introduction to Using Units of Mass and Weight (B)

Students will get a glimpse of what they will learn about in the lesson. They will also read the lesson goals and keywords. Have students select each keyword and preview its definition.

Multiples of 10, 25, 50, and 100 Math Facts Game

Students will practice working with multiples of 10, 25, 50, and 100.

LEARN AND TRY IT

LEARN Converting Customary Units of Weight

Students will learn how to convert customary units of weight from larger to smaller units and smaller to larger units.

TIP It is common for students to confuse conversion facts between fluid ounces and ounces. This leads to a common error of thinking there are 8 ounces in a pound because there are 8 fluid ounces in a cup. Remind students that a pint and a pound have the same number of ounces. A pint holds 16 fluid ounces and a pound is 16 ounces.

TRY IT Convert Customary Units of Weight

Students will practice converting customary units of weight. Support will be provided to help students overcome misconceptions.

LEARN Converting Customary Units of Weight to Solve Problems

Students will learn how to convert customary units of weight to solve real-world problems.

TRY IT Convert Customary Units of Weight to Solve Problems

Students will practice converting customary units of weight to solve real-world problems. Support will be provided to help students overcome misconceptions.

TRY IT   Practice Converting Customary Units of Weight

Students will complete online practice problems. Then they will complete Practice Converting Customary Units of Weight from *Summit Math 5 Activity Book.*

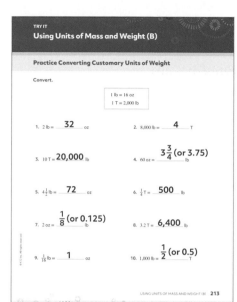

WRAP-UP

Converting Customary Units of Weight

Students will solve a problem to show that they understand how to convert customary units of weight.

Using Units of Mass and Weight (C)

Lesson Overview

ACTIVITY	ACTIVITY TITLE	TIME	ONLINE/OFFLINE
GET READY	Introduction to Using Units of Mass and Weight (C)	**2** minutes	🖥️
TRY IT	Review Using Units of Mass and Weight	**18** minutes	🖥️
QUIZ	Using Units of Mass and Weight	**25** minutes	🖥️
WRAP-UP	More Math Practice	**15** minutes	🖥️

Lesson Goals

- Review converting within metric units of mass and within customary units of weight and converting units to solve real-world problems.

- Take a quiz.

GET READY

Introduction to Using Units of Mass and Weight (C)

Students will read the lesson goals.

TRY IT

Review Using Units of Mass and Weight

Students will answer questions to review what they have learned about using units of mass and weight.

QUIZ

Using Units of Mass and Weight

Students will complete the Using Units of Mass and Weight quiz.

More Math Practice

Students will practice skills according to their individual needs.

Customary Units and Line Plots (A)

Lesson Overview

ACTIVITY	ACTIVITY TITLE	TIME	ONLINE/OFFLINE
GET READY	Introduction to Customary Units and Line Plots (A)	**2** minutes	🖥️
	Look Back at Adding Fractions and Mixed Numbers	**8** minutes	🖥️
LEARN AND **TRY IT**	Representing Data on a Line Plot	**15** minutes	🖥️
	Represent Data on a Line Plot	**10** minutes	🖥️
	Practice Representing Data on a Line Plot	**20** minutes	🖥️ and 📄
WRAP-UP	Representing Data on a Line Plot	**5** minutes	🖥️

Content Background

In this lesson, students will represent data on a line plot. Each data set includes metric or U.S. customary measurements of length, liquid volume, mass, or weight. Data values include fractions and/or mixed numbers.

Lesson Goals

- Create a line plot for a data set that includes fractions.

GET READY

Introduction to Customary Units and Line Plots (A)

Students will get a glimpse of what they will learn about in the lesson. They will also read the lesson goals and keywords. Have students select each keyword and preview its definition.

NOTE While any mark can be used on a line plot, Xs and dots are most commonly used. Each line plot in this lesson uses Xs.

Look Back at Adding Fractions and Mixed Numbers

Students will practice the prerequisite skill of adding fractions and mixed numbers.

LEARN   Representing Data on a Line Plot

Students will represent data on a line plot.

TRY IT   Represent Data on a Line Plot

Students will practice representing data on a line plot. Support will be provided to help students overcome misconceptions.

TIP   When students complete a line plot, have them count the number of Xs to be sure they have the same number as the number of data values.

TRY IT   Practice Representing Data on a Line Plot

Students will complete online practice problems. Then they will complete Practice Representing Data on a Line Plot from *Summit Math 5 Activity Book*.

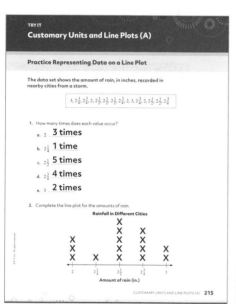

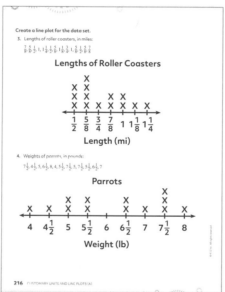

Representing Data on a Line Plot

Students will solve a problem to show that they understand how to represent data on a line plot.

Customary Units and Line Plots (B)

Lesson Overview

ACTIVITY	ACTIVITY TITLE	TIME	ONLINE/OFFLINE
GET READY	Introduction to Customary Units and Line Plots (B)	**2** minutes	🖥️
	Multiples of 15, 20, 30, and 60 Math Facts	**8** minutes	🖥️
LEARN AND **TRY IT**	Interpreting a Line Plot	**15** minutes	🖥️
	Interpret a Line Plot	**10** minutes	🖥️
	Practice Interpreting a Line Plot	**20** minutes	🖥️ and 📄
WRAP-UP	Interpreting a Line Plot	**5** minutes	🖥️

Content Background

In this lesson, students will interpret data displayed in a line plot to solve problems. Each problem requires students to add, subtract, multiply, or divide. Students should read each problem carefully to determine which data values and operation should be used.

Many problems require students to use the greatest or least of something. Other problems might ask students to find the total measurement for the data value that occurred the most. Some students struggle to understand the difference between the greatest amount of something and the data value that occurs the most. To find the greatest amount, identify the number farthest to the right on the number line that has a mark above it. To find the data value that occurs the most, identify the number that has the most marks. There is only one greatest (or least value), but there can be multiple data values that occur the most.

> ### Lesson Goals
> • Solve problems using a line plot.

MATERIALS

Supplied
• *Summit Math 5 Activity Book:* Practice Interpreting a Line Plot

GET READY

Introduction to Customary Units and Line Plots (B)
Students will get a glimpse of what they will learn about in the lesson. They will also read the lesson goals.

Multiples of 15, 20, 30, and 60 Math Facts

Students will practice working with multiples of 15, 20, 30, and 60.

LEARN AND TRY IT

LEARN   Interpreting a Line Plot

Students will learn how to interpret data displayed in a line plot to solve problems.

TRY IT   Interpret a Line Plot

Students will practice interpreting data displayed in a line plot to solve problems. Support will be provided to help students overcome misconceptions.

TRY IT   Practice Interpreting a Line Plot

Students will complete online practice problems. Then they will complete Practice Interpreting a Line Plot from *Summit Math 5 Activity Book*.

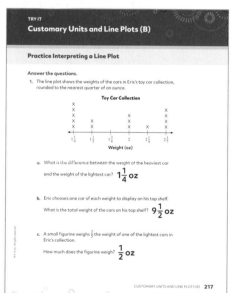

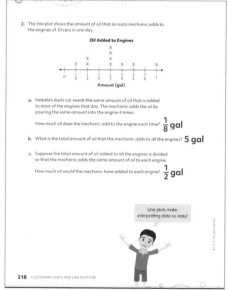

WRAP-UP

Interpreting a Line Plot

Students will solve a problem to show that they understand how to interpret data displayed in a line plot to solve a problem.

Customary Units and Line Plots (C)

Lesson Overview

ACTIVITY	ACTIVITY TITLE	TIME	ONLINE/OFFLINE
GET READY	Introduction to Customary Units and Line Plots (C)	**2** minutes	🖥️
TRY IT	Review Customary Units and Line Plots	**18** minutes	🖥️
QUIZ	Customary Units and Line Plots	**25** minutes	🖥️
WRAP-UP	More Math Practice	**15** minutes	🖥️

Lesson Goals

- Review creating a line plot for a data set that includes fractions and solving problems using a line plot.

- Take a quiz.

MATERIALS

There are no materials to gather for this lesson.

GET READY

Introduction to Customary Units and Line Plots (C)

Students will read the lesson goals.

TRY IT

Review Customary Units and Line Plots

Students will answer questions to review what they have learned about customary units and line plots.

QUIZ

Customary Units and Line Plots

Students will complete the Customary Units and Line Plots quiz.

More Math Practice

Students will practice skills according to their individual needs.

Big Ideas: Mini-Project

Lesson Overview

Big Ideas lessons provide students the opportunity to further apply the knowledge and skills acquired throughout previous units. Each Big Ideas lesson consists of three parts:

1. **Cumulative Review:** Students keep their skills fresh by reviewing prior content.

2. **Preview:** Students practice answering the types of questions they will commonly find on standardized tests.

3. **Synthesis:** Students complete an assignment that allows them to interweave and apply what they've learned. These synthesis assignments will vary throughout the course.

   In the Synthesis portion of this Big Ideas lesson, students will complete a small, creative project designed to tie together concepts and skills that students have encountered across units. These small projects are designed to emphasize a real-world application that connects mathematics to other subjects, including science, technology, engineering, art, and history. Students will need to use pencil and paper and/or technology to show their work.

   LEARNING COACH CHECK-IN   Make sure students complete, review, and submit the assignment to their teacher.

All materials needed for this lesson are linked online. The materials are not provided in this Lesson Guide or in the Activity Book.

> **MATERIALS**
>
> **Supplied**
> - Mini-Project Instructions (printout)

Classification of Two-Dimensional Figures

Triangles (A)

Lesson Overview

ACTIVITY	ACTIVITY TITLE	TIME	ONLINE/OFFLINE
GET READY	Introduction to Triangles (A)	**2** minutes	📶
	Classification of Two-Dimensional Figures in 60 Seconds	**3** minutes	📶
	Look Back at Identifying Right, Acute, or Obtuse Angles	**5** minutes	📶
LEARN AND **TRY IT**	Classifying Triangles by Angle Measures	**15** minutes	📶
	Classify Triangles by Angle Measures	**10** minutes	📶
	Practice Classifying Triangles by Angle Measures	**20** minutes	📶 and 📄
WRAP-UP	Classifying Triangles by Angle Measures	**5** minutes	📶

Content Background

In this unit, students will learn that all shapes can fit into categories and subcategories and that all characteristics of a category apply to its subcategories. For example, acute, right, and obtuse are all subcategories of triangles. All triangles have 3 sides and 3 angles, so acute, right, and obtuse triangles also have 3 sides and 3 angles. Students will also learn that categories and subcategories of polygons can be classified in a hierarchy based on shared characteristics.

In this lesson, students will start by learning how to classify triangles based on angle measures. Every triangle has at least 2 acute angles. Therefore, the measure of the third angle is used to classify a triangle. If the third angle is a right angle, the triangle is a right triangle. If the third angle is an acute angle, the triangle is an acute triangle. If the third angle is an obtuse angle, the triangle is an obtuse triangle.

TIP Remind students that an image is not always drawn to scale. If students use a protractor to measure the angles, they could get a different measurement than what is given in the image. In that case, students should always use the measure given in the image.

MATERIALS

Supplied
- *Summit Math 5 Activity Book:* Practice Classifying Triangles by Angle Measures

KEYWORDS

acute triangle – a triangle with 3 acute angles

obtuse triangle – a triangle with 1 angle greater than 90°

polygon – a plane shape made of 3 or more straight sides that separate the inside of the shape from the outside

right triangle – a triangle with a right angle

Lesson Goals

- Classify triangles based on their angle measures.

- Describe the attributes that are shared by acute triangles, right triangles, and obtuse triangles.

GET READY

Introduction to Triangles (A)

Students will get a glimpse of what they will learn about in the lesson. They will also read the lesson goals and keywords. Have students select each keyword and preview its definition.

Classification of Two-Dimensional Figures in 60 Seconds

Students will watch a short video designed to spark their interest in upcoming topics.

Look Back at Identifying Right, Acute, or Obtuse Angles

Students will practice the prerequisite skill of identifying right, acute, or obtuse angles.

LEARN AND TRY IT

LEARN Classifying Triangles by Angle Measures

Students will learn how to classify a triangle based on the measures of its angles. They will also learn how to describe the characteristics shared by categories of triangles.

TRY IT Classify Triangles by Angle Measures

Students will practice classifying triangles by angle measures and describing shared characteristics of triangle categories. Support will be provided to help students overcome misconceptions.

TRY IT   Practice Classifying Triangles by Angle Measures

Students will complete online practice problems. Then they will complete Practice Classifying Triangles by Angle Measures from *Summit Math 5 Activity Book*.

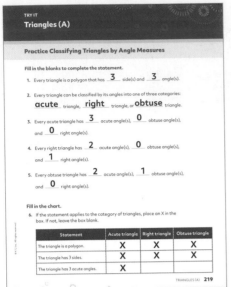

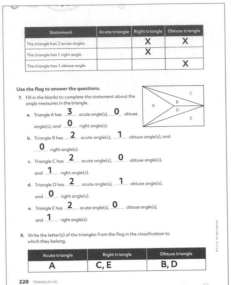

WRAP-UP

Classifying Triangles by Angle Measures

Students will solve a problem to show that they understand how to identify acute, right, and obtuse triangles.

Triangles (B)

Lesson Overview

ACTIVITY	ACTIVITY TITLE	TIME	ONLINE/OFFLINE
GET READY	Introduction to Triangles (B)	**2** minutes	🖥️
	Multiples of 15, 20, 30, and 60 with Instant Recall	**3** minutes	🖥️
	Classifying Triangles by Side Lengths	**5** minutes	🖥️
LEARN AND **TRY IT**	Classifying Triangles by Side Lengths	**15** minutes	🖥️
	Classify Triangles by Side Lengths	**10** minutes	🖥️
	Practice Classifying Triangles by Side Lengths	**20** minutes	🖥️ and 📄
WRAP-UP	Classifying Triangles by Side Lengths	**5** minutes	🖥️

Content Background

In this lesson, students will classify triangles by side lengths. They will also classify triangles by angle measures and side lengths. A triangle is a polygon with 3 sides and 3 angles. Students can classify a triangle based on its angle measures, the relationship among the lengths of its sides, or, in some cases, a combination of both.

A triangle with no sides that are the same length is an *scalene* triangle. A triangle with at least 2 sides that are the same length is an *isosceles* triangle. A triangle with 3 sides that are the same length is an *equilateral* triangle. Therefore, an equilateral triangle is a special type of isosceles triangle. A drawing of a plane geometric figure often shows tick marks on the sides of a figure. Identical tick marks shows sides that are equal in length.

equilateral triangle

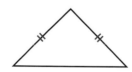
isosceles triangle

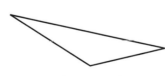
scalene triangle

MATERIALS

Supplied
- *Summit Math 5 Activity Book:* Practice Classifying Triangles by Side Lengths

KEYWORDS

equilateral triangle – a triangle that has all sides equal in length

isosceles triangle – a triangle that has at least 2 sides equal in length; an equilateral triangle is a special type of isosceles triangle

scalene triangle – a triangle that has no sides equal in length

Students can often classify a triangle by its angles and the lengths of its sides.

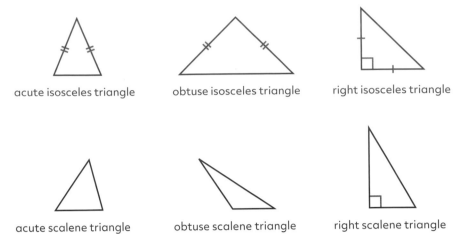

acute isosceles triangle   obtuse isosceles triangle   right isosceles triangle

acute scalene triangle   obtuse scalene triangle   right scalene triangle

An equilateral triangle is always an acute triangle; however, it is never labeled an "acute equilateral triangle."

Lesson Goals

- Classify triangles based on their side lengths.
- Classify triangles based on their angle measures and side lengths.
- Describe the attributes that are shared by scalene triangles, isosceles triangles, and equilateral triangles.

GET READY

Introduction to Triangles (B)

Students will get a glimpse of what they will learn about in the lesson. They will also read the lesson goals and keywords. Have students select each keyword and preview its definition.

Multiples of 15, 20, 30, and 60 with Instant Recall

Students will practice working with multiples of 15, 20, 30, and 60.

LEARN AND TRY IT

LEARN   Classifying Triangles by Side Lengths

Students will learn how to classify a triangle based on the lengths of its sides. They will also learn how to describe the characteristics shared by categories of triangles. Finally, students will classify a triangle based on both its angle measures and side lengths.

TRY IT   Classify Triangles by Side Lengths

Students will practice classifying triangles by side lengths and describing shared characteristics of triangle categories. Support will be provided to help students overcome misconceptions.

TRY IT   Practice Classifying Triangles by Side Lengths

Students will complete online practice problems. Then they will complete Practice Classifying Triangles by Side Lengths from *Summit Math 5 Activity Book*.

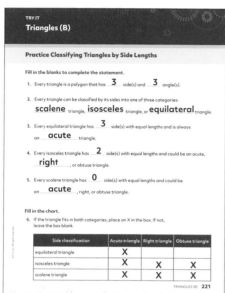

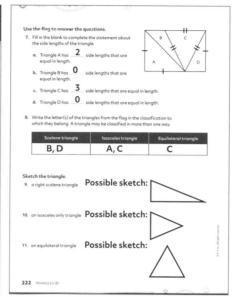

Classifying Triangles by Side Lengths

Students will solve a problem to show that they understand how to classify a triangle by its side lengths.

Triangles (C)

Lesson Overview

ACTIVITY	ACTIVITY TITLE	TIME	ONLINE/OFFLINE
GET READY	Introduction to Triangles (C)	**2** minutes	📡
TRY IT	Review Triangles	**18** minutes	📡
QUIZ	Triangles	**25** minutes	📡
WRAP-UP	More Math Practice	**15** minutes	📡

Lesson Goals

- Review classifying triangles by angle measures, side lengths, or both and describing the attributes that are shared by acute, right, obtuse, scalene, isosceles, and right triangles.

- Take a quiz.

MATERIALS

There are no materials to gather for this lesson.

GET READY

Introduction to Triangles (C)

Students will read the lesson goals.

TRY IT

Review Triangles

Students will answer questions to review what they have learned about triangles.

QUIZ

Triangles

Students will complete the Triangles quiz.

More Math Practice

Students will practice skills according to their individual needs.

Polygons (A)

Lesson Overview

ACTIVITY	ACTIVITY TITLE	TIME	ONLINE/OFFLINE
GET READY	Introduction to Polygons (A)	**2** minutes	🖥️
	Look Back at Identifying Parallel Lines	**8** minutes	🖥️
LEARN AND **TRY IT**	Classifying Polygons	**15** minutes	🖥️
	Classify Polygons	**10** minutes	🖥️
	Practice Classifying Polygons	**20** minutes	🖥️ and 📄
WRAP-UP	Classifying Polygons	**5** minutes	🖥️

Content Background

In this lesson, students will classify polygons by the number of sides it has. A polygon is a plane shape made of 3 or more straight sides. The ends of each side must connect to another side so that the inside of the shape is separated from the outside of the shape. This lesson includes polygons with 3, 4, 5, and 6 sides, respectively called triangles, quadrilaterals, pentagons, and hexagons.

OPTIONAL   Some students may be curious to know the names of shapes with more than 6 sides. They likely know that an octagon has 8 sides and may even know that a polygon with 10 sides is a decagon. (*Decade* and *decagon* have the same prefix *dec*– meaning "ten.") Less commonly known are the heptagon with 7 sides, the nonagon or enneagon with 9 sides, the hendecagon with 11 sides, and the dodecagon with 12 sides. Any polygon can also be named using the term *n*-gon, where *n* is the number of sides. So, a heptagon could also be called a 7-gon.

Lesson Goals

- Classify polygons by their number of sides.

MATERIALS

Supplied
- *Summit Math 5 Activity Book:* Practice Classifying Polygons

KEYWORDS

hexagon – a 6-sided polygon

pentagon – a 5-sided polygon

quadrilateral – a 4-sided polygon

triangle – a 3-sided polygon

GET READY

Introduction to Polygons (A)

Students will get a glimpse of what they will learn about in the lesson. They will also read the lesson goals and keywords. Have students select each keyword and preview its definition.

Look Back at Identifying Parallel Lines

Students will practice the prerequisite skill of identifying parallel lines in two-dimensional figures.

LEARN   Classifying Polygons

Students will learn how to classify polygons based on their number of sides.

TRY IT   Classify Polygons

Students will practice classifying polygons based on their number of sides. Support will be provided to help students overcome misconceptions.

TRY IT   Practice Classifying Polygons

Students will complete online practice problems. Then they will complete Practice Classifying Polygons from *Summit Math 5 Activity Book*.

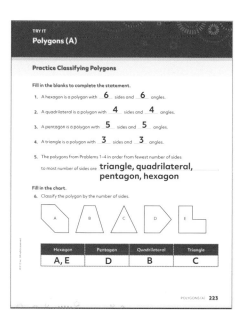

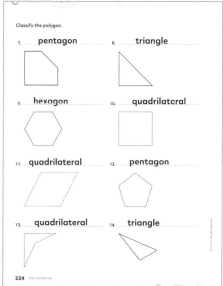

WRAP-UP

Classifying Polygons

Students will solve a problem to show that they understand how to classify polygons by their number of sides.

Polygons (B)

Lesson Overview

ACTIVITY	ACTIVITY TITLE	TIME	ONLINE/OFFLINE
GET READY	Introduction to Polygons (B)	**2** minutes	📶
	Multiples of 15, 20, 30, and 60 Math Facts Game	**8** minutes	🖥️
LEARN AND **TRY IT**	Describing Quadrilaterals	**7** minutes	🖥️
	Describe Quadrilaterals	**7** minutes	📶
	Classifying Quadrilaterals	**7** minutes	📶
	Classify Quadrilaterals	**7** minutes	📶
	Practice Describing and Classifying Quadrilaterals	**20** minutes	📶 and 📄
WRAP-UP	Describing and Classifying Quadrilaterals	**2** minutes	📶

Content Background

In this lesson, students will describe and classify different quadrilaterals. A *quadrilateral* is a 4-sided polygon. Many quadrilaterals have special names based on characteristics, such as the lengths of their sides, their angle measurements, and whether opposite sides are parallel. A drawing of a polygon often shows tick marks on the sides of a figure. Identical tick marks show sides that are equal in length, or congruent. If 2 or more sides have the same number of tick marks, those sides are congruent. A small square in a corner shows that the angle is a right angle. Small arrowheads show sides that are parallel. If two sides have the same number of arrowheads, those sides are parallel.

> ### MATERIALS
>
> **Supplied**
> - *Summit Math 5 Activity Book:* Practice Describing and Classifying Quadrilaterals

Students will describe and identify trapezoids, parallelograms, rectangles, rhombuses, and squares. If a 4-sided polygon does not fit into a specific category, it is simply called a quadrilateral. This lesson will also show that some quadrilaterals fall into overlapping categories. Often, a flowchart or Venn diagram is used to illustrate the relationships among categories of quadrilaterals.

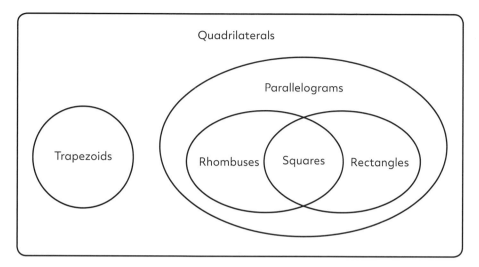

The Venn diagram shows the following relationships.

- A quadrilateral cannot be both a trapezoid and a parallelogram.

- Rhombuses and rectangles are each special types of parallelograms.

- A square is a special type of rhombus, a special type of rectangle, and a special type of parallelogram.

Lesson Goals
- Describe the attributes of different quadrilaterals.
- Classify quadrilaterals by their attributes.

Introduction to Polygons (B)
Students will get a glimpse of what they will learn about in the lesson. They will also read the lesson goals and keywords. Have students select each keyword and preview its definition.

Multiples of 15, 20, 30, and 60 Math Facts Game
Students will practice working with multiples of 15, 20, 30, and 60.

KEYWORDS

parallelogram – a quadrilateral with two pairs of parallel sides

rectangle – a parallelogram with four 90° angles; a square is a special type of rectangle

rhombus (plural: rhombuses) – a parallelogram that has all sides equal in length; a square is a special type of rhombus

square – a parallelogram that has all sides equal in length and four 90° angles

trapezoid – a quadrilateral with exactly one pair of parallel sides

LEARN   Describing Quadrilaterals

Students will learn how to describe and identify different types of quadrilaterals.

TRY IT   Describe Quadrilaterals

Students will practice describing and identifying quadrilaterals. Support will be provided to help students overcome misconceptions.

LEARN   Classifying Quadrilaterals

Students will learn how to classify quadrilaterals by their attributes.

TRY IT   Classify Quadrilaterals

Students will practice classifying quadrilaterals. Support will be provided to help students overcome misconceptions.

TRY IT   Practice Describing and Classifying Quadrilaterals

Students will complete online practice problems. Then they will complete Practice Describing and Classifying Quadrilaterals from *Summit Math 5 Activity Book*.

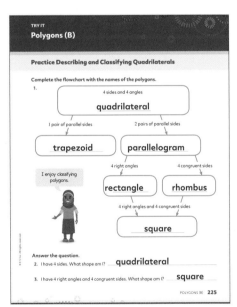

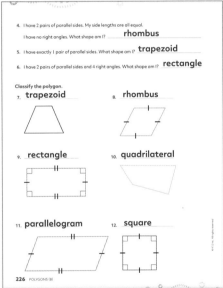

Describing and Classifying Quadrilaterals

Students will solve problems to show that they understand how to describe and classify quadrilaterals.

Polygons (C)

Lesson Overview

ACTIVITY	ACTIVITY TITLE	TIME	ONLINE/OFFLINE
GET READY	Introduction to Polygons (C)	**2** minutes	
TRY IT	Review Polygons	**18** minutes	
QUIZ	Polygons	**25** minutes	
WRAP-UP	More Math Practice	**15** minutes	

Lesson Goals

- Review classifying polygons by their number of sides, describing the attributes of different quadrilaterals, and classifying quadrilaterals by their attributes.

- Take a quiz.

MATERIALS

There are no materials to gather for this lesson.

GET READY

Introduction to Polygons (C)

Students will read the lesson goals.

TRY IT

Review Polygons

Students will answer questions to review what they have learned about polygons.

QUIZ

Polygons

Students will complete the Polygons quiz.

More Math Practice

Students will practice skills according to their individual needs.

Big Ideas: Extended Problems

Lesson Overview

Big Ideas lessons provide students the opportunity to further apply the knowledge and skills acquired throughout previous units. Each Big Ideas lesson consists of three parts:

1. **Cumulative Review:** Students keep their skills fresh by reviewing prior content.

2. **Preview:** Students practice answering the types of questions they will commonly find on standardized tests.

3. **Synthesis:** Students complete an assignment that allows them to interweave and apply what they've learned. These synthesis assignments will vary throughout the course.

   In the Synthesis portion of this Big Ideas lesson, students will complete multistep problems that go beyond the short answer and multiple choice problems they encounter in their regular lessons. These problems give students an opportunity to demonstrate problem solving, reasoning, communication, and modeling skills. Students will need to use pencil and paper and/or technology to show their work.

   LEARNING COACH CHECK-IN This is a graded assessment. Make sure students complete, review, and submit the assignment to their teacher.

All materials needed for this lesson are linked online. The materials are not provided in this Lesson Guide or in the Activity Book.

End-of-Year Project

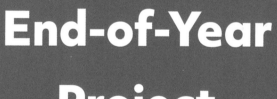

End-of-Year Project

Project Overview

The end-of-year project is an extended, inquiry-based activity that is designed to build a deeper understanding of mathematics. Students use critical thinking skills and creativity as they explore an authentic, real-world problem. The project cuts across curricular areas, showing the impact and relevance of math while building twenty-first-century skills.

The project is structured around a driving question that is both engaging and relevant to students and their community. To find answers to the question, students will apply the mathematics they already know and then expand their knowledge to fill in the gaps. They will create and submit a final product that demonstrates what they have learned.

To complete the project, students should

1. Download the project packet.

2. Read the instructions and complete the project.

3. Submit the project.

   LEARNING COACH CHECK-IN   This is a graded assessment. Make sure students complete, review, and submit the end-of-year project to their teacher.

All materials needed for this project are linked online. The materials are not provided in this Lesson Guide or in the Activity Book.

Advance Preparation

Read the project packet. Gather any required materials.